JANUS IN THE DOORWAY

The memorial to Marjory Fleming in Abbotshall Churchyard, Kirkcaldy (see page 125)

JANUS IN THE DOORWAY

Douglas Guthrie

London
Pitman Medical Publishing Co. Ltd

First published 1963

PITMAN MEDICAL PUBLISHING COMPANY LTD.
46 Charlotte Street, London, W.1

Associated Companies

SIR ISAAC PITMAN AND SONS LTD.
Pitman House, Parker Street, Kingsway,
London, W.C.2
The Pitman Press, Bath
Pitman House, Bouverie Street, Carlton, Melbourne
22–25 Beckett's Buildings, President Street,
Johannesburg.

PITMAN PUBLISHING CORPORATION
20, East 46th Street, New York

SIR ISAAC PITMAN AND SONS (CANADA) LTD.
(Incorporating the Commercial Text Book Company)
Pitman House, 381–383 Church Street, Toronto.

W Z 40

PRINTED AND BOUND IN ENGLAND BY
HAZELL WATSON AND VINEY LTD
AYLESBURY, BUCKS

CONTENTS

V

ILLUSTRATIONS

PREFACE

JANUS, THE GOD OF DOORWAYS who gave his name to the first month of the year, was represented on Roman coins as having two faces, looking in opposite directions, backward into the past and forward into the future.

This dual point of view, so natural to a doorkeeper, is essential in education, because the past is the best guide to the future, and the most logical introduction to any branch of knowledge is the study of its origin, growth and development.

During the present age of spectacular advance in every field of learning, we would do well to imitate Janus, who did not forget to glance over his shoulder as he passed through the doorway into the new world.

History, despite all its failings and inconsistencies, remains the foundation of today's knowledge and the basis of tomorrow's discoveries. Although Janus was not a God of Medicine, his viewpoint may well be adapted by every disciple of Aesculapius. He forms a fitting emblem for this collection of essays, which deal mainly, though not exclusively, with various aspects of medical history. It is hoped that it may be of interest not only to the doctor but also to the general reader, who may recognize within its pages some familiar figures of a bygone age who well deserve to be remembered.

D. G.

21, Clarendon Crescent,
Edinburgh.
October 1963.

ACKNOWLEDGEMENTS

THE MAJORITY of these papers have already appeared in print, and the author is indebted to the editors for their kind permission to reproduce the articles in book form: the Editor of the *British Medical Journal* for 'The medical and scientific exploits of King James IV of Scotland', and 'Harvey in space and time', and for 'Doctor William Heberden' which appeared in the *Annals of the Rheumatic Diseases*; the Editor of the *Canadian Medical Association Journal* for 'Sherlock Holmes and medicine'; the Editor of *Health Horizon* for 'Arabian medicine'; the Editor of *Irish Journal of Medical Science* for 'The way of the investigator'; the Editor of *Journal of the Royal College of Surgeons of Edinburgh* for 'The Surgeon-apothecaries and Physick Gardens of old Edinburgh'; the Editor of *The Lancet* for 'Religio Medici: a tercentenary tribute' and 'The search for a philosophy of medicine'; the Editor of the *London Hospital Gazette* for 'The pursuit of the infinitely small'; the Editor of *The Scotsman* for 'Dr. Francis Adams of Banchory'; the Editor of *Scottish Geographical Magazine* for 'Ancient Greece and the healing art'. The author thanks Messrs. Lloyd-Luke for their kind sanction to reprint the paper on 'The Hippocratic oath', which appeared in *Medical Ethics*, edited by Dr. Maurice Davidson, and Messrs. Spink & Son for the illustration of the Janus coin from *The Coinage of the Roman Republic* by E. A. Sydenham.

'On writing a history of medicine' and 'Ancient and primitive drugs' first appeared in *International Review of Medicine and General Practice Clinics*; 'The rise of medical education in Scotland' in *Bulletin of the New York Academy of Medicine*; 'Coryat's Crudities' in *University of Edinburgh Journal*; 'A hundred years of chloroform', 'John Hunter, surgeon and naturalist' and 'Laënnec and his stethoscope' in *Edinburgh Medical Journal*; and 'Dynasties of doctors' in *The Quarterly Journal of the Scottish Genealogy Society*.

The author also expresses his cordial thanks to Sir Zachary Cope for much helpful advice and encouragement, and to the publishers for their invaluable aid.

To Jean

THE HISTORICAL
APPROACH TO MEDICINE

THE SEARCH FOR A
PHILOSOPHY OF MEDICINE*

THE MOST LOGICAL INTRODUCTION to any field of learning is a study of its history. If we are unfamiliar with the past, we cannot hope to understand the present. The teacher of art, economics, philosophy, music, or of various other branches of knowledge is wont to preface his course of instruction with an account of the rise and development of the subject, and of its advance and progress towards the present-day standard.

In medicine, and perhaps also in some of the sciences, there is an unfortunate tendency to belittle or even to neglect the past. The medicine of our forefathers is regarded as something quaint and curious, often absurd, and at times amusing, but useless and obsolete when viewed in the light of modern knowledge.

This narrow view is as unfortunate as it is fallacious. The enormous accumulation of facts and the multiplication of discoveries have increased, rather than diminished, the necessity for a backward view. Many scientists confront the vast mass of new knowledge with a feeling of apprehension, and it is not surprising that some of our leading thinkers have dared to suggest that the pace has been too rapid, and that a little slackening of the speed might enable us to make a fuller use of the information already at our disposal. Although there is this strong temptation to apply the brake, clearly there can be no delay in the advance of medicine. Nevertheless the balance may be readjusted by cultivating a closer acquaintance with the great masters, by noting how they, too, faced the difficulties of their times, and by reading for ourselves some of their classic writings, which still deserve to be remembered.

* Inaugural lecture to the class of History of Medicine delivered at the University of Edinburgh, on 22 January 1946.

NEED FOR AN HISTORICAL BACKGROUND

The need for an historical background to the study of medi-' cine is becoming more and more obvious. Unfortunately, however, the student is almost overwhelmed by the mass of technical detail with which he must be familiar, at least on the day of examination, if not also in the subsequent practice of his profession. He graduates an expert in modern medical technique yet knowing little of the pioneer work upon which modern medicine is founded. It is obviously inadvisable to add another subject to the overcrowded curriculum, but every medical school might well provide optional facilities for the instruction of the student in the history of his profession. Professor Whitehead has somewhere remarked that "the main business of universities is to promote among students a balance of mind devoted in equal measure to detailed facts and abstract generalizations." Of detailed facts we have more than enough in medicine; let us beware lest the general principles be neglected.

No doubt some such argument has led the university court of Edinburgh University to revive the lectureship in the history of medicine, so ably filled for more than thirty years by the late Dr John D. Comrie, a scholarly historian who achieved an international reputation by his contributions to the subject, especially by his excellent *History of Scottish Medicine*. It is only fitting that due tribute should be paid to one whose teaching has influenced many generations of students. Dr Comrie was not the first in Edinburgh to give courses of lectures on the subject. An earlier physician to the Royal Infirmary and a consultant of high repute, Dr James Warburton Begbie, delivered a short annual series of lectures on the history of medicine, in the Extramural School, for eight years, beginning in 1857.

APPROACH TO MEDICAL HISTORY

History has been made since Begbie's day and even since Comrie's day, and the methods of presenting the subject have altered considerably. The field is so vast and varied that it may be approached from many angles, and he who would teach it may find himself embarrassed by the numerous gates through which he may enter. Naturally, he must maintain a chronological order. Unfortunately for the student, as for the schoolboy, some knowledge of dates is essential. But that is almost the only definite rule. In the manner of presentation a wide choice is open to the teacher. He may present a series of chosen biographies, giving an account of the lives and work of the pioneers. History approached from the biographical angle supplies a stimulus and an encouragement, and acts as a leaven to the technical detail of modern medicine.

Oliver Wendell Holmes, when he was professor of anatomy at Boston, used to tell his class how the great French surgeon Velpeau, who was the son of a blacksmith, came to Paris as a lad, almost starving, and walking in his wooden shoes. "You see, gentlemen," said Oliver Wendell, "a good head over a pair of wooden shoes is a great deal better than a wooden head belonging to an owner whose feet are shod in calf-skin."

History may also be studied from the national or local point of view; the student being naturally interested in the rise and development of medicine in his own country, or in his own medical school. The history of diseases, and of the changes which have taken place in the incidence and severity of various maladies, is a suggestive study; and even more far-reaching in its interest is the history of epidemics and of the influence which such plagues as the Black Death or the Sweating Sickness exerted on the march of civilization.

Sometimes the lives of whole nations have been altered by disease, as also have the lives of individuals. And if the individual is a talented person, the result of his ill-health may affect the course of art, literature, or politics. Recollect the effect of the blindness of Milton, the deafness of Beethoven, the vertigo of Dean Swift, the gastritis of Napoleon; all of which have been chronicled in detail.

Again, the history of public health and of what is now known as social medicine is well worthy of attention. When Greece and Rome were the centres of civilization, the individual was of less importance than the State, and the seed of social medicine was planted then. During later times Christianity emphasized individualism, but quite recently the pendulum has swung again towards the socialization of medicine.

Each special branch of medicine has its history. Some are very ancient; others have arisen from the invention of new techniques or instruments, such as Röntgen rays and the laryngoscope. War has sometimes initiated discoveries and advances in naval and military medicine and surgery, which have been adapted subsequently to meet civilian needs.

The medical literature of the past offers another great field for study. Although it contains much that is now obsolete, it is also rich in sensible advice and clear description. The history of medicine is not all contained in books. One may learn much from a study of skulls of prehistoric date, of Egyptian mummies, of drug jars, of ancient instruments, of coins and commemoration medals, and of postage stamps. So even philately is linked with medical history, which is indeed a many-sided subject.

PHILOSOPHY OF MEDICINE

There is another aspect of the history of medicine, more important and far-reaching than any of those already mentioned. It is the study of the systems and trends and motives in medicine, the age-long search for a philosophy.

The earliest medical man was a magician or sorcerer. He moved in an aura of mystery and, regarding disease as devil possession, he sought to expel the demon by trephining the skull of the patient, by administering some particularly nauseous remedy, or by the use of charms or incantations.

The next stage was that in which the medical man appeared as a priest. He practised the healing art in the temples, dedicated first to Apollo and subsequently to Aesculapius. This cult persisted for centuries, and traces of it may still be found in Southern Europe.

The passage of medicine from the hands of the priest into those of the philosopher was a notable advance, and it was in ancient Greece, the birthplace of philosophy and of scientific medicine, that the transition took place. Philosophy paved the way for medicine in Greece, where many philosophers were also physicians; and since that time medicine has been deeply influenced by current philosophy.

In the first great medical school of Europe, that of Salerno, the study of medicine was preceded by a three-year course of logic—a most sensible rule. The leading exponent of British medicine of the eighteenth century, William Cullen, was wont to preface his lectures with the statement: "It shall be my endeavour to make you philosophers as well as physicians." And in our own day, when medicine has become mechanized and specialized almost beyond recognition, the need for a philosophic basis is greater than ever. The edifice has grown almost too massive for the foundations, and it seems desirable that the builders should pause, to ascertain whether those foundations can support any further addition to the superstructure.

At this stage it may be advisable to define the term "philosophy", as it is one of those words which has changed its meaning and is now applied somewhat loosely. "Philosophia", the love of wisdom, was the name given by Pythagoras to the study of the principles and causes of all things. It was originally an all-embracing subject, "the completely-unified knowledge", as Herbert Spencer called it, although now, owing to the growth of daughter sciences, its field is more limited. The word is often used in an adjectival sense, and as a synonym for "theory". Accordingly, we speak of the philosophy of science, or of medicine, meaning the first principles or theoretical basis of the subject, in contradistinction to its practice.

The philosophy of medicine is not merely a "system" or dominating idea. Many systems have been tried and found wanting, because medicine is not an exact science but, like navigation and agriculture, it is an art, subject to conditions over which man has little or no control. Medicine can never become entirely and exclusively scientific.

There are those who affirm that medicine is undergoing a change from a practical art to an applied science. But surely that change can never become complete. Art and science both remain essential in medicine. Art is sense, science is reason; art asks "how?" and is concerned with treatment; science asks "why?" and is curious about causation.

The two points of view are apparent in the lives of Sydenham and Harvey; Sydenham, following the teaching of Hippocrates, writing admirable descriptions of diseases, insisting that "the art of medicine is to be properly learned only from its practice and exercise"; Harvey, curious to know why veins had valves, whence came all the blood pumped along by the heart, and whither it all went, pondering his solution of the problem for twelve years before putting it into print. Those two great men exemplify the extremes of art and science, each contributing to the progress of medicine.

Nevertheless a greater concentration on the art, as opposed to the science, of medicine, however desirable, does not supply the complete answer to our problem. The art of medicine is not its whole philosophy. One must search more deeply in history in order to construct a philosophy which will serve as a basis for modern medicine. Let us begin by glancing at the views current in ancient Greece.

SYSTEMS AND PHILOSOPHIES OF EARLY MEDICINE

Some of the early Greek philosophers practised medicine, and all were interested in the subject. There was Democritus, who was the first to state that all things were composed of infinitely small "atoms"; Alcmæon, who showed that the seat of intelligence was the brain and not the heart, as had been supposed; and Empedocles, who described the four elements, fire, air, earth, and water, and founded the doctrine of humours, which was the basis of medical practice for centuries.

It was Socrates who first humanized philosophy by applying it to man, rather than merely to the universe or the stars. Socrates, however, left no written records, and it is to Plato that we are indebted for a complete statement of his own views as well as those of his master. Unlike the greatest of scientific philosophers, Aristotle, who followed them, Socrates and Plato were not students of nature. They chose rather to examine the metaphysical world of pure logical concepts or ideas. Nevertheless Plato freely commented on the medicine of his time and emphasised the interdependence of soul and body. "The great error of the day," he writes, "is that the physicians separate the soul from the body." "The nature of the body can only be understood as a whole. To think of treating the eyes alone, without the head, or the head alone, without the rest of the body, is the height of folly." "Neither ought you to attempt to cure the body without curing the soul."

Of course the greatest of Greek physicians was Hippocrates, who did for medicine what Socrates did for philosophy. Not only did Hippocrates set medicine free from the domination of magic and from the control of the supernatural, but he speedily realized that so vast a subject must no longer be a mere branch of philosophy. He rendered great service by proving that no disease had a divine or sacred origin, but that all diseases arose from natural causes. Furthermore, he laid a solid foundation for therapeutics by teaching that "our natures are the physicians of our diseases". His case-records were careful and

8

accurate; he laid great emphasis upon prognosis, and his ethical standard supplied a noble ideal which is followed to this day.

It was indeed strange that the teaching of the Hippocratic School became overshadowed 600 years later by that of Galen, and that the greatness of the Father of Medicine was not fully appreciated until after the Renaissance. Certainly his profound regard for the *Vis Medicatrix Naturæ* was not shared by his immediate followers, who formed themselves into various sects, such as Dogmatists, Methodists, or Pneumatists, and so provided a problem for medical historians.

Among the Methodists, for example, was Asclepiades, one of the earliest Greek physicians to practise in Rome. He completely denied the healing power of nature and asserted that the physician must grapple actively with the disease and cure it *cito, tuto et jacunde*—"safely, swiftly, and smoothly". Such a physician, however dangerous in reality, is often highly popular and fashionable. "Masterly inactivity" is no easy doctrine when it comes to be applied in practice.

Hippocrates separated medicine from philosophy. Galen, in the second century A.D., strove to reunite them, but with little success. Galen's contribution to philosophy was slight. Yet his service to medicine was immense. He followed the teaching of Hippocrates, to whom he accorded full credit, and he made many discoveries of his own, which he described in his extensive writings. His views, including his errors, were accepted and blindly followed for more than a thousand years.

THE MEDIEVAL SCENE

After the time of Galen, medicine, and indeed all learning, entered a period of darkness and stagnation, when the quest for philosophy became a mere search for the philosopher's stone which would turn all to gold. Chemistry became alchemy, and astronomy degenerated into astrology, although it is true that there were some great physicians, such as Rhazes and Avicenna, among the Arabs of the Moslem Empire, and that the sciences of chemistry and pharmacology made some progress.

Moreover, it is easy to criticize astrology, but it may be a mistake to regard it as an entirely foolish science. In quite recent times it has been shown that the majority of distinguished men have been born in the early months of the year. There may be an optimum time for birth; in other words, some may be born "under a lucky star". Astrology, therefore, may contain some grain of truth, and medieval wisdom need not all turn to folly in the light of modern science. The influence of climate and weather, that is to say, of the sun and moon, upon the incidence of disease is still an interesting though somewhat neglected study. Furthermore, those Dark Ages may appear to us more dark than they really were, owing to the contrasting brilliance of the ages which preceded and which followed.

The torch of medical learning was not kept alight during those centuries by the Arabs alone. The Christian Church recognized the value of knowledge and, while it discouraged progress in medicine and forbade anatomical dissection, it preserved the learning of the ancients until the dawn of better times. In many a medieval monastery the work of transcription and translation was carried on; hence the classic Greek texts were preserved until, with the invention of printing, they became available for all. Another great service rendered by the Church was the care of the sick; the earliest hospitals were founded by Church leaders about this time. And now came an era of dramatic changes.

THE RENAISSANCE AND ITS RESULTS

The wonderful revival of learning known as the Renaissance, which marked the transition from the Middle Ages to the modern world, was no sudden revolution but rather a gradual movement—a dissatisfaction with the existing tradition and a receptive attitude towards new discoveries. Beginning in Italy as a renewed appreciation of art and literature, it permeated all branches of learning and gradually spread to other countries. The year 1543 was important for medicine and science, since it marked the appearance of the works of Copernicus and Vesalius with their new and exciting discoveries in astronomy and in anatomy. Contemporary with Vesalius lived Ambroise Paré, that noble and humane surgeon, and Paracelsus who, notwithstanding his eccentricity, inaugurated a new epoch in medicine.

A golden age was indeed dawning, when scholars in various branches of learning coöperated with each other and showed a breadth of outlook which has never since been equalled. Medicine was profoundly affected by advances in other fields. Philosophers such as Francis Bacon and René Descartes showed how the search for knowledge ought to proceed, the former

reviving the Platonic method of reasoning, the latter expound-
ing the dual existence of body and soul. Galileo introduced
mechanics, William Gilbert enunciated the principles of
magnetism, while William Harvey completely revolutionized
medicine by his discovery of the circulation.

Before this period surgeons and physicians had banded themselves together or separately into various guilds. In Edinburgh
the barber surgeons and the surgeons received in 1505 from the
Town Council a "seal of cause" to which royal assent was
granted, and from this event arose the Royal College of Surgeons of Edinburgh. A similar union, ratified by Henry VIII at
London in 1540, led to the founding of the Royal College of Surgeons of England, although there were those who regretted the
separation of surgery from medicine. As John Banester wrote at
the time, "Some have affirmed that the surgeon hath not to deal
in physic. Small courtesy it is to break faithful friendship, for one
cannot work without the other, nor the other practise without
the aid of both". This view was shared by Peter Lowe, when he
founded the Faculty* of Physicians *and* Surgeons of Glasgow in
1599.

CHEMICAL AND MECHANICAL VIEWS OF MEDICINE

It is not surprising that the eager race after new facts, which
began at the Renaissance, led to the introduction of some
curious trends. The desire to explain all vital processes in terms
of physics and chemistry was favoured by two schools of thought,
the iatrophysical and the iatrochemical. The former, like Descartes, regarded the human body as a machine; the latter
looked on it as a test-tube in which chemical reactions took
place.

Thomas Willis, the leading exponent of iatrochemistry in
England, compared the physician to a brewer or vintner, watch-
ing the fermentations in the human body and prepared to
rectify any irregularity. A strong supporter of iatrophysics was
Archibald Pitcairne, whose name is linked with that of Alexander Monro as a founder of the Edinburgh School of Medicine,
and who was one of the first to bring to Edinburgh the methods
of the Leyden school. He boldly championed the views of
Harvey at a time when much incredulity prevailed regarding
the discovery of the circulation.

* Now Royal College (1962).

Although those two views were widely discussed, it soon became obvious, as it is again becoming obvious today, that there were certain aspects of health and disease which could not be explained in terms of physics and chemistry. Some further stimulus was required to free medicine from medieval scholasticism. The numerous new facts which had accumulated in bewildering profusion could not be built into the fabric of medicine after the fashion of the physical sciences. Medicine concerned the human body, and the human body was more than a machine.

At this stage there came upon the scene the dominant figure of Thomas Sydenham, who, like Boerhaave and Cullen in the following century, took a wide and humane view of medicine and advocated a return to the methods of Hippocrates. The attributes of a good doctor do not change; they remain the same for us as they were for Hippocrates and for Sydenham. Sydenham's views were not of the academic variety, but they were full of sound sense and deep human insight. Unlike his contemporary, Harvey, who was a Royalist, Sydenham was an officer in Cromwell's army. He lived in stormy times, and it is not surprising that the value of his writings was not fully appreciated until after his death. Nevertheless he was one of those men whose value cannot be assessed from the printed word. Personality, that elusive factor, counts for much. Perhaps the best of a man like Sydenham dies with him, as his friend John Locke pointed out. There is a knowledge which cannot be written down, though it may be passed down by example. Personal insight and human kindness cannot be transmitted by book learning. This explains why the old-fashioned system of apprenticeship was a most valuable part of medical education, unfortunately lacking today.

THE EIGHTEENTH-CENTURY OUTLOOK

As we proceed to survey the eighteenth-century scene, we find that, in spite of the Sydenham tradition and the sound teaching and example of such intellectual giants as Cullen, Mead, Fothergill, and Lettsom, the hankering after systems persisted, and here we encounter John Brown, with his "Brunonian" system, treating all diseases either by stimulants or sedatives in large doses, because, in his view, tension and relaxation were the only sources of every malady. At the opposite extreme in point of dosage was the method of Samuel Hahnemann, whose principle of homœopathy still exists. It represents perhaps the last effort to systematize medicine.

In those stately and spacious eighteenth-century days it was possible for a man of culture to have a fair knowledge of all the sciences. Fothergill had a botanical garden which rivalled the royal garden of Kew, and Mead had the best library and private art collection in London. The greatest surgeon of the century, John Hunter, built up a museum which was no mere collection. There was an object lesson in every specimen. Hunter founded the science of surgical pathology, but he also did much more, for he was keenly interested in all living creatures, from bees to elephants. His was that eager curiosity which characterizes so many men of genius.

His oft-quoted remark, "Why think? why not try the experiment?" was made in a letter to his friend and pupil, the country doctor, Edward Jenner, with whose assistance he was investigating the body temperature of hibernating hedgehogs. Hunter explored the whole field of biology. He also strove to reunite medicine and surgery, which were developing along diverging lines.

Hunter's broad outlook is one which might well be revived today.

SCIENTIFIC AND EXPERIMENTAL MEDICINE

The nineteenth century found medicine still in quest of a philosophy, but the nature of the search had changed. It had become obvious that, to use the words of Claude Bernard, "Systems exist, not in nature, but only in men's minds". Bernard was not only a pioneer physiologist who made great discoveries; he was one of those who stepped aside from the path of research in order to guide others, by showing how investigation should be conducted. The true scientist studied the facts of nature, framed a hypothesis, and then, by experiment, tested the truth or fallacy of the hypothesis. Imagination had no place in the experiment. All facts, however unusual and curious, must be accepted. As Bernard was wont to say, "Imagination must be put on, like one's overcoat, on leaving the laboratory." Imagination was of service only in framing the hypothesis and in planning the experiments. Such was the philosophy of Claude Bernard. His *Introduction to the Study of Experimental Medicine* is a classic which should be read by every student.

SOCIALIZATION OF MEDICINE

Bernard's work appeared in 1865 during a period of spectacular advance in medicine. It was the year of Lister's discovery, Pasteur was nearing the height of his career, and very soon the proof of a bacterial cause of many diseases was to alter the whole fabric of pathology.

Meanwhile the public conscience was awakening to the importance of health for all. Individualism was giving place to socialism; men like J. P. Frank on the Continent and Jeremy Bentham in England were stating that rulers were responsible for the health of their subjects, and that private philanthropy must now be replaced by public legislation in all matters concerning health and sickness. The socialization of medicine was partly a result of the industrial revolution, the change from handicraft to machinery, from small workshops to huge factories; all of which so altered the mode of life of the people as to impose new and heavy responsibilities upon medical science. This new environment of medicine produced the National Insurance Act of 1911 and the further changes which prevail today. During the nineteenth century it had become more and more obvious that the general practitioner could not supply, single-handed, facilities for all the complicated laboratory tests and methods of treatment which were essential to modern scientific medicine. Nor could the average patient afford the expense associated with such progress.

Moreover, the treatment of the sick was only part of a vast programme of health legislation. No longer was medicine merely the curing of the sick and injured; the era of preventive medicine had arrived. Disease must be fought in its earliest stages, even before it had become disease. The promotion of health of body and mind by every possible means was desired, and this led to the development of what we now term social medicine. Today, the problem of maintaining the health of a nation, without too greatly interfering with the freedom of the patient or of his medical attendant, calls for great tact and statesmanship.

But a discussion of the future of medical practice does not come within the scope of the present subject. It is mentioned merely as indicating how the importance of the crowd is now tending to outweigh the importance of the individual, and each one must decide for himself whether this is a sign of progress or not.

DISADVANTAGES OF SPECIALISM

Reference must be made to another strong trend of modern medicine, the increase of specialization. The inventions and discoveries of the past hundred years have given rise to many new branches of medicine. The specialist, absorbed in the study of his own particular portion of the human body or his own skilled technique, is in danger of losing touch with generalities, and of becoming an isolated unit.

As a result, medicine faces today the urgent need of unifying and integrating all this highly specialized knowledge. The word "integration" is not an elegant term, but it ought to be the slogan of modern medicine. No specialty should be allowed to develop as a detached entity.

Throughout a long history, medicine has been continually subjected to an alternation of separations and reunions. The present fragmentation of medicine has probably reached its climax, and soon it may be succeeded by a phase of reunion. The specialties may become rearranged in groups. In the field of neuro-psychiatry this has already been accomplished, and other subjects may follow this example. Even medicine and surgery may again join forces, as many diseases have an interest in both.

Perhaps the medicine of the future may be taught as one vast subject, each specialist participating as his sphere of activity comes under discussion. In the meantime the isolation of the specialist should be avoided. If he cannot take a general post-graduate course every five years, the "quinquennial brain-dusting" advised by Osler, at least he should retain an interest in general medicine and general science, seeking out such generalities as still exist in these segmented times. Fortunately, modern science has accepted as a duty the task of translating new knowledge into language which the average citizen can understand, and such knowledge is in great demand. Nowadays everyone knows something about atomic energy and penicillin therapy. The specialist can no longer afford to be ignorant of the work of his colleagues, because even his patients may already be familiar with the latest discovery.

Of course extraneous knowledge and interests should be

carefully controlled, and limited in time and place. The patient usually prefers a doctor whose mental activity is entirely medical, or at least appears to be so. One of Queen Victoria's doctors, Sir Henry Holland, in his autobiography, tells of a leading statesman of the time who was reproached by his friends for employing a doctor of very mediocre attainment. He replied that Dr X was so ignorant of everything else that he could not be otherwise than profound in medicine. There may be some truth in such a remark; and yet, the physician's knowledge should surely extend beyond his physic. And it is not only desirable that the branches of medicine should be more closely linked together, and that medicine should continually learn from science. There might well be reciprocity with the arts and even with music, and a general interchange of knowledge and opinions.

THE UNKNOWN FACTOR

The arts and music, things of the spirit, remind us of that deep unfathomable human aspect of medicine which must be considered in any search for a philosophy. In an earlier part of this lecture it was mentioned that medicine could never become completely scientific. There enters into it an unknown and unknowable factor. As Sir Thomas Browne remarked, "There are many things true which are neither inducible by reason nor confirmable by sense". Perhaps this elusive but essential factor reaches its greatest height in medicine. Today philosophy, which has so greatly influenced the march of medicine, is undergoing vast changes, and many distinguished scientists are acknowledging that there is an indefinite "something" which lies beyond the reach of methods known to science. Scientists are becoming philosophers, and thus science and philosophy, which appeared to be drifting apart during the rapid scientific advance of last century, are again tending to come together, as in the days of ancient Greece. It is true that they are not yet entirely united. They do not completely understand each other. Perhaps medicine may act as the catalyst. Medicine, which so deeply concerns mankind, is both scientific and philosophic, and in the near future it may provide a meeting-place for other forms of knowledge, becoming the link between science and philosophy. Science and philosophy have each given much to medicine. It seems not unreasonable to expect that medicine will furnish to her benefactors, namely, to science and to philosophy, a common ground of understanding. Meantime, medicine might do well to cultivate broader interests and to study theory besides practice. Otherwise, in gaining the whole world, medicine may be in grave risk of losing its own soul.

PLACE OF HISTORY IN MEDICINE

A final important clue to the search for a philosophy has not been mentioned, although, in a sense, nothing else *has* been mentioned. It is the need for retrospection, for a closer study of that heritage of medicine which remains the only foundation for further progress. The trends and ideas which have influenced our forefathers are still at work today, although in a very different medium.

Yesterday's contribution cannot be neglected. It may be true that the medical student has no time to study history. Yet the greater the pace, the more the need for the backward glance. We may be running away from something more valuable than the thing we pursue. Perhaps we may learn this lesson in time, and perhaps before long there may be a department of the history of medicine in every university and school of medicine. It would not merely provide lectures but would be a centre for the promotion of all that pertains to the cultural aspect of medicine.

And if, as some would have us believe, medicine is about to enter a new and glorious era and to become the chief factor in promoting the welfare of mankind to an extent which we now discern but dimly, a study of the historical background appears to be essential. History may well furnish the chief source of inspiration and may even provide an answer to our quest for a philosophy.

ON WRITING A HISTORY OF
MEDICINE

IN A PAPER OF THIS NATURE, dealing with the problem of writing medical history, I am now faced with the more difficult problem of writing on the writing of medical history. Considerable self-examination was essential before I could answer the questions of the why and the how in medical historiography. Whether or not my introspection has been successful, I leave the reader to judge.

THE NEED FOR MEDICAL HISTORY

I am often asked *why* we should study the history of medicine— an interesting occupation for senile doctors, a quaint and curious story of bygone days, a side line for the antiquarian, only that and nothing more.

"And why," continues the critic, "why should we impose such a study upon the overworked medical student?"

To such enquirers I reply that medical history is an essential basis and background to medical practice. Not only does it provide a stimulus to those who are carrying on the great tradition that is their heritage, but it supplies a cultural and ethical foundation to modern medicine. It gives us ideals to follow, inspiration for our work, hope for the future. Many read history for information only, out of sheer interest, but whatever the motive, the reader is influenced by what he reads. History widens the horizon, it links medicine with other branches of knowledge, and, above all, it counteracts the present-day tendency of medicine to become more and more specialized, more and more technical. Written history is the main source of information; knowledge is best acquired and interest is best fostered by reading, rather than by lectures. Indeed, the lecture ought to serve merely as a stimulus and as a guide to the individual studies of the reader. Long courses of lectures on the history of medicine are of little value to the average student, who requires merely an outline on the subject that he can amplify for himself by reading. Six or eight lectures at most will satisfy all needs, and although in so short a series the whole ground cannot be covered, the series of cross-sections should be presented in such a manner as to leave the student with the desire to know more, and to search the literature for himself.

HISTORY IN THE MEDICAL CURRICULUM

While I regard history as an essential component of medical education, I do not think it should ever become "just another special branch" of medicine. Indeed, history, in medicine, should never be a specialty; it ought to be, rather, an integral part of each department of medical knowledge, permeating all the branches and helping to bring medicine into line with all other fields of knowledge that contribute to the welfare and happiness of mankind.

Every teacher of medicine, whatever be his special affinity, ought to direct the students' attention to the lessons of history, while he unfolds his discipline in its latest phases. He may even give, with advantage, a special lecture, perhaps an introductory lecture, on the early history of his subject, with due references to the pioneers. It is also highly desirable that the student should be acquainted with the history of his own medical school. In Edinburgh, we can conduct a medical pilgrimage around such ancient shrines as still exist, and we always include Greyfriars Churchyard in the tour. There is much to be learned from the graves of the great. For some years I have been invited by a number of my colleagues to address their students each term, and I have always regarded those lectures as more useful and significant than the lectures that constitute my short annual course on the history of medicine in general. Whatever method be adopted, history ought to be administered to medical students in small and well-spaced doses.

Another important means of teaching medical history is use of exhibits of early books, manuscripts, instruments, photographs, etc. arranged in prominent showcases so that even he who runs from classroom to classroom may observe and read. Such visual education awakens interest and suggests further lines of inquiry and reading.

CHANGING VIEWS OF HISTORY

We have considered why history should be studied as part of medicine and how it may be taught, but we have not yet answered the question, in my own case a very pertinent one, "Why write another history of medicine? Surely many histories are already available, and in any case, the facts of history must surely remain unchanged". My answer is that there is ample scope and need for more histories of medicine.

History is never static. While it is true that the hard facts continue as unaltered records, the attitude toward those facts and the interpretation of the facts undergo changes with each succeeding generation. History does not, and cannot, repeat itself, despite the oft-quoted phrase. It becomes a different story, even within an average lifetime. The idea of the "second chance" is a complete delusion, though it has been exploited by many authors. If it were possible for each of us to have a second chance to relive this life, would the result be better or worse? Who has not asked himself this question? Nevertheless it is a foolish fantasy, because in the meantime, conditions of life and of environment have so entirely changed that the new life could not possibly follow the same pattern as the old one. In the same way, the appeal of history undergoes changes as each new chapter is added to the age-long tale. From this, it follows that a new version of history in general, and of the history of medicine in particular, will be in constant demand as time goes on. We find ourselves continually revising our views and reshaping our reactions to meet each new situation. The telling of the old tale again in the language of today and to suit the needs of modern readers is just as essential in history as it is in any other aspect of medicine.

MODERN MEDICAL HISTORY

In speaking of history up to this point I have had in mind *early* history. Although it may be argued that the events of yesterday have already become history, a period of time, even many years, must elapse before those events come within the field of the historian. Of course there have been many excellent books and articles on "The past fifty years in medicine" or some such topic. Nevertheless, I submit that history of so modern a date is in a class by itself, and is best taught and written, not by the medical historian, but by the expert in the subject under review. Historical facts do not at once fall into their correct perspective. As Bishop Mandell Creighton said, "The lessons of history are best learned in periods which do not challenge direct comparisons with the present. We are calmer and more impartial when the conditions of the problem are somewhat remote." Furthermore, as is well known, a new remedy does not at once assume its permanent place in therapeutics. In time it may be improved, or superseded, or even discarded. Medical history takes at least half a century to mature, and to write of modern history, as of prehistory, may be guesser's ground.

THE ALPHA AND OMEGA OF HISTORIOGRAPHY

Now let us deal with the technique of the medical historian— how he approaches the task, and how he begins and how he ends the story that he sets out to tell. He must first delineate the field with which he proposes to deal; his first duty is the collection and analysis of the recorded facts. Historical observation is always indirect; the information is always secondhand. The original records that form the quarry of the historian have been made by others, usually in writing, although before the invention of writing, they consisted of tools, implements, bones, and other relics—the source books of unwritten history. Even the written records have been copied and recopied, and many of the originals no longer exist. Still, the mass of available material is enormous, and the historian's task is one of choice and selection rather than one of mere collection.

Moreover, the difficulty is increased by the constant expansion of history. History is expanding at both ends, as well as in the middle. More and more records of the activities of mankind in the past are becoming available. Meanwhile, as the years pass, the events of each decade, of each year, and even of each day are becoming historical. Even prehistory, which has often been regarded as a mere field for speculation, is yearly yielding up its ancient secrets and adding to the mass of facts available to the inquiring historian.

The medical historian will do well to pay special attention to the prehistory of medicine and to primitive medicine and medical folklore, the most ancient aspects of the healing art, which still survive and even flourish today, in spite of modern advances. Man's greatest discoveries—the use of tools, cooking, agriculture, etc.—were made in prehistoric times, long before the invention of writing. A study of the primitive mind may furnish the key to some of the problems of the present. The supernatural still has a place in medicine.

Collecting his data, indexing the essential facts, noting the trends and fashions that have affected medical practice, reading biographies of the pioneers, studying the growth of medical education, the development of hospitals and nursing, and the classic books, the historiographer enters upon his task. This period of collecting may extend over a number of years, but it should not be too long. In George Eliot's remarkable novel *Middlemarch*, which Stephen Paget urged all his medical students to read, there is the character of Casaubon, engaged in the lifework of writing a "key to all the mythologies". He piles up data upon data until he is engulfed in the great mass of material regarding which no conclusion has been reached. He ends as he began, a mere collector.

> *Nothing so difficult as a beginning*
> *In poesy, unless perhaps the end.*

So wrote Byron, and what is true of poesy applies with equal force to history. The beginning is hard enough, but one must know also where and when to stop. The end of the stage of collection is only the beginning of the real enterprise. After collection comes selection, together with analysis; finally, the time arrives for presentation, in writing. Sifting the mass, discarding here, and adding there, the historian at length designs the pattern of his writing.

Apart from notes or a skeleton or framework of the book, with perhaps chapter headings and the like, he has not yet put pen to paper. Leaving the scientific period of his task he now enters the phase that is, rather, an art.

SCIENCE VERSUS ART IN THE WRITING OF HISTORY

Half a century ago, history passed through a period of criticism and revaluation such as we have witnessed much more recently in medicine. Certain distinguished historians of the last century told us that history should be regarded as "a science, no less and no more", and that it was not a branch of literature. To clothe the story in an acceptable literary dress was no part of the historian's job.

After much heated argument, a more common-sense view has been reached and is now generally accepted. It would have been pitiable if history had yielded then to the temptation of becoming a specialized study, for scholars only. The study of the past can never be the monopoly of a select group. Amateur historians do much valuable work, but above all in history, as in medicine too, there is great need for interpreters who can make available for the ordinary intelligent man the work of the specialist. This indeed is a most useful art. Even in medicine, now so highly specialized and fragmented, and so "scientific", it is becoming clearer every day that science has its limitations, and that many problems lie beyond the bounds of the most advanced dreams of scientific endeavour.

History, then, is both science and art. The collection of data is science; the analysis and presentation of history based on the data is art.

The facts themselves are of undoubted value, and a mere chronology of events has its uses. But how dry and unreal are dates of kings and battles, which gave such headaches to the schoolboys of a generation ago. That brilliant historian, G. M. Trevelyan, has shown very clearly how much more important are the lives of the people than are the doings of their rulers. He has written a "Social History" which he defines as "history with the politics left out". Nothing is lost and much is gained by this plan. So also in medical history, the writer should use his art of bringing medicine into line with daily life; the patient then enters the picture; his attitude toward the doctor, his food and clothing and housing, as well as his diseases, all are to be studied, as the scroll of past records is unrolled. It is indeed fortunate that history has escaped from the bondage of science and still talks the language of the ordinary man. But can history assist medicine to achieve a similar position of freedom? This may be possible, although the medical historiographer who works with this end in view is faced with a formidable task.

MAKING HISTORY INTO LITERATURE

A history may be defined as "a critical review of past events in the light of present-day knowledge". Above all, the work should be critical and explanatory. The day of scientific history, if it ever really existed, is over, and although perhaps the history of science may remain "scientific", the history of medicine, like the practice of medicine, must ever be an art, and a branch of literature. The exposition and commentary, so essential if a history is to be something more than a dictionary of dates or a bundle of biographies, are the major portion of the work, and, of course, the difficult part to write. A mere record is not a history.

Robert Louis Stevenson wrote of Dr John Brown, the author of the immortal tale *Rab and His Friends*:

> *Ye didnae fash yoursel' to think,*
> *Ye stapped your pen into the ink,*
> *An' there was Rab!*

It is doubtful if the good doctor really found his literary work so easy.

For most of us it is a toilsome business, requiring much revision and many corrections. Numerous are the sources of error, and the ship of history requires careful handling as it is steered through the stormy seas. Controversies are many, numerous are the problems. Was Hippocrates real? Was Paracelsus a charlatan? What was the effect of Christianity on medicine? Who was the true discoverer of anaesthesia? Questions such as these are scattered throughout history, and the historian must face and answer them, if he is to fulfil his true function. Few of his readers are experts; they therefore demand guidance in the solution of dubious matters. This is right and proper, but sometimes the historian propounds an extreme view, and he may even revel in the dethronement of a great pioneer. This kind of historical analysis, under the ugly name of "debunking", has become very popular, though it is really a mean trick to play on our ancestors. Of course they had their faults, but why lay such stress on this negative side of their lives? The converse attitude, that of "whitewashing" some historical personage who has usually been regarded as a villain, is not so common a practice. Unless he is very sure of his ground, the writer of history should avoid extreme views in either direction. Sensational matter, written to shock some and to surprise others, or to form a kind of historical "thriller", ought to have no place in a history of medicine.

A greater difficulty, and, indeed, the main difficulty that confronts every historian, is that of making his story run smoothly, so as to assume the form of a readable narrative.

24

UNHISTORIC ACTS AND UNRECORDED FACTS

The historiographer's first duty is to tell the tale in an attractive manner. A bare statement of facts and events makes a lamentably dull book. Good history should be literary and, at the same time, human. Impersonal history is no history at all; without biography it becomes very dry indeed.

At first, the writer may be tempted to exaggerate the importance of great discoveries and to lay great stress on the lives of famous men. It should be remembered that this is only one aspect of history, a survey of the peaks and not of the valleys, a study of milestones rather than of the miles between. Of course the trail of the pioneers is a noble theme, but it leaves untold the more significant unhistoric acts and unrecorded facts. The discoveries may be the bricks, but the untold tale is the cement that binds them together. "The growing good of the world is partly dependent on unhistoric acts", wrote George Eliot in the last sentence of *Middlemarch*, and two centuries earlier, Sir Thomas Browne reflected that there might be "more remarkable persons forgot, than any that stood remembered in the known account of time".

The lives and deeds of many unknown practitioners form the material out of which the history of medicine is fashioned. These were the men who made possible the work of the famous discoverers.

No definite pattern of progress may be discerned in history, and no one now refers to an imagined steady growth of goodness. The temperature chart of history shows violent oscillations, which seem to have escaped the notice of complacent Victorians. Indeed, the word progress, in history, denotes only a movement, not always a betterment by any means.

THE VALUE OF REVIEWS

The publication of a book and, most of all, of a history does not bring to an end the responsibility of the author. There are still reviews to be faced and criticisms to be answered. There may even be the possibility of future editions and of translations into other languages.

Reviews are widely read, for various reasons. Some read a review to save themselves the trouble of reading the book, others to ascertain whether the book is worth reading or even worth buying. Accordingly a review ought not to be simply a criticism of defects and errors together with a statement of how the reviewer himself would have written the book. A review ought rather to give a brief synopsis of the contents and construction of the work, of its interest and readability, and especially of whether it supplies new knowledge or approaches the existing knowledge from a new point of view that brings it into line with modern thought. In a history, the reviewer will look for the change of view regarding events long since fixed in time and place.

My history of medicine had the good fortune (I never learned why) to be reviewed in the *Observer* by Mr George Bernard Shaw. Mr Shaw followed none of the usual rules of reviewing. He simply wrote an entertaining essay, using the book as a starting point, and dealing with the fallacies of antisepsis and the follies of vaccination, in his own inimitable style. It was not surprising (or was it?) that the history became a "best seller". Many bought the book simply because G.B.S. had reviewed it; they had no special interest in the subject and none, needless to say, in the author.

Strangely enough, the reviewing of books is a fairly recent trend in literature. It was unknown in ancient and medieval times and became prominent only at the beginning of the last century, under the stimulus of the *Edinburgh Review* and the *Quarterly Review* and similar publications, sponsored by the leading literary men of that time. Now it has become an essential stage in the career of every book, of whatever merit.

HINTS FOR HISTORIOGRAPHERS

Having strayed a little way from the main object of this paper, let me now set down a few conclusions for the benefit and guidance of future writers of a medical history. It would be presumptuous of me to lay down rules, and in any case there can be no rules for the pursuance of an art. All that I can do is to offer a few remarks that may save others from errors of which I am all too conscious in my own work.

1. Do not lay too much stress on famous men and great discoveries. Never forget the part played by the unknown doctor and the still more obscure patient. The histories of epidemics, of special branches of medicine and surgery, of drugs and instruments, of hospitals, of medical schools, of early classic

books, and of many other aspects of the wide field should enter the picture and provide material quite as significant as the occasional outbursts of genius.

2. Although a chronological order is essential, one need not be a slave to dates. The average student dislikes history when it is portrayed in the battles-and-reigns manner of former school days. Nevertheless, the historian should imagine himself to be living during the period under review. He will then be less likely to fall into the error of criticizing past events as though they were happening in the environment of the present day. If the truth were known, our forebears were often much wiser than we are, though their advantages were infinitely fewer than ours.

3. Cultivate a style of writing such as will make your story come to life. Take as your models some of the masters; for example, Sir William Osler, whose charming historical essays are such a joy to read. The appreciation of good literature comes to a child at an earlier age than most of us imagine. Oliver Wendell Holmes envied the boy or girl who had "tumbled about in a library", though today the remark has lost its point, since few homes possess libraries. During my own early years, in a Scottish "manse", I was obliged to commit to memory many chapters of the Bible. These I can still recollect, and I know now that they formed the best possible introduction to literature and to history, as, indeed, to the whole business of living happily. It was irksome at the time, but of lifelong value.

4. Verify all your references, from originals if possible. Guide the reader to the sources and give chapter and verse so that he may pursue the quest for himself, and roam even further than you.

Remember to link medical history, at each period, with the history of national and social events. The tale needs to be placed in its own setting, against the contemporary background. Epidemics had a profound effect on many nations. The laws governing medical education and practice and the attitude of the public toward the medical profession naturally influenced the march of medicine, as also did the World Wars of our own time. Readers of medical history should be led to associate it with their general historical knowledge; history, medicine, and literature are the components of every work on the history of medicine.

5. A good index is indispensable, and illustrations add to the

attraction and value of any volume. "What is the use of a book," said Alice in Wonderland, "without pictures or conversations?"

The pictures need not all be portraits; indeed, portraits of eminent persons are familiar enough. A physician teaching, or a surgeon operating, is better than any posed portrait, and shows the fashions of the period. Every illustration should tell its own story—Charles II "touching" for king's evil, Leeuwen-hoek's microscope, an operation in Lister's day are examples.

As for the index, it should be as complete as possible since it will often be the first part of the book to be consulted.

MEDICAL HISTORIES OF THE FUTURE

Will the history of medicine that someone will write in another fifty years follow the pattern of its predecessors? It is to be hoped that the single volume book will remain in demand, as it seems unlikely that the student of the future will have the time to digest the larger and more comprehensive works, which, of course, will be valuable as reference tools.

Perhaps some other means of recording events, such as micro-films, television, museums, and the like, will take the place of printed books, at least to some extent. It is idle to speculate on what may happen. Certain it is that the study of the history of medicine will no longer be focused on Europe alone, so long regarded as "Christendom". Already the centre of activity has swung toward America. For years, medical history has had an accredited position in the medical schools of the United States, in strange contrast to the British schools, which have neglected the subject for the most part. Moreover, medical education, even in the countries of Latin America, provides for the teach-ing of medical history at almost every university. South American republics are already conscious of their own contri-butions to medicine, and there are excellent historical works on Brazilian, Cuban, Venezuelan, and Peruvian medicine. Many of those works appear to have been sponsored by the health departments of their various governments, an encouraging sign of the times.

There is great need for more medical historians, especially in Britain. The field is wide and unexplored. Local medical history is hardly noticed in the numerous works on British topography; the medical folklore of other countries has been more fully studied. America has accorded far greater honour to the pioneers of horse-and-buggy days than Britain has to her pioneers of general practice. Australia, however, has set a good example by the publication of many papers describing the medical work of the early settlers; indeed, the time is now ripe for a complete history of medicine in Australia, which would be valuable and stimulating.

So let us have more and more contributions to the history of medicine, whether as short articles or on a larger scale. By this means, we may have an opportunity of viewing the past history of medicine in each country and, as so many people are interested in history, of drawing the nations together by the fascinating story of each other's heritages. As has been proved time and again, without a knowledge of the past, we are ill equipped to face the future.

THE GENESIS OF
MEDICAL THOUGHT

ANCIENT GREECE AND THE HEALING ART*

THE LOVELY LITTLE ISLAND OF DELOS, in the Cyclades, was originally a floating island, anchored to the bed of the sea to provide a resting-place for the goddess Leto, who there gave birth to the twins Apollo (Phoebus) and Diana (Artemis). Here begins the story of medicine, with ancient Greece as its cradle.

Although Delos, at one time a prosperous city with a famous market in which ten thousand slaves were sold in a single day, is now a mass of ruins, one may still visit, near the summit of Mount Cynthus, the Grotto of Apollo, a cleft in the rocky hillside, roofed by a double row of huge slabs of stone forming a primitive arch. The famous lions of Delos are of two varieties: the marble sea-lions, believed to be votive offerings, and the more recent mosaic lion on the floor of one of the villas.

At an early age Apollo left for Delphi. High up on the side of Mount Parnassus, approached by a steep and winding road from the port of Itea on the Gulf of Corinth, Delphi is a most eerie and awe-inspiring place even today, and one can readily understand why it occupied the central point in maps of ancient Greece, just as Jerusalem was placed in the centre of Christendom. It was said that Zeus released two eagles at opposite ends of the earth, and, flying towards each other, they met at Delphi. There, therefore, was the centre or navel of the earth, and it was marked by a conical boulder, the *Omphalos*, which may still be seen beside the Sacred Way, the marble-paved approach to the temple. There is another *omphalos*, at the local museum at Kastri, the village which occupied the site of Delphi, and which was bodily transplanted half a mile eastwards by the French excavators before they unearthed the treasures which may now be seen.

* Adapted from a Lecture delivered to the Royal Scottish Geographical Society on 21 February 1940.

33

But to return to Apollo. On arrival at Delphi his first act was to slay a python or monster which had rendered the site untenable. Delphi remained for centuries a shrine of worship of Apollo, the most sacred spot in Greece. Its chief claim to fame, however, arose from the famous oracle. Beside the Sacred Way there was a chasm or cleft in the rock from which issued intoxicating fumes. Over this was the tripod on which the priestess sat, chewing laurel leaves and uttering her ravings, which, however incoherent, were cleverly transcribed into hexameter verse which usually conveyed an ambiguous meaning. Apparently the priestess was a sort of medium. Her ego, under the influence of fumes or laurel (the exact cause is very obscure), became submerged, and a dissociated personality replied to enquirers. So numerous and valuable were the gifts to Delphi for professional services rendered, that safe deposits or treasuries were built, and these, in ruins or partially restored, still adorn the sacred precinct. One of the finest of the offerings, discovered only a few years ago, is the bronze charioteer, complete even to the painted ivory eyes and bronze eyelashes, so amazingly lifelike.

Although the problems submitted to the oracle were mostly political and strategic, many were domestic and personal, and there can be no doubt that an opinion was sought in cases of serious illness. The enquirer did not always ask for treatment, still less did he demand a diagnosis. A prognosis, a life or death verdict, was what he most desired. The importance of prognosis was emphasized by Hippocrates, and even today it is a fear of the future which impels many a patient to consult his doctor. It is only a step from the Delphian Oracle to the cult of Aesculapius. Indeed, it was at Delphi that Aesculapius, about 1250 B.C., ventured to use his art to restore the dead to life. Zeus punished this presumption by slaying Aesculapius, who then became a god, and was worshipped in hundreds of temples, or Asklepieia. One of the most famous was at Epidaurus; there were others at Cos, Pergamos, Athens, and many other places. To the Asklepieia came many sick persons for the healing ritual known as temple sleep, or "incubation". After such preliminaries as bathing and offering of sacrifice, the patient lay down to sleep in the "abaton", a long colonnade, open to the air at each side. During the night Aesculapius appeared in a dream and gave advice, or even performed an operation, which resulted in a cure. Sometimes the harmless snakes of the temple assisted in the treatment by licking the eyes or sores of the patient. The part played by the priests also varied widely according to the case. Our knowledge of incubation is derived from local inscriptions describing the cases, from the satirical account by Aristophanes in his *Ploutos*, and from the sacred orations of Aristides, who was himself a patient, and obviously a hypochondriac. One of the inscriptions at Epidaurus tells of a paralytic who was ordered to bring into the abaton as large a stone as he could find. He did so, and there the stone may still be seen.

No doubt incubation was a very effective form of psychotherapy. Although as a rule the cure was completed, as by a miracle, in a single night, the patient sometimes remained for days or weeks, taking the waters and baths, and following a routine of diet and exercise as at any modern spa. The temples of Aesculapius were in healthy places with natural springs and fine scenery. Even in its present ruined state Epidaurus is a lovely spot, and on the occasion of our visit its beauty was enhanced by the abundant anemones and other spring flowers.

The theatre, excavated only a few years ago, is one of the finest in Greece, seating about 20,000 spectators. One may also visit the sports ground or stadium, and may use the massive stone seats which were originally available for patients.

Incubation was practised in the eighth century B.C., and continued till paganism gave way to Christianity; even today traces of the ancient cult still remain. In certain churches of Greece and Italy, on certain days in the year, sick pilgrims pass the night, and cures are reported.

The next phase takes us from priestcraft to prescribing, from Aesculapius to Hippocrates, from Epidaurus to Cos. In the island of Cos, the home of Hippocrates, there was a great Asklepieion discovered in 1903, the reconstruction of which was undertaken by Italians. The association of the Father of Medicine with the temple has been argued and questioned. Certainly the Hippocratic principles were directly opposed to magic and ritual, but the influx of patients to the Asklepieion may have created a demand for healers other than those who held office as priests. We know little of the life of Hippocrates, save that he was descended from Aesculapius, who had two daughters, Hygeia and Panacea.

Born in Cos in 460 B.C., Hippocrates lived a long life, and it

35

may be true that he taught his students under the huge oriental plane tree which is still a prominent landmark in the town, and which measures thirty-six feet in circumference (Plate I). He first separated medicine from philosophy, and disproved the idea that disease was a punishment sent by the gods.

Although we know little about the man, a study of the books known as the Hippocratic Collection, which were inspired, if not entirely written, by Hippocrates, reveals his high standard of ethics, his accuracy of case-recording, and his insistence upon prognosis. The Aphorisms, Prognostics and Oath are almost certainly the work of Hippocrates. The ethical code, or Hippocratic Oath, has been adopted as a pattern by medical men throughout the ages. His genius for exact observation is shown in many of his writings, notably in the terse aphorisms, the first of which is well known, "Life is short, the art long, the opportunity fleeting, experiment fallacious, judgement difficult", and he goes on to advise the doctor to do the right thing at the right time. He discusses the age incidence and the seasonal incidence of various diseases, and in studying the patient he notes the facial appearance, the position in bed, the movement of the hands, the extent of sleep, and many other signs which we are apt to overlook in these days of instrumental and chemical methods. His critics have said that he paid more attention to causes and prognosis than to diagnosis and treatment. It is true that many of his patients died, but that simply indicates his honesty in recording all he saw, so different from the records of Asklepieia which seem to consist of a series of miraculous cures.

To Hippocrates prognosis was all-important. Perhaps his own long life was conducive to his study of prognosis. As Sir James Mackenzie remarked, "No doctor lives long enough to write a reliable book on prognosis." Prognosis is not merely a forecast of how disease will progress. It is, to quote Dr Singer, "knowing things about a patient before you are told them". Hippocrates viewed disease as a natural phenomenon. "Every disease", he writes, "has its own nature, and arises from external causes, from cold, from the sun, from changing winds, from occupation." In showing that there was, in most diseases, a tendency to a natural cure, he formulated the great principle of *Vis Medicatrix Naturæ*. "Our natures are the physicians of our diseases." "Do not disturb a patient during or after a crisis, and try no experiments with drugs or instruments, but leave him alone."

Hippocrates used few drugs, but his advice regarding diet, exercise and mode of life is often surprisingly modern.

These are some of his hints on professional deportment: "The doctor should keep himself clean and be respectably dressed, and should make use of ointments spreading an agreeable but not suspicious aroma." "On entering the sickroom he should sit down, should not speak much, nor let himself become embarrassed." And here are some maxims for the surgeon: "He must use both hands with equal celerity, and it is a favourable circumstance if the thumb is in good apposition to the forefinger." "The nails should not project beyond the finger tips, and yet not be too short."

In point of time Hippocrates was closely followed by Aristotle, the great biologist and comparative anatomist, whose work was of inestimable value to medicine. Then the scene shifts to Egypt, where there was a famous medical school at Alexandria, and then to Rome, where Celsus wrote his voluminous work.

The greatest exponent of Greek medicine after Hippocrates was Galen, who was born at Pergamos in A.D. 130. Pergamos, or Bergamum, is in Asia Minor, fifty miles north of Smyrna (Izmir), and it may be visited by those who are prepared to negotiate in springless motor-cars one of the roughest roads in Asia. The site of the Asklepieion is magnificent. There is a huge theatre, but the temple, with its wonderful sculptures, has been removed and reconstructed in the Pergamon Museum in Berlin, and is one of the finest art treasures of Germany. That Galen was a hard worker is shown by the number of his writings. He dissected many animals, described many of the muscles, traced the cranial nerves, noted the effect of section of the spinal cord, and of the recurrent laryngeal nerve. He was the first to show that the arteries contained blood and not air, and he very nearly discovered the circulation of the blood. All these discoveries and those of his predecessors were recorded by Galen in a number of works which were destined to remain the standard textbooks of medicine for more than a thousand years.

Throughout the dull-witted period of the Middle Ages, no one thought of questioning the authority of Galen. Then came the Renaissance, when Paracelsus prefaced his Lectures by publicly burning the works of Galen, when Vesalius showed that much of the Galenic anatomy was false, as it had been based on animal dissections, and when Ambroise Paré introduced simple dressings instead of boiling oil. Nevertheless their criticism does not detract from the value of the medicine of Ancient Greece. Nor is Greek medicine a matter of mere historic interest. Even today it is useful to recall the Hippocratic tradition. Our natures are the physicians of our diseases. The physician, and the specialist, whatever his field, should study the entire patient and his environment, and view disease with the eye of a naturalist. After all, he can only assist Nature.

REFERENCES

The Legacy of Greece: Ed. by R. W. Livingstone, 1921.
Incubation, or The Cure of Disease in Pagan Temples and Christian Churches: Mary Hamilton (St Andrews), 1906.
The Delphic Oracle: H. W. Parke, 2 vols, Oxford, 1956.

THE HIPPOCRATIC OATH*

IN THE HALL of the Mayo Foundation House at Rochester, Minnesota, formerly the home of Dr Will Mayo and now serving as "a meeting-place where men of medicine may exchange ideas for the good of mankind", there is a stained-glass window that commemorates the progress of medicine down the ages, along the three parallel lines of education, practice and, research. One of the central panels represents Lister at work, and it bears the motto: "To cure sometimes, to relieve often, to comfort always."

THE HIPPOCRATIC IDEAL

Cure and relief may be brought to the patient by science, but comfort is the work of an art that lies outside the fields of physical diagnosis and mass treatment. The science of medicine is today so powerful and efficient that there seems to be less actual need for the art, which, in consequence, is likely to be neglected. Our "journals of medicine" are now "journals of medical science", from which art has disappeared. With the advent too of nationalization and specialization, medical practice has become less intimate and less personal. Never before, perhaps, has there been greater necessity for closer attention to the ideals embodied in the Hippocratic Oath, that great code which magnifies the art of medicine, and which, in various versions, has guided the conduct of each successive generation of practitioners during many centuries.

OTHER ETHICAL CHARTERS

Long before the time of Hippocrates the practice of healing was regulated by laws and rules. No doubt prehistoric man, like primitive man as existing today, followed such regulations.

* An abridged version of Chapter XIV of *Medical Ethics*, edited by Dr. Maurice Davidson and published by Lloyd-Luke (Medical Books), Ltd., London, by whose kind permission it is here reproduced.

Some regard the "Hippocratic" Oath as the work of the Greek philosopher Pythagoras. Be that as it may, the earliest known code is that of Hammurabi (about 2250 B.C.), engraved on a pillar of hard stone and still on view in the Louvre. This code was, in fact, a law, with statements of medical fees—ten talents of silver to the physician who successfully opened an abscess of the eye, but two talents if the patient was a slave. On the other hand, there were severe penalties; for example, if the sight of the eye was lost or if the victim died, the hands of the surgeon were to be cut off. If the patient happened to be a slave, the surgeon was simply to supply another slave in his place. There is no mention of any penalties in the Hippocratic Oath, which is a set of ideals rather than a law.

Other codes of conduct and of bearing, framed after the time of Hippocrates, include that of the Indian surgeon Susruta who, early in the Christian era, made rules for the selection of medical students or pupils, who were to be chosen for "a noble countenance, a cheerful spirit, and a readiness to endure pain and weariness".

Not until about A.D. 1230 do we find definite regulations for medical education. It was then that the enlightened monarch, Frederick II, decreed that the medical course should be preceded by three years' study of logic and that no one might practice medicine without having passed the examination of the School of Salerno.

Still later, at the beginning of the fourteenth century, we find Lanfranc, of Milan and Paris, advising the physician "to be true and humble, to speak no ribaldry, to avoid any self-praise, and to help poor men without reward".

The ethical code of Maimonides (A.D. 1135–1204) is often placed alongside that of Hippocrates. Born of a well-known Jewish family in the city of Cordoba, Maimonides practised there, and later in Cairo where he became physician to Saladin the first Sultan of Egypt. In his philosophy Maimonides attempted to reconcile Jewish and Moslem beliefs. His best-known work is his *Guide to the Perplexed*. The *Prayer of a Physician*, ascribed to him, begins thus : "Endow me with strength of heart and mind so that both may be ever ready to serve the rich and poor, the good and wicked, friend and enemy,—and may I never see in the patient anything else but a fellow creature in pain."

HIPPOCRATES AND HIS DOCTRINE

By far the most significant of the codes of medical conduct was, and still is, the Oath of Hippocrates, which has outlived all other similar documents.

The discovery of a principle is always more significant than the discovery of a fact, and the first statement of those ethical principles that regulate the practice of medicine was surely a discovery of the first importance, for which Hippocrates well deserves his title of Father of Medicine. We need not pause to argue whether Hippocrates existed at all, whether there were three physicians bearing that name, and whether the Hippocratic works were written by a school, or team, of physicians. It is simpler and more practical to believe, as most of us do, that Hippocrates was born on the Isle of Cos about 460 B.C., that he taught and practised there and elsewhere in Greece, that it was he who separated medicine from magic, stating that no disease was sacred, but that all diseases arose from natural causes, and that nature was the chief healer, the *Vis Medicatrix Naturæ*. Hippocrates was a shrewd and exact observer who used his unaided senses with excellent effect. He also emphasized the value of prognosis, or foreknowledge, and all his writings are still worthy of study. Among the best known of his writings is *The Oath*, a simple and straightforward charter of medical ethics or conduct.

DATES AND EDITIONS OF THE OATH

Authorities are by no means agreed regarding the original date of the Oath usually associated with the name of Hippocrates. Edelstein states that it was introduced by Pythagoras about 500 B.C., while Singer thinks that it may not have appeared until Roman times. Many manuscripts are extant; one of the earliest, dating from the tenth century and bearing the name of Urbinas, is preserved in the Vatican Library. The best manuscripts, tenth to fourteenth century, are listed by W. H. S. Jones in his indispensable work, *The Doctors' Oath* (Cambridge, 1924). The first Latin edition to appear in print is dated, from Rome, 1525; the earliest Greek printed edition was issued a year later. Four English versions of the sixteenth century, by Securis, Newton, Read, and Lowe, have been described by S. V. Larkey.[1]

In the original version of the Oath there is no mention of free treatment for the poor, but in Thomas Newton's work, *The Old Man's Dietarie* (1586), the Oath, which forms part of this book, includes the promise "that I shall not be squeamish to bestow my skill upon the poor and needy, freely and without fee". Although he did not mention it in *The Oath*, Hippocrates, in *Precepts*, advised his followers "not to be too unkind, but to consider carefully the patient's means . . . and sometimes give your services for nothing". The Oath included by Maister Peter Lowe in his textbook *A Discourse of the Whole Art of Chirurgerie* (1597), contains the following phrase, "I shall patiently sustain the injuries, reproaches, and loathsomeness of sick men, and all other base railings", thus suggesting that every doctor should cultivate the virtues of equanimity and self-mastery, so highly praised by Sir William Osler in his splendid essay, *Aequanimitas* (1889).

The excellent French translation by Littré was published in 1839, and in 1849 there appeared the English version by Francis Adams, the general practitioner of Banchory, Deeside, who translated many Greek medical classics. Later English renderings are by W. H. S. Jones (Loeb Library), 1923, and by John Chadwick and W. H. Mann, 1950.

It need hardly be added that the Oath is not the only Hippocratic work relating to ethics. Scattered throughout his works are many wise ethical counsels. An oft-quoted phrase, which goes to the root of the matter, states that "Where the love of man is, there is also love of the Art". The Oath is a charter or ideal, and not in any sense a law. No penalties are mentioned; it is an appeal and not a threat.

THE HIPPOCRATIC OATH (Translation by W. H. S. Jones)

I swear by Apollo Physician, by Asclepius, by Health, by Heal-all, and by all the gods and goddesses, making them witnesses, that I will carry out, according to my ability and judgement, this oath and this indenture:

To regard my teacher in this art as equal to my parents; to make him partner in my livelihood, and when he is in need of money to share mine with him; to consider his offspring equal to my brothers; to teach them this art, if they require to learn it, without fee or indenture; and to impart precept, oral instruction, and all the other learning, to my sons, to the sons of my teacher, and to pupils who have signed the indenture and sworn obedience to the physicians' Law, but to none other.

I will use treatment to help the sick according to my ability and judgement, but I will never use it to injure or wrong them.

I will not give poison to anyone though asked to do so, nor will I suggest such a plan. Similarly I will not give a pessary to a woman to cause abortion. But in purity and in holiness I will guide my life and my art.

I will not use the knife either on sufferers from stone, but I will give place to such as are craftsmen therein.

Into whatsoever houses I enter, I will do so to help the sick, keeping myself free from all intentional wrong-doing and harm, especially from fornication with woman or man, bond or free.

Whatsoever in the course of practice I see or hear (or even outside my practice in social intercourse) that ought never to be published abroad, I will not divulge, but consider such things to be holy secrets.

Now if I keep this oath and break it not, may I enjoy honour, in my life and art, among all men for all time; but if I transgress and forswear myself, may the opposite befall me.

THE CHRISTIAN VERSION

There have been many renderings and many interpretations of the Hippocratic Oath. The first important digression from the original was the Oath as adopted by the early Christian Church, of which the best known manuscript is that of Urbinas in the Vatican Library of tenth century date. The Christian Oath is modified, "so that a Christian may follow it"; there is no mention of "swearing" the Oath. It is written in the form of a cross.

The first important difference is the omission of any reference to pagan deities. The initial invocation is not "I swear", etc., but is a beatitude: "Blessed be God the Father of our Lord Jesus Christ who is blessed for ever and ever; I lie not."

There is no praise of the teacher, nor any preferential treatment of him or of his sons or other pupils. Obviously the early Christian Church discouraged all secret societies and trade unions. Christian benevolence should be universal, and an exclusive circle of practitioners could not be permitted by those who held all men as brothers.

43

Another feature of the Christian Oath is the absence of the clause that prohibits surgery, or at least lithotomy. It was natural, perhaps, that the early Christians, who attributed healing power to God alone, should disapprove of operative interference, just as they discountenanced dissection of the human body.

MEDICAL ETHICS OF EIGHTEENTH AND NINETEENTH CENTURIES

Before dealing with the administration of the Hippocratic Oath, let us glance at the development of medical ethics in comparatively recent times. The term "medical ethics" came into general use after Thomas Percival of Manchester (b. 1740) published, in 1803, his well-known treatise bearing that title.

This book was an advance on the earlier work of Professor John Gregory of Edinburgh, the father of James Gregory of powder fame. Gregory's six lectures, entitled *The Duties and Qualifications of the Physician*, printed in 1772, reaffirmed the dignity of the medical profession, or rather of the physician, who had been the victim of many a satire since the days of Molière. This work dealt with medical etiquette, or the personal qualities of the physician, and his duty to his colleagues.

Percival's treatise took a wider view. It was called *Medical Ethics*,[2] not merely *etiquette*, although it did lay stress on a good bedside manner, as was the custom of the time. Percival was a man of distinction, had studied at Edinburgh and graduated M.D. at Leyden in 1765, an F.R.S., and was the friend of Voltaire, Franklin, Hunter, and others. Percival had already made important contributions to sociology before he wrote the book for which he is chiefly remembered. His interest in ethics arose from the difficulty of staffing the Manchester Infirmary during a typhoid epidemic, and he set himself to enunciate a code of precepts for the professional conduct of physicians and surgeons. The book met with much criticism, but it led to the better conduct of practice and it was highly regarded by the newly founded medical schools in the United States, as was also the work of Gregory. Percival's is one of the most interesting of medical classics; it has formed the basis of all subsequent work on the subject.

A treatise entitled *The Young Practitioner*, by J. de Styrap, Physician to Salop Infirmary, dated 1890, is a guide to medical

44

etiquette rather than medical ethics. The newly qualified physician, just starting practice, is advised to purchase a good-looking horse and to write his prescriptions in clear and legible Latin.

The eminent American neurologist, Silas Weir Mitchell, covers much the same ground in his *Doctor and Patient*, published in 1888. Another book, which was highly regarded during the early years of the present century, was Robert Saunby's *Medical Ethics, a guide to professional conduct*, dated, from Bristol, 1902.

A more modern view was adopted by W. G. Aitchison Robertson, who gave good counsel for his time in a work entitled *Medical Conduct and Practice* (1921). Those, and other works of similar nature, while they give an interesting picture of the state of medical practice, have been rendered obsolete and redundant by the profound changes that have taken place in the practice of medicine during recent years. A book still well worth reading, containing much wise advice applicable even today, is *The Physician's Art*, by A. G. Gibson of Oxford (1933). It is "an attempt to expand the fragmentary work written in 1669 by John Locke, the philosopher and physician, entitled *De Arte Medica*", which is reprinted as the first chapter of Gibson's scholarly work.

During the past two decades the ethical basis of medical practice has altered vastly and an entire revaluation of medical ethics, such as the present work provides, is much to be desired. The Oath of Hippocrates should ever be regarded as the ideal to be followed, although, of course, it requires modification to bring it into line with current thought and practice. In 1953 the British Medical Association rendered a useful service by publishing a 20-page booklet on *Ethics and Members of the Medical Profession*, which contains all the information likely to be required by the practitioner.

THE ADMINISTRATION OF THE OATH

It must be clearly understood that the Oath was devised not as a law but as a precept. Unlike the Code of Hammurabi, it makes no mention of penalties. The Hippocratic Oath was a counsel of perfection; an attempt to set up a high moral standard. For centuries, and indeed until the establishment of such courts as the General Medical Council, founded in 1858,

45

an appeal to conscience was the only means of elevating the moral tone of the medical profession, and of showing that character was as important as knowledge in the practice of medicine. Whether the Oath was actually "administered" in early times is a matter of controversy.

When medical schools and universities were established, it was natural that some form of promise should be given by those who were about to graduate. As already mentioned, the School of Salerno adopted the rules made by Frederick II about A.D. 1230, although those rules concerned the period of study and standard of examination, rather than the conduct of the physician. One of the earliest bodies to adopt the Hippocratic Oath as a form of promise on graduating in medicine was the University of Montpellier (1181). The graduand repeated the words: "I promise and swear, in the name of the supreme Being, in the presence of the masters of this school and of my dear fellow-students, and before the image of Hippocrates, to be faithful to the laws of man and of honour in the exercise of medicine." He further promised to attend the poor without fee, to maintain silence when entrusted with secrets, to maintain a high moral standard, and to pass on to his children the knowledge imparted by the masters. The University of Vienna, founded in 1365, requires of its graduates that they shall "hold ever sacred the name of this University", shall cultivate and increase knowledge and use it "for the well-being and prosperity of man", and "perform all the duties befitting an upright physician, with that humanity which is meet and proper". The graduand of the University of Basel, founded in 1460, promises to "hold the investiture this day in the light of a sacred ordinance", also "never to use quack nostrums or harmful drugs", and "to undertake the tasks of your profession with becoming piety". Those, and other early universities, continue the practice to this day, and it is only right and proper that every medical school should follow their example.

I have recently tried to ascertain the extent to which the Hippocratic Oath is adopted in some academic circles, and the results of the inquiry are rather surprising. In South Africa (University of Cape Town), candidates, before being admitted to the qualifying degree, must sign a declaration stating that they "will exercise their profession for the good of all persons in their care, will hold in due regard the honourable traditions of the profession, and will be loyal to the University and endeavour to promote its welfare". In Canada the use of the Hippocratic Oath is almost universal. At the University of Western Ontario medical graduates recite the Oath in unison in addition to signing it. At the French University of Montreal it is read out by one of the graduates, and subscribed by all.

The Royal Colleges of Physicians and of Surgeons, in England, Scotland, and Ireland, demand of their Licentiates and Fellows a promise to promote the reputation and Dignity of the College and to be obedient to the Laws, but there is no reference to the Hippocratic Oath.

At Oxford University there is no administration of the Hippocratic Oath to medical graduands, although, as students, they may see the version prominently displayed in the Radcliffe Library. Liverpool University prints the Oath of Hippocrates in the Calendar, so that students "may read it with profit", but it is not administered or signed at graduation ceremonies.

At the University of Edinburgh, since 1947, the graduands all stand at the graduation ceremony while the Dean reads to them the Declaration, to which they assent by raising their right hands. The procedure at the University of Glasgow is very similar to that at Edinburgh, but the administration of the Oath is conducted by the Dean at a private ceremony before the graduation ceremony.

Perhaps it would be a good idea if all universities would combine in formulating a clearly worded declaration, based on the Hippocratic Oath, which would be generally acceptable. It would be for the good of the medical profession if the universities were to take more account of the great code of conduct that, in one form or another, has been adopted by many generations of physicians and has profoundly influenced the practice of medicine since the days of Hippocrates. Medicine demands character as well as knowledge. Today it is more essential and desirable than ever that medicine should remain a vocation and a profession, rather than a technique or a business, and should, in fact, remain "The Art", as Hippocrates called it. The maintenance of a high ethical standard would be greatly assisted if every medical graduand, at a solemn ceremony, were to dedicate himself to his calling by publicly adopting those principles that for centuries have guided the healing art toward its highest destinies.

REFERENCES

[1] LARKEY, S. V., The Hippocratic Oath in Elizabethan England, *Bull. Hist. Med.* **9** : no. 3, 1936.
[2] PERCIVAL, T., *Medical Ethics*, 1803.

GREAT EPIDEMICS OF THE PAST

ONE OF THE MOST INTERESTING CHAPTERS in medical history is provided by the violent and widespread outbreaks of disease which have appeared from time to time. Of the earliest epidemics we have no record, but it may be surmised that they did exist, greatly to the alarm and consternation of prehistoric man who, regarding disease in the individual as the work of a devil or enemy, must have been deeply impressed when he saw crowds of his fellow men smitten by a malady which he could in no wise explain. Even when we come to a time when epidemics were duly described in writing by historians, or by physicians, we must remember their ignorance of the causes as we study their records.

Among the many epidemics of recorded history there were three which must be regarded as almost cataclysmic, and which were certainly pandemic. In his great work on epidemics, Creighton remarks that: (1) "the Plague of Justinian in the sixth century turned the key of the medieval prison house; (2) the Black Death, in the fourteenth century, unlocked it after 800 years." It is certainly remarkable that the so-called Dark Ages began and ended with the greatest pestilences of history. Gibbon tells us that the Black Death caused a "vast decrease of the human species" which has never been repaired. (3) As for the third vast epidemic, the influenza outbreak of 1918, the worldwide effect of it has not yet been assessed by historians.

Nevertheless we must not over-estimate the social effects of great epidemics. Mankind has a wonderful power of recuperation, even after the most devastating war or pestilence.

One of the most obvious difficulties in the study of recorded epidemics is the uncertainty of diagnosis. All that is called "plague" is not plague as we now know it, as we shall see presently. Furthermore, diseases change. Some become extinct,

49

like sweating sickness; others appear to be new, like epidemic encephalitis. Also, there is great variation of severity and virulence in the diseases which occur in epidemic form.

THE CAUSATION OF EPIDEMIC DISEASES

Perhaps the most interesting and significant aspect of the epidemics of former times lies in the varying views regarding their causation, which were current at the time of their appearance. And although bacteriology has explained many diseases, there are still many unsolved problems in epidemiology.

Prehistoric man, like primitive man today, did not admit that disease could arise from what we call "natural causes".

It was a step in advance when it came to be realized that the spirit or god who inflicted the disease might also accomplish the cure. Apollo, who spread pestilence with his arrows, was worshipped in the temples of healing; the temples of Apollo, which became temples of Aesculapius. Arrows of plague are mentioned in the Rig-Veda of the Hindus, written about 1500 B.C., and it is significant that St Sebastian, who was pierced by many arrows before his martyrdom in A.D. 288, became, at a much later date, the patron saint of plague.

In the Saxon "Leechbook of Bald" of tenth century date, disease is attributed to elf-shot; so that this idea of arrows, of something projected into man's body to make him sick, the first glimmering of the idea of bacterial invasion, is a very old idea indeed.

In Biblical times, disease, and especially epidemic disease, was regarded as a punishment for sin. It was inflicted by a righteous God, who was also the healer. The idea of arrows is paralleled in the Bible by serpents. We read of "the great and terrible wilderness wherein were fiery serpents" and also that "The Lord sent fiery serpents and they bit the people, and much people of Israel died". Then came the cure, when "the Lord commanded Moses to make a fiery serpent of brass and put it on a pole so that everyone who looked on it should live".

Some historians have explained that this serpent was guinea worm, but the prevailing view is that it was simply an emblem, like the arrow. The flesh of serpents was used as a remedy, non-poisonous snakes were kept in Aesculapian temples, and to this day, the serpent remains a sign of healing.

We shall return to the plagues of the Bible presently, but

meantime as we continue to trace the outlook upon epidemics we find that Hippocrates, about 400 B.C., introduced a great change by attributing disease to nature, and refusing to admit magical or supernatural causes. Hippocrates laid great stress upon climate and weather as causes of disease. He states that pestilence was caused by air and he appears to have attributed it to vapours or miasma, a view which persisted for centuries.

The historian, Varro, who died in 27 B.C., wrote: "Swamps breed animalculae which cannot be seen, and which we breathe through the nose and mouth into the body where they cause grave maladies."

Hippocrates made no reference to contagion, which apparently he did not recognize, as did Galen, second century A.D., who mentioned that "it is dangerous to be associated with those who are suffering from plague". The doctrine of contagion had a long way to go before it was accepted. Although it is mentioned in the Bible, which is very advanced in its views on the control of the disease called Leprosy, and although Thucydides regarded plague as transmissible by contact, nevertheless the idea was slowly adopted, and we find that even Sydenham, who lived during the Great Plague of London, paid little or no attention to the question of contagion.

More than a century before Sydenham's day, Fracastorius of Verona, brilliant alike as poet, philosopher and physican, had published in 1546 his great work *De Contagione*. With a vision far ahead of his time, Fracastorius described contagion by direct contact, contagion by fomites (a word coined by him and still used), and contagion at a distance, carried by air. He also wrote of the seeds of disease, or "seminaria", imperceptible particles which spread infection, although it is very doubtful if he visualized such particles as living organisms. Proof of the "contagium vivum" was obliged to await the invention of the microscope. It is said that Kircher, a German Jesuit priest, was the first to discover organisms in the blood of plague patients, which he described as "living effluvia". Whether that is correct or not, Kircher's *Scrutinium Pestis*, 1659, was an important defence of the idea of contagion.

Meanwhile there arose a wordy strife regarding the spontaneous generation of small living creatures. Men still believed that maggots appeared in meat, and mites in cheese, generated out of nothing, and that was even after Francisco Redi, the

51

Italian poet and parasitologist, had shown in 1685 that if the meat was protected from flies, no maggots would appear. The argument narrowed down to the smallest germs, the existence of which was taken for granted, and Lister, when he borrowed from Pasteur the "germ theory" upon which to found his "antiseptic principle", was obliged to prove that fermentable fluids if boiled and protected from dust, remained sterile, and that fermentation was a biological and not a chemical change. The further work of Pasteur and Koch and their followers, and the discovery in rapid succession of the organisms of plague, cholera, typhoid and other diseases, furnished conclusive evidence of the cause of epidemics, and the "miasma" idea was forgotten in the immense advance of scientific medicine during the second half of the nineteenth century.

EPIDEMICS OF ANCIENT TIMES

Let us now study a little more closely the great epidemics and attempt to interpret the records.

Biblical Plagues

Among the earliest records are those of the Old Testament, and numerous plagues are mentioned, mainly in order to drive home the lesson that disease is a punishment for sin. There is little reference to prevention or cure nor any conception of contagion, save in relation to leprosy. The ten plagues of Egypt recorded in Exodus ix were not all diseases; there was the plague of frogs, of flies, of darkness, and so on: the sixth plague, a murrain which attacked man and beast alike, described as "boils breaking forth" and regarded by some authorities as anthrax. In the Book of Numbers xi, we read of a plague caused by eating quails. This may have been ptomaine poisoning, although the onset was remarkably rapid, the people being smitten while they were still chewing the flesh.

Among other plagues was the pestilence which killed seventy thousand and ceased only after David had built an altar and offered a sacrifice. The Plague of David has been recorded by Mignard, a seventeenth-century artist who has taken some liberty with the environment by introducing recent architecture. But perhaps the best known and most devastating of Biblical plagues was that which smote the people of Israel at

Ashdod as a punishment because they placed the Ark of the Covenant in a heathen temple. This plague is of special interest as it was associated with "emerods" (a word meaning swellings), and the trespass offering made on this occasion consisted of "five golden emerods and five golden mice". This reference to buboes and rats stamps the epidemic as bubonic plague.

Graeco-Roman Plagues

Passing to Graeco-Roman times we discover greater detail in the account by the historian Thucydides of the plague which devastated Athens in 430 B.C., during the second year of the Peloponnesian War. "Many in perfect health", he writes, "were suddenly seized with violent heats in the head and redness of the eyes. The throat and tongue were suffused with blood and the breath became fetid. There was sneezing and hoarseness and cough, also distressing vomiting. Sufferers died on the seventh day or, if they survived, the disease descended to the bowels and produced severe diarrhoea which carried them off, with few exceptions. Some lost fingers or toes, others suffered loss of their eyes. Some who recovered had forgotten all things and knew neither themselves nor their friends."

The majority of those who have studied this description have concluded that the epidemic was one of typhus fever, although others have regarded it as smallpox. It broke out in the garrison town of Athens, which was overcrowded by inhabitants of the surrounding country who sought sanctuary there during the siege. Thucydides recognized that it was contagious, as he speaks of "men dying like sheep, through having caught the infection in nursing each other". Pericles and his two sons died of the disease, and Thucydides himself was attacked, but recovered. It was believed to have been caused by poisoning of the wells at Piraeus by the invading army, an idea which recurs repeatedly during subsequent epidemics.

To Galen we are indebted for an account of the great Antonine plague which attacked Rome in A.D. 165 and lasted for fifteen years. It was said to have been brought from the East by a Syrian army. Galen's description shows evidence of having been borrowed from Thucydides. He stated that there was "an eruption all over the body, a dark efflorescence, which left scars on healing", a description which suggests confluent smallpox. The mortality in Rome was high and among the victims was the Emperor, Marcus Aurelius, to whom Galen was personal physician.

There was a plague in Rome which began in A.D. 252 and which was as long and virulent as the Antonine plague. It is sometimes called after Cyprian, the Bishop of Carthage who described it and who used it as a lever for obtaining converts to Christianity. It was very contagious, and spread rapidly over the known world. Some have regarded it as bubonic plague, others assert that it was dysentery, but the evidence is not very strong on either side.

Still more devastating and significant was the severe and world-wide epidemic which appeared at Byzantium in A.D. 542 when Justinian was Emperor, and which probably contributed to the final fall of the Roman, or rather the Byzantine, Empire. Procopius, the historian who describes this plague, states that "the whole human race was near being exterminated". He speaks of pestilential demons as the cause and he rejects the idea of contagion. As the disease was associated with burning fever, buboes of the groins, and the vomiting of blood, there is little doubt that it was true plague, although smallpox cannot be entirely ruled out. Many fell as though stricken with apoplexy, and those who held out longest died on the fifth day. All work in the city of Byzantium came to an standstill. The accumulation of dead bodies was so great that burial was impossible and they were piled up to the roof in unoccupied buildings which were then closed, a procedure naturally conducive to the spread of the epidemic. This pandemic lasted for fifty years. Gibbon asserts that one hundred millions died. Arles and Narbonne were devastated in A.D. 549, and corpses littered the streets as there was no one to bury them. Rome shared in the pestilence, and St Gregory led the people to one of the great churches in a procession of penitence which has been the subject of many paintings.

MEDIEVAL EPIDEMICS

There were various epidemics during the Crusades and it was natural that such a movement should spread disease. But all the medieval pestilences seem insignificant in comparison with the Black Death of the fourteenth century. This devastating plague, and true plague it certainly was, took its origin in China in 1347, after an unusual season of flood and earthquake. Soon it reached Europe, and at the city of Caffa in the Crimea, during a state of siege, the attacking Tartar army threw over the walls into the city the dead bodies of plague victims, with a view to infecting the defenders. This is perhaps the first record we have of bacteriological warfare. The epidemic spread inland from the sea just as fast as a rat could run, though its spread by rats was unsuspected then. It approached Italy in the form of a "dense pestiferous fog" or "a thick stinking mist" in the sky, and it passed rapidly north through Italy and Spain to France, by 1348, thence to Germany and the Netherlands. England became infected in 1350 and by this time all Europe was plague stricken.

All accounts of the Black Death are agreed as to the heavy mortality. Some say that half the population of Europe perished; some even more, others less. Two-thirds of the people of Florence died and nine-tenths of the people of Avignon. Trade and all social activities were at a standstill. Ships lost entire crews from plague and drifted about in the Mediterranean until driven ashore to spread plague on land. The state of affairs was graphically described by Boccaccio: "Many stalwart men and fair ladies breakfasted at home with their families, but supped with their ancestors in the next world." One of the best eye-witness descriptions is given by Guy de Chauliac who was at that time Physician to the Pope at Avignon. Guy distinguished the two varieties: (1) Pneumonic, and (2) Bubonic. If you visit Avignon you may see the great hall in the Papal Palace where large fires were kept alight with a view to destroying the infecting agent of unknown nature. At the foot of the hill on which the Palace is built there flows the broad river with its half-finished bridge, the famous Pont d'Avignon. During the Black Death the bodies of the dead accumulated so rapidly that they were cast into the river as means of disposal, and Pope Clement consecrated the Rhone for the purpose. Guy de Chauliac manfully stuck to his post, and did what he could for the stricken, which was little. "As for me," he writes, "I dared not absent myself, but still I was in continual fear." Actually he did become infected, but recovered after a long illness. Most of the cases were of the fatal pneumonic type. By way of prevention Guy advised flight from the infected area and the use of purgatives, which must surely have added to the difficulties of escape. Of course the plague was recognized

55

as contagious, but the contagion was a corruption of air or water, and no writer even hints at a living contagion. Many believed that the wells had been poisoned. For this, the Jews were blamed, and were burned alive in great numbers. Some of the suspected wells were sealed so that they could not be used, but the plague continued.

The Black Death disrupted public morale: the Church and the Law lost their hold on the people. One of the most curious results consisted of processions or pilgrimages by crowds of people who sought to allay the epidemic by their own penitence. "Each carried a scourge of leather which they applied to their limbs until blood flowed. Town and country resounded with their cries." Those Flagellants marched from place to place and were not only a great nuisance, as they were fed and housed wherever they went, but also became a source of anxiety to the Church which saw its authority undermined. In many towns of Germany and Austria one may still see plague crosses and memorials, marking the site of such pilgrimages. It was also the Black Death which led artists to choose the Dance of Death as a favourite theme.

It was natural that plague, like other medieval diseases—St Anthony's Fire and St Vitus Dance—should have its patron saints. Mention has already been made of St Sebastian who shares with St Roch the power of healing the plague-stricken. St Roch was born at Montpellier in 1295. He was a man of noble birth who devoted his life and his means to the relief of plague patients. During the Black Death he travelled from place to place until he himself contracted plague and crawled outside the city of Piacenza to die. But while he lay there he was kept alive by a dog which brought him a loaf each day. Eventually he recovered and returned to Montpellier after many years of absence. None recognized him and he was imprisoned as a spy and died in prison. His identity was established by the jailer, who found in his cell a piece of parchment bearing the words, "All those attacked by plague, if they pray through the medium of St Roch shall be healed". St Roch was an outstanding example of the courage and resignation so often displayed during the Black Death. Yet it was not until the fifteenth century that the Cult of St Roch became widespread.

Between the Black Death in 1348 and the much more localized Great Plague of London in 1665 there were many outbreaks of plague in Britain. Plague was made notifiable in Edinburgh in 1505, which must be one of the first examples of the notification of an infectious disease. Throughout that century there were frequent plague epidemics in Europe. For example, there was a severe outbreak at Milan in 1576, in which Carlo Borromeo, Bishop of Milan, played a heroic part and was canonized as a patron saint of plague, almost rivalling St Roch in popularity.

One result of the Black Death was a fall in the literary output, but the Renaissance brought many advances, and among them, the introduction of printing. Many of the early printed medical works were tracts dealing with plague. The first medical book to be printed in England, dated 1485, was written by the Bishop of Aarhus, in Denmark, and the oldest original medical work printed in Scotland is *Ane Breve Description of the Pest*, by Gilbert Skene, who practised at Aberdeen and later in Edinburgh. It is dated 1568. Scotland was very progressive in its regulations to prevent the spread of the disease and there is even the record of the appointment of a plague medical officer, James Henrysoun, at Edinburgh, in 1565. The last epidemic of plague in Scotland was at Glasgow, in 1648.

EPIDEMICS FROM FIFTEENTH TO SEVENTEENTH CENTURIES

Another saint whose name is linked with a disease is St Anthony. The disease, *St Anthony's Fire*, was probably ergotism, which produced burning pain and cramp in the limbs and which was of epidemic prevalence in the tenth and eleventh centuries and appeared in Russia as late as the nineteenth century. It arose from the use of bread made from grain infected by rye disease or ergot.

The next widespread epidemic after the Black Death was of entirely different nature. The *Sweating Sickness* was curiously confined to England, where it broke out in the summer of 1485 just as Henry VII was about to ascend the throne. The epidemic spread rapidly, killing two Lords Mayor and six Aldermen within a week. Thousands of people died, some of them while walking in the street, for the disease spared none and indeed it appeared to fall more severely upon the young and vigorous. The onset was very sudden, with headache, fever, and profuse perspiration, and death often occurred within the

57

first few hours. There appeared to be no immunity and many persons suffered from two or more attacks. There were five epidemics of Sweating Sickness between 1485 and 1551, each occurring during summer and lasting but a short time. The most virulent epidemic was in 1528 and the mortality was then very high. The final visitation, which appeared in 1551, was described by John Caius, one of the most famous physicians of his time, who rebuilt Gonville College, Cambridge, and who was Physician to four sovereigns in succession. His tomb, bearing the terse epitaph, "Fui Caius", may still be seen in Caius College Chapel. Caius wrote *A Boke of Conseill against the Disease commonly called the Sweat or Sweating Sickness* in 1552 and it is the classic account of the disease. Sweating Sickness seems to have been confined to England, but long after its disappearance there was, in Northern France, a series of epidemics of what was called the Picardy Sweat. The first was in 1718 and it returned almost every year for a century.

There have been various attempts to diagnose sweating sickness, which does not seem to conform to any known disease. Some say it was influenza; others, typhus, but it was probably a virus infection which could be classed today as miliary fever. The Sweating Sickness acted like a spur upon medical progress, as did another disease which seemed also to be a new creation. This was Syphilis, which broke out with all the appearance of an epidemic during the siege of Naples in 1495. It was said to have been brought from America by the sailors of Christopher Columbus, but this fact has been much disputed. At all events it assumed a severity which has never since been equalled, and it caused many deaths. The name was given to it by Fracastorius, to whose work on contagion reference has been made. He described the disease and its treatment by mercury and guaiacum, and began by relating the story of a young shepherd named Syphilus who had incurred the anger of the gods and was smitten with a dreadful and contagious disease. There were various epidemics during the next century and a half, but the Great Plague of London of 1665 eclipsed them all in fury. It was called The Poore's Plague, as it began in the poor quarter of the city where the wooden houses, devoid of fresh air and light and innocent of sanitation, would favour the spread of any epidemic. Defoe tells us that "whole streets of families were swept away" and that "the plague defied all medicine, while the very physicians were smitten with it, with their preservatives in their hands". Defoe's account in his *Journal of the Plague Year* was hardly that of an eye witness, as he was only six years old at the time.

Samuel Pepys kept his diary in the plague year, although he must have been strangely unmoved by the suffering when he wrote "I have never lived so merrily as I have done this plague time". In an earlier entry he records how he saw the homes marked with a cross and "Lord, have mercy upon us". Notification was not compulsory, but the practice of printing weekly Bills of Mortality had been introduced in 1532 and had been analysed by John Graunt in 1662. In September, Pepys, noting that over 8,000 had died that week, entered in his diary "The biggest Bill yet; very grievous to us all. Settling my things in order, lest it should please God to take me."

Praiseworthy but ineffective efforts to ascertain the cause by post-mortem examination were made by George Thomson and others. One of the physicians who fought the plague was Nathaniel Hodges, who wrote an excellent account called Loimologia (1672). He had a great belief in sack as a preventive, and in angelica root as a remedy. But remedies were numerous and quacks flourished, while mascots were in great demand. The Plague water of the Pharmacopoeia of that day contained twenty-one ingredients. Fires were kept alight in the streets as it was thought that this measure might purify the contagious air, but it merely added to the discomfort of an unusually warm summer. Tobacco was one of the preventive agents, and at Eton the boys were thrashed if they neglected to smoke each day. It was thought that dogs carried the infection and they were slaughtered in great numbers, while rats, the real offenders, were allowed to go free. By this date, the massacre of Jews, which characterized earlier epidemics, had been shown to be ineffective. More than one-fifth of the inhabitants of London died of plague, and other towns suffered, though less severely. London was purified by the Great Fire in the following year and Britain has never since experienced a major plague epidemic.

Plague was one of the scourges with which Napoleon's army had to contend in Egypt and a famous painting represents Napoleon visiting plague-stricken soldiers and even touching their bubonic swellings to give them confidence. Napoleon's chief physician, Desegnettes, went even further and deliber-ately inoculated himself with pus from a plague abscess. For-tunately he escaped the disease.

EPIDEMICS OF TODAY

There is no space here to tell the full story of other epidemic diseases—diphtheria, cholera, smallpox, yellow fever and typhoid fever. Nor can we study today the interesting discover-ies of inoculation and vaccination. But one final epidemic must be mentioned in conclusion, regarding the most recent of the great pandemics of history. The conclusion of the war in 1918 was marked by a serious and widespread outbreak of *influenza*. The mortality was not so great as that of other pandemics. The Black Death killed ninety per cent, cholera eighty per cent, influenza only about three per cent. Nevertheless, the greatest losses were among men and women in the prime of life, and the death rate was much greater in persons under forty. All over the world, even in the remote South Seas, this epidemic raged, and there was much disorganization of trade and of essential services. Measures of prevention were instituted. Early isolation was of value, as also was the use of masks, which was made compulsory in certain countries. In Chicago the police were empowered to arrest anyone who coughed or sneezed without using a handkerchief. The full story of the influenza epidemic has not been told.

Epidemic diseases are still with us, although each year shows some progress towards this control. Nevertheless epidemiology remains an essential and important branch of medicine, and a study of the great plagues of earlier times can supply many a clue to the control of modern epidemics.

SUGGESTIONS FOR READING

The Epidemics of the Middle Ages: J. F. K. Hecker, Eng. trans. 1844.
Plague and Pestilence in Literature and Art: R. Crawford, 1914.
A History of Epidemics in Britain: C. Creighton, 2 vols. 1891–94.
Rats, Lice and History: H. Zinsser, 1935.
The Great Plague of London in 1665: W. G. Bell, 1924.
Epidemics and Crowd Diseases: M. Greenwood, 1936.
The Conquest of Epidemic Disease: C. E. A. Wilson, 1943.

ARABIAN MEDICINE

A THOUSAND YEARS AGO the Arabs were pre-eminent in Medicine; they alone held the key to the art of healing. Their entry into the world of scientific culture was one of the most surprising phenomena of history. It was strange indeed that the nomadic children of the desert should have become the leading scholars and investigators of their time and should have bridged with such conspicuous success the years between the decline of Greek culture and the appearance of the Renaissance. Those years are often called The Dark Ages, but they were dark only in contrast with the dazzling brilliance of the preceding and of the succeeding epochs.

ARABIAN MEDICINE DEFINED

In approaching the study of Arabian Medicine, two facts must be clearly remembered; first, the scope of the term Arabian, and second, the paucity of the information. The words Arab or Arabian, as applied to this period of medical history, refer only to the Arabic language. Of those who contributed to Arabian Medicine, few were natives of Arabia, although all spoke Arabic and dwelled within the Moslem Empire. Many were Persians, some were Syrians, others were born in Spain. Nor were they all followers of Islam. Just as there was no racial barrier, so also there was no distinction of creed. Christian, Jew and Moslem collaborated in the common interest.

A second important fact, and one which adds considerably to the difficulty of the student of Arabian Medicine, is that the available data are relatively scanty. Only a small proportion of the literature has been studied and translated. Masses of manuscripts, in the libraries of Istanbul, Cairo, and elsewhere, still await investigation. In 1931 there was discovered a ninth-century Arabic text of the lost treatise of Galen "On Medical Experience" and this has only recently (1944) been translated and published in English. Many original Arabic works may yet come to light and may surprise those who regard the physicians of that time as mere imitators.

SOURCES OF ARABIAN MEDICINE

Bearing the above facts in mind, we are not surprised to find that John Freind, writing his *History of Physick* (1775) during his imprisonment in the Tower of London on account of Jacobite sympathies, prefaces his account of Arabian Medicine with the remark: "Here I am entering a most confused and disagreeable wilderness, where one may walk till one is tired, without being able to find the way out."

Yet it is not so very difficult to explain how Medicine passed into Arabian hands, how the scholars undertook the task of translating into Arabic the classic works of Hippocrates, Galen and others, how the physicians and scientists also revised the medical knowledge of ancient India and Persia, to which they added some original observations of their own, how hospitals were founded and medical teaching instituted and how eventually, about five centuries later, the accumulated literature was translated from Arabic into Latin, and was handed on to Medieval Europe when the Moslem Empire came to an end.

The fall of Rome had marked the conclusion of the wonderful achievement of the Greeks in medicine. Greek physicians at Rome had continued the work, so well inaugurated in Greece during the Hellenistic period.

Eventually, in the fourth century A.D., the Emperor Constantine endeavoured to prolong the life of the Empire by transferring the capital from Rome to Byzantium (Constantinople) and during the three following centuries there arose a group of men, including Oribasius, Aëtius, and Alexander of Tralles, whose writings, though lacking in originality, served to perpetuate much of the classical medical work which otherwise might have been lost. The last of the Byzantine compilers, as they are sometimes called, was Paul of Aegina, who lived during the seventh century and was highly esteemed by the Arabs, upon whom the mantle of medical learning had fallen even then.

THE SCHOOL OF TRANSLATORS IN PERSIA

Even during the Byzantine period this transition from Greek to Arabic was fostered by a great school of translators. When

Nestorius, Bishop of Constantinople, was banished for heresy in A.D. 431, he fled with a band of followers to Edessa (Urfa) in Asia Minor and thence to Jundi Shapur (Gondisapor) in South West Persia, not far from Ctesiphon, where the Sassanian king had established his capital. At Jundi Shapur, of which no trace now remains, there was a large hospital, but the chief service rendered at this centre of learning was the translation by the followers of Nestorius of many of the Greek classic works. These were rendered into Arabic, either directly, or through the medium of Syriac.

Thus there was a nucleus of medical learning in the Arabian world before the birth of Mohammed, and it was ready to develop under the stimulus of the new faith. Mohammed was born at Mecca in A.D. 570, and before his death at the age of sixty-two he had established a great religion and a mighty empire. The religion he called Islam (reconciliation) and its followers, Moslems (the reconciled). Under the stimulus of Islam the Moslem armies made vast conquests. Sweeping along the northern coast of Africa they reached Morocco. Two generations after the death of the Prophet they crossed into Spain. Then, moving through France, they might have encircled the Mediterranean had they not been repelled at the gates of Tours in A.D. 732 by the Frankish army under Charles Martel. Yet they founded an empire extending from India to Spain and established a magnificent capital at Baghdad, not far from the ruins of Babylon. Thus, the Arabs became masters of about one half of the civilized world of their day. At Baghdad (A.D. 762), as at such other great centres as Damascus and Cairo, and later at Cordova in Spain (A.D. 960), large mosques were built, and, connected with each mosque there was a school and a hospital.

Learning was held in high esteem by the conquering Moslem. As Withington tells us, "A Byzantine emperor was astonished to find that the right of collecting and purchasing Greek manuscripts was among the terms dictated by a victorious barbarian". Mohammed found ample room for learning in his new creed and he revered all scholars, whatever might be their religious views. To quote from the *Koran*, "Science is the remedy for the infirmities of ignorance, a comforting beacon in the night of injustice".

After the death of Mohammed, the "Caliphs", or substitutes,

continued to favour the spread of learning. Under such sympathetic administration the Nestorian School of Jundi Shapur
could not fail to benefit and its reputation was enhanced when
Jurjis Bukht-Yishu, the chief physician of the hospital, was
called to attend Al-Mansur, the Caliph of Baghdad.

This family of Bukht-Yishu (servants of Jesus) supplied the
leaders of medicine during six generations and for more than 250
years. Although wealth is no criterion of success in medicine, it
is worth mentioning that Jibra'il (Gabriel) Bukht-Yishu
(d. A.D. 830), grandson of Jurjis (George) already mentioned,
was one of the richest physicians in history and was said to have
amassed from fees a fortune equivalent to three million pounds
sterling.

Another distinguished physician of the ninth century was
Yuhanná ibn Másawayh (Mesues or Mesue in Latin), whose
chief claim to fame, apart from his translations, was his insistence on the use of mild remedies in place of the drastic treatment adopted by some of his predecessors. As a translator,
Mesue was eclipsed by his dispenser and pupil, Hunayn ibn
Ishág (Hunain or Johannitus), who spent two years in Greece
learning the language, and then returned to Jundi Shapur to
become the most accomplished scholar of his day. Indeed, his
translations were paid for by their equivalent weight in gold.
His industry must have been immense, as he is said to have
translated all the works of Galen, besides many other writings.
That he was not devoid of originality is evident from his *Ten
Treatises on the Eye*, said to be the earliest known textbook of
ophthalmology. Hunain was the last of the great translators.
The seat of learning became transferred from Jundi Shapur to
Baghdad, and there was inaugurated a Golden Age of Arabian
Medicine which continued during the ninth and tenth centuries,
and, in the Western Caliphate (Spain) even longer.

It was at Baghdad that the first attempt was made to establish a medical register. In A.D. 931, a patient having died
through an error on the part of his physician, the ruling Caliph
ordered all medical practitioners, except those in official positions, to submit to an examination by Sinan ibn Thabit, chief
of the hospital. The examination was not of very searching
nature. Among the 800 candidates was a dignified and impos-
ing old man who, though unable to read or write, begged for
leniency, as he was the sole support of his family. On learning

that he did not employ bleeding nor purgatives, but only syrups and juleps, Sinan granted the licence to practise.

It was in the use of drugs that the Arabs excelled. Their contribution to medicine is largely in the domain of pharmacology. Many words connected with the science are of Arabic origin; such as benzoin, jujube, syrup, sugar, senna, camphor, alkali, alcohol, cassia, and the word drug itself.

No account of Arabian Medicine is complete without some mention of the alchemist Jábir ibn Hayyán who became well known in medieval Europe under the name of Geber. Little is known of his life, and some of the works bearing his name are now regarded as fictitious. Nevertheless he invented and improved many chemical processes such as sublimation, distillation, crystallization, etc., and he described the preparation of the salts of various metals and other substances. Alchemy was true chemistry in the hands of Geber; only in later medieval times did it degenerate into a species of magic.

RHAZES AND HIS WORK

The greatest of the Arabian physicians and one of the greatest medical men of all time was Abu Bakr Muhammad ibn Zakariyya ar-Razi, whose name has fortunately been shortened into Rhazes. Born about A.D. 860 at Ray near Teheran, he was a Persian who devoted the early part of his life to music and philosophy, an excellent introduction to the study of medicine, to which he was attracted by an old dispenser with whom he was friendly. Eventually he attained distinction, and was consulted regarding the most desirable site for the hospital of Baghdad. This he chose by hanging pieces of meat in various parts of the city and selecting that quarter in which the meat was slow to decompose. To the great hospital Rhazes became chief physician. His writings suggest that he was a true follower of Hippocrates; no slave of fashion, nor adherent of any cult, but one who made his own observations and drew his own deductions. He differed from the doctors of his time who claimed ability to make a diagnosis from inspection of the urine alone, without seeing the patient, a form of practice which had been long in vogue and which persisted for centuries after that time. Rhazes made a careful clinical examination and recorded his observations. Although the experimental method had not been adopted in science, and the study of anatomy was neglec-

65

ted by the Arabs, there is reason to believe that Rhazes paid some attention to anatomy and that he tested the effects of drugs by administering them to animals. He regarded fever as Nature's reaction to disease. His treatment was simple, and he used no drug when he thought that diet would effect a cure. He recommended the game of chess as a cure for melancholia.

Rhazes was a voluminous writer, although many of his books have perished. His largest work was the encyclopaedic *El Hawi*, or *Liber Continens*, an immense undertaking, the Latin translation, dated 1486, being the largest and heaviest of medical incunabula. He advised his readers to study the writings of the ancient physicians, as by this means, along with some experience, they might greatly increase their efficiency. A synopsis of the great work prepared for the benefit of the ruler Al Mansur, entitled *Liber Almansoris*, is a sort of medical compendium, dealing with the bites of venomous animals, with medicine for travellers, with hints on slave-buying and with many other topics of interest and value.

Probably the best of Rhazes' writings and the one which most clearly reveals his clinical insight, is his treatise *On Smallpox and Measles*, written about A.D. 910. An English translation was published by the Sydenham Society in 1847.

The two diseases had been confused until Rhazes drew a clear distinction between them. "Excitement, nausea and unrest", he wrote, "are more prominent in measles than in smallpox, whilst the aching in the back is more severe in smallpox than in measles." His explicit account is still worth reading. Although perhaps less famous than Avicenna, Rhazes was perhaps the greatest of all Arabian physicians. Towards the end of his long life he became blind, the result, it is alleged, of an injury which resulted from a quarrel with the ruler of Bokhara. It was thought that his sight might be improved by an operation but he refused. According to one commentator, he said that he had already seen enough of the world's misery; according to another, he discovered that the operator was unfamiliar with the anatomy of the eye.

During the lifetime of Rhazes there lived another distinguished physician, Isaac Judaeus, an Egyptian Jew, and physician to the rulers of Tunisia, whose writings were highly esteemed, even as late as the seventeenth century. His *Guide of Physicians* contains a number of pithy aphorisms. He states, for example, that "the chief task of the physician is to prevent disease", and that "the majority of diseases are cured by nature". "Comfort and soothe the patient," he advises, "for by that means dost thou support nature." Another maxim is: "Treating the sick is like boring holes in pearls—the work must be carefully done so as not to mar the jewel." Another classic Arabian medical book of the tenth century was the *Maliki* or *Liber regius*, a treatise which enjoyed wide popularity until it was superseded by Avicenna's *Canon*. The author was a Persian named Haly Abbas, and he referred to his work as "a complete book on medical art containing all that is necessary for the physician". His descriptions of diseases reveal an originality unusual in Arabian medical writers.

AVICENNA, "PRINCE OF PHYSICIANS"

The most famous of all Arabian physicians was Avicenna (his lengthy Arabic name need not be quoted). Like Rhazes and Haly Abbas, he was a Persian born near Bokhara about A.D. 980. He must have been an infant prodigy, as he knew the *Koran* by heart at the age of ten and was already writing on medicine at sixteen years of age. Such was his early reputation that he was summoned to attend the ruler of Baghdad who, by way of recompense, granted him the free use of the Royal library, a boon which was of the greatest value to Avicenna. His relations with other rulers were less friendly, as he suffered imprisonment and hardship. It is said that in the intervals of hard study he applied the stimulus of alcohol and that this accounted for his death at the age of fifty-eight.

Many of the works of this prolific writer are lost, but the greatest, the *Qánún* or *Canon of Medicine*, has survived as a medical classic and part of it has been translated into English. It had an immense reputation, was used as a textbook at the University of Montpellier until 1650, and is said to be still in use by native practitioners in the East. It did not win the approval of all critics. Arnold of Villanova called it "mere scribblings", and Avenzoar regarded it as "so much waste paper". Nevertheless it passed through numerous editions in manuscript and print and is by far the most celebrated work in Arabian medicine. Like the Maliki of Haly Abbas, the *Canon* of Avicenna dealt with the entire range of medical knowledge.

Avicenna disapproved of astrology and he attempted to

67

reduce medicine to a science of mathematical accuracy. There-in lay his error; medicine must ever be an art as well. The *Canon* begins with an account of personal hygiene, of the impor-tance of diet, of the effect on health of climate, sleep, music and other factors. There are notes for travellers, and advice on the care of the aged. Although Avicenna made no original discovery his descriptions of disease could have been written only by a keen observer. Little can be added today to his word-picture of meningitis, of pleurisy or of jaundice. The last-mentioned he classifies as obstructive, haemolytic (he calls it corruption of the blood), and toxic. What could be more modern than this account?

Avicenna did not confine his attention to medicine. He wrote on geology, on astronomy, and on philosophy. Moreover he was something of a poet, and some of his poems have even been identified, although on very slender evidence, with those of Omar Khayyam, who really lived a century later. Avicenna led a wandering life, practising medicine at Baghdad, at Khiva, at Ispahan, and at Hamadan, where he died and where his tomb is still pointed out to the visitor. Whether he deserved his title, the Prince of Physicians, or not, is open to argument, but it is certain that he exercised a profound effect upon the progress of medicine.

ARABIAN MEDICINE IN SPAIN

In the work of Avicenna Arabian Medicine reached a high level. Its contribution was by no means ended, however, and it progressed for two more centuries, mainly in Spain, under the guidance of a number of scholars to whom reference will now be made. The medical centre had now been transferred from Baghdad to Cordova, a large and important Spanish city, with a university founded in the eighth century, an extensive library, and many hospitals. In A.D. 936 there was born at Cordova the greatest of Arab surgeons, whose ideas were far ahead of his time.

Albucasis, or Abulcasis as he is sometimes called, did much to raise the status of surgery which "had passed into the hands of the vulgar and uncultivated". When one remembers that anatomy was almost wholly neglected by the Arabs, one is not surprised that surgery made little progress. Under Albucasis, however, it acquired new life, and his book, called *Tasrif*,

68

remained the authority on surgery for centuries. It is the first surgical textbook to contain illustrations, although most of those represent instruments and appliances. The Arabs refrained as far as possible from shedding blood in operating, and the cautery was the favourite instrument. Although a number of operations are described, Albucasis never tired of repeating his motto—"Caution!"

The twelfth century witnessed a revival of medical learning which, had it progressed farther, might have become an actual renaissance. This took place in the Western Caliphate, where Arabian Medicine showed some signs of originality and of a spirit of critical enquiry.

The greatest physician of his time, worthy to rank alongside Rhazes and Avicenna, was Avenzoar, who was born near Seville in 1113 and who acquired great fame as a practitioner. He is said to have discovered the itch mite (acarus scabei), "a very small beast, so small that he is hardly visible". This was by no means the only original observation made by Avenzoar. He was an astute clinician who relied upon his own experience and he had a sound knowledge of the actions of drugs. He was the first writer to describe cancer of the stomach. His treatise, entitled *Thesir*, or "Assistance", appeared in many Latin editions after the invention of printing.

Of slightly later date was Averroes of Cordova (b. 1126), better known as a philosopher than as a physician. His work, the *Colliget*, contains a complete system of medicine but is simply a compilation, and much of his argument consists of a defence of Aristotle and of his views, as opposed to those of Galen.

THE CONTRIBUTION OF MAIMONIDES

The last of the great exponents of Arabian Medicine was one who attained eminence, alike in medicine and in philosophy. Moses Maimonides was a Jew who was born in Cordova in A.D. 1135. Doomed to banishment because he would not accept the Moslem faith, he went to Cairo where the law was more lenient and where he acquired a reputation so great that he became physician to Saladin, the Saracen leader who opposed the Crusaders. Maimonides is said to have been the original of the physician El Hakim of Sir Walter Scott's *Talisman*. For the eldest son of Saladin, Maimonides wrote a treatise on personal health, the *Book of Counsel*, and he also wrote a compendium of all that was best in the works of Galen, entitled *Aphorisms according to Galen*. Another of his books was *On the Causes and Nature of Disease* and in this work he condemned all forms of magic and astrology and advised the use of simple drugs and suitable diet.

Maimonides had a large practice in Cairo, and the fact that his literary work was of high quality shows that he was a keen and tireless scholar. For him the patient was never a case, always a human being, and in his *Guide to the Perplexed* which is, perhaps, his most famous work, he reconciled religion with medicine and showed how each might assist the other.

Maimonides was one of the greatest of the many Jewish physicians who have advanced medicine, and it is not surprising that his tomb, at Tiberias, is still a place of pilgrimage.

Despite all its defects, its ignorance of anatomy, its neglect of experiment, its craze for classification and theory, its pedantry and verbosity, and its slavish adherence to Galen and Aristotle, Arabic Medicine did make a substantial contribution to the sum of medical knowledge. Its exponents laid the foundations of modern chemistry and pharmacology. Ophthalmology, always an important speciality in the East, made progress in their hands. Great stress was laid upon the provision of hospitals.

EARLY HOSPITALS IN THE MOSLEM EMPIRE

Mention has been made of the great teaching hospital of Baghdad, and there were similar institutions at Damascus and at Cordova. The Mansur Hospital at Cairo was completed in A.D. 1284 and was built by voluntary labour. Loiterers or visitors, whatever their rank, were obliged to assist in the work, and one historian records that "most people avoided going that way". This hospital had special wards for eye diseases and for fevers, courtyards for lectures, a herb garden, a dispensary and a large library. Fifty speakers chanted the *Koran* day and night, while soft music was played to lull the sleepers. Each patient, on departure, was given a sum of money to support him until he should be fit to work. When this hospital was opened, the Moslem Empire was already declining and the famous medical school of Salerno was already well established. Constantine the African (1010–87), in the monastery of

Monte Cassino, had translated many Arabic works into Latin, while Gerard of Cremona (1114–87) performed similar service a century later in the school of translators at Toledo, which had taken the place of Cordova as the centre of learning. Arabic Medicine was highly esteemed in medieval times but the Renaissance produced a reaction against "Arabism" which persisted for many years. Even today it is difficult to assess the Arab contribution at its true value, and further research may prove that the period was illumined with greater originality than has been hitherto supposed.

ARAB MEDICINE TODAY

It is indeed strange that so little of the original Arabian Medicine is known or practised in the Moslem world today. Some years ago M. W. Hilton-Simpson, during a number of visits to Algeria, made a study of the methods of native medical practitioners and recorded the results in his book, *Arab Medicine and Surgery* (1922). Those doctors based their diagnosis upon the doctrine of "humours" first enunciated by the ancient Greeks. Their treatment was entirely empiric, but they were familiar with the uses of many drugs derived from plants. In Surgery, they were concerned mainly with the treatment of injuries, and they applied splints to fractures and secured good results. They were even familiar with bone-grafting and for the purpose freshly-obtained animal bones were employed, usually from a dog. For fractures of the skull they practised trephining, using a small saw to remove the bone, after removing a portion of scalp with a red-hot punch. No anaesthetic was used, nor was any attention paid to asepsis, yet good results were secured. Apparently few other attempts have been made to interpret modern native medicine in Moslem lands. It offers a field for investigation which might yield interesting results, even today. In general, however, it may be said that modern native Arabian Medicine contains little that has been derived from its early exponents, and it is now of little account. This fact need not deter us from paying homage to the great Arabian physicians of past ages whose work we have discussed. They preserved the medical learning of the Greeks when it was in danger of being lost, they added some original work of their own and they handed on to Europe the accumulated knowledge. Although Arabian Medicine fell into disfavour at the Renaissance, it had served a useful function, and today it deserves to be accorded a high place in the history of medical progress.

REFERENCES

JOHN FREIND, *History of Physick*, 2 Vols., 1725–26.
M. NEUBURGER, *History of Medicine*; 2 vols., 1910–25.
E. G. BROWNE, *Arabian Medicine*, 1921.
D. CAMPBELL, *Arabian Medicine and its Influence on the Middle Ages*, 2 vols., 1926.
HILTON-SIMPSON, M. W., *Arab Medicine and Surgery*, 1922.
The Legacy of Islam: Ed. Sir T. Arnold and Dr Guillaume, 1931.

THE EVOLUTION OF OBSTETRICS

A COMPLETE COURSE OF INSTRUCTION in any subject must necessarily include the study of its history. This rule applies with special force to the various branches of medicine, which cannot be properly learned unless the student knows something of the foundations upon which the modern knowledge rests. How true is the remark of Sir William Osler: "By the historical method alone can many problems in medicine be approached profitably."

The history of medicine is of great interest, although mere interest does not justify its inclusion in a medical curriculum which is already over-filled. Of course the past contains much obsolete and useless information, just as our present-day studies will be regarded as out of date a hundred years hence or probably less, but we must know what happened yesterday if we are to do good work today, and we must have some idea of the medical practice of our forefathers if we are to improve upon their efforts. In no branch of medicine is history so important as in obstetrics.

Obstetrics emerged as a science as recently as the eighteenth century. Before then it had been in the hands of midwives who, about the sixteenth century, began to call in the aid of the surgeon in cases of difficulty. The eighteenth century saw the appearance of the man-midwife, but obstetrics did not even then secure such status as the subject deserved. It is only today consolidating its deserved position as the third member of the great medical tripod—Medicine, Surgery, Obstetrics.

In reviewing the history of any subject, chronological order is of the first importance. The usual method of studying the past is to begin with the earliest times and to march steadily onward to the present. A more attractive plan is to select a central focal point and to note what happened before and since. The point in question is usually a revolutionary discovery such as that of Harvey in Medicine or Lister in Surgery. Each of those men effected a complete change in practice and outlook. In Obstetrics, to whom must this honour be accorded? Undoubtedly to William Smellie, who well deserves his title of founder of modern midwifery.

WILLIAM SMELLIE, THE MASTER OF BRITISH MIDWIFERY

The career of this Scottish general practitioner who became the leading obstetrician of his time, perhaps even of all time, is one of the most interesting in the history of medicine. Little is known of Smellie's early life. He was born in or near Lanark in 1697, and he practised in his native town for nineteen years. We do not know where or how he received his medical education. In later life he became an M.D. of Glasgow, but as he lived long before a qualifying degree was necessary, he was probably apprenticed to some doctor of experience, after the fashion of the day. While engaged in practice at Lanark between 1720 and 1739 he was increasingly attracted to midwifery and he kept careful notes of his cases, which form the second volume of his great book. Of course, midwifery was still in the hands of midwives, but in rural districts midwives were neither numerous nor skilled and they were probably only too pleased to transfer their responsibilities to this young and energetic doctor.

It is not known what impelled this country practitioner, after all those years of practice, to go to study in Paris and then to teach and practise in London. It was a bold step for one who was unknown outside his own area, and who had no influential friends to assist him. Paris was at that time the centre of obstetric teaching. The work of both surgeons and midwives there was of high standard, and for the information brought from France by Smellie there was a demand, as is shown by the fact that the courses of instruction he gave in his London house at Wardour Street, Soho, were very popular and successful.

The mannikin which he used in teaching consisted of a pelvis covered with leather and a foetus of similar construction. Despite the sarcastic remarks of his critics, these were much better than the wickerwork contrivance used in France. After teaching and practising with great success in London for twenty

74

years, William Smellie retired and returned to Lanark where he had bought a small estate which he named Smyllum. There he died four years later. He and his wife, Euphemia Borland, are buried in Lanark churchyard. The memorial, which may still be seen, was repaired some years ago at the joint instance of the Obstetrical Societies of Edinburgh and Glasgow.

Smellie's famous *Treatise on Midwifery*, published in 1752, marks him as the founder of scientific midwifery. One reason for the popularity of the book is that it is so well and clearly written. It is said that Smellie was assisted in his literary task by his friend Tobias Smollet, whose novel *Roderick Random* is, or should be, well known to every medical student.

Smellie corrected many errors, and he improved the forceps (as we shall presently mention), but his chief service was his accurate description of the mechanism of labour. Before his time it had been imagined that the head of the child maintained an antero-posterior position relative to the mother, during birth. It had been also believed that the foetus lay head uppermost in the uterus until the seventh month. Then, the head became heavier, toppled over, and thus approached the mouth of the uterus. In this position it was, as one writer (Burton) stated, "ready to escape out into the world on its hands and knees".

Smellie showed that this view was fallacious, and, from careful measurement of the head and the pelvis and from close observation of his patients in labour, he noted that the path followed by the head was not straight. It took the line of least resistance and, as he wrote, "sometimes it is placed diagonal in the cavity". A century earlier Henry van Deventer of the Hague, the goldsmith who became an obstetrician, had drawn attention to the influence of pelvic deformities upon parturition. Smellie carried the argument further. He made careful measurements of the pelvis, and of the foetal head, and finding that the traditional belief was incorrect, he worked out a description of the mechanism, which remains true today, although it was Smellie's successor, Thomas Denman, who divided the process of labour into stages.

Before Smellie's day the practice of obstetrics was almost entirely in female hands as it had been from the earliest times; and not only in the hands of women, but of women who were ill-instructed in their art.

75

OBSTETRICS IN GREEK AND ROMAN TIMES

Hippocrates, who lived about 400 B.C., besides being a physician and surgeon was also an obstetrician. It is he who is responsible for the statement that a child born at the eighth month cannot live; a legend which persisted for many centuries and which is one of the errors disproved by Smellie. Hippocrates believed the process of birth to be the result of the infant's own efforts. In his view, the baby when it has acquired sufficient strength, tears the membranes and makes its way out. This was another error perpetuated for centuries, and even upheld by William Harvey, who stated that "the foetus promotes his own delivery by his efforts, like a butterfly emerging from a chrysalis".

Hippocrates recognized that, normally, babies were born head first and that any other presentation was dangerous. Accordingly he advised that in all mal-presentations an attempt should be made to replace the head in the normal position, and this advice was followed for centuries, even after the introduction, by Soranus, of podalic as opposed to cephalic version. In cases of delay, Hippocrates recommended that the patient be strapped to a table or board which should then be repeatedly struck on the ground.

A more progressive and sensible system of obstetrics was introduced by Soranus, who practised at Rome during the first century A.D. He was a native of Ephesus who, like many other Greek doctors, had come to seek his fortune in Rome. Soranus was a man of high principles and a sound clinician, and if his teaching had been followed obstetrics would soon have been established on a scientific basis. But his teaching was forgotten and his writings were lost. Indeed his chief manuscript was discovered in the Vatican library as recently as 1838. Soranus condemned the shaking method of Hippocrates. For all abnormal presentations he advised delivery of the child by the feet, and he was the inventor of podalic version, a procedure which was forgotten until revived by Ambroise Paré 1,400 years later. Soranus stated that he had delivered many living infants by version. In difficult head presentations he advised embryotomy, sacrificing the child to save the mother. As might be expected, this barbarous practice continued during the Middle Ages, but it is astounding to find that it has only recently been abandoned, or reserved for most unusual cases.

Medieval methods had little to commend them, and although the Arabs made some progress in pharmacology, they did little to advance surgery or obstetrics. The only obstetric instruments were hooks and knives and strong forceps, used to dismember or to crush the unborn baby. Galen added nothing to obstetric knowledge, and the methods of Albucasis and others were retrograde. Even the first medical school of Europe, that of Salerno, which came into being in the eleventh century, produced little original work, despite the fact that its staff included such women as Trotula, Rebecca, and others known in History as "The Ladies of Salerno".

EARLY TEXTBOOKS OF OBSTETRICS

The introduction of printing gave an enormous impetus to all branches of learning. The first textbook of midwifery to be printed, in 1513, was the work of Eucharius Roesslin of Frankfurt and it bore the quaint title, *Der Schwangern Frawen und Hebammen Roszgarten*. It was translated into many languages and enjoyed a vast reputation, in numerous editions, although now it is one of the rarest prizes of the book collector. Edinburgh University Library possesses the editions of 1565 and 1626. There were fourteen English editions, the first dated 1540, and all bear the name of Thomas Raynalde although it is uncertain whether Raynalde was a medical man or simply a printer. *The Byrth of Mankynde*, as the English translation was called, remained in demand as a textbook until the end of the seventeenth century. The Latin edition was called *De Partu*. This famous book showed no originality and was simply a compilation of all previous work. It was based on tradition and book-learning, not upon experience—so different from the treatise of Smellie, which was entirely the fruit of years of observation and practice. The "Roszgarten" even revives the ancient Hippocratic method of cephalic version. The various positions of the foetus in utero are illustrated in curious figures which resemble, fairly closely, those of Soranus, fourteen centuries earlier. The birth stool is shown, a very ancient piece of obstetric apparatus mentioned in the Bible and in all the older works on Midwifery. In the seventeenth century, and even later, it formed part of the dowry of every bride in many countries. It was not until the eighteenth century that it became usual to deliver the patient in bed.

So important an event as birth was naturally mixed up with astrology in those early times, and another sixteenth-century work, *De Conceptu* by Rueff of Zurich, shows an astrologer at the window of the birth chamber, forecasting from the stars the fate of the child.

AMBROISE PARÉ AND OTHERS

Midwifery did not remain for long in this stagnant condition. The Renaissance had brought enlightenment to all fields of learning and, although the midwives retained their monopoly of obstetrics, they were not only better educated for the work but also more willing to call in the assistance of a surgeon in cases of difficulty. Thus it was that Ambroise Paré, surgeon to three successive kings of France, a man of great ability, skill and originality, included midwifery in his practice and introduced "improvements equal to his remarkable advances in the treatment of gun-shot wounds". That he was as cautious as he was humane is obvious from the remark so often repeated in his writings—"I dressed him, God healed him". It is true that Paré accepted without question some of the age-long errors. For example, he attributed the time of birth to the fact that the foetus, having used up all the available nourishment, became restless, burst its bonds and so escaped into the world. Paré further believed that at the time of birth the ilia became separated from the sacrum, in other words that the sacro-iliac synchondrosis gave way, but he could not agree that the pubic symphysis also opened, as had been imagined.

This fallacy regarding the pelvic bones was finally refuted by François Mauriceau, author of the leading French textbook of the seventeenth century—*Traité des maladies des femmes grosses* (1668). Mauriceau wrote: "The woman in labour can walk very well, which she could never do if the Os Pubis or Ilia were separated the one from the other. I have dissected the bodies of women a few days after delivery and could never find the least separation." Paré introduced various improvements. He advised delivery in bed, with the pelvis supported on a pillow, instead of the traditional obstetric stool. He also sutured the ruptured perineum; this had not been practised before. He favoured the liberal use of oil and ointments to lubricate the parts and so facilitate delivery. But by far his most important service was his reintroduction of podalic version, the method originated by Soranus of Ephesus. Paré, however, was the first to advise podalic version in head presentations when difficulty arose, and it was his favourite method of dealing with all manner of emergencies in midwifery. One advantage of this method was that it often replaced the destructive operation of embryotomy.

The friendly association of midwives with surgeons was at this time very usual in France although it often aroused strong opposition from the patient.

Paré's writings are still interesting to read, especially his vivid account of his adventures as an Army Surgeon. Like many other writers of that age, Paré devoted much attention to the study of monstrosities, although some of them were impossible exaggerations of the actual facts. He was also concerned with multiple births, and among his extraordinary records he refers to the case of the Italian woman Dorothea, who produced twenty infants at two births, at the first, nine, and at the second, eleven, and who during pregnancy was obliged to support her abdomen by a broad scarf slung round her neck. One must not judge too harshly the credulity of Paré: his fictions are mild in comparison to those of his contemporaries.

WILLIAM HARVEY AND THE CHAMBERLENS

The most distinguished obstetrician of the following century, the seventeenth, was none other than William Harvey. Towards the end of his long life he was fortunately persuaded by his friends to put into print his work on embryology, which was second in importance only to his discovery of the circulation of the blood. *De Generatione*, which appeared in 1651, can scarcely be regarded as a book on Midwifery, although there are those who look upon Harvey, and not Smellie, as the founder of scientific midwifery. This work on generation is concerned mainly with the development of the chick in the egg and with the reproductive processes in deer, which he demonstrated to King Charles I (Plate 8). Only thirty pages of the work deal with obstetrics, but illustrative cases described by Harvey show that he drew from an ample practical experience. He mentions that all animals come into the world head foremost; he also affirms the belief that a child born in the eighth month seldom lives. He relates cases of living children born as early as the fifth month and as late as the thirteenth month, though his facts are unconvincing. Harvey was a great believer in the power of Nature and he deplored the ill-advised efforts of midwives to hasten the process of birth. "Nature herself", he

79

wrote, "must be our adviser; the path she chalks must be our walk."

Harvey did well to draw attention to the deplorable ignorance of the midwives of that date; in his words: "the young, giddy and officious midwives do persuade poor women to use their birth stool before the time and do bring them in danger of their lives."

A contemporary of Harvey, Peter Chamberlen, to whose association with the obstetric forceps we shall refer presently, wrote in 1646 a pamphlet entitled "A Voice in Rhama, or the cry of women and children echoed forth in the compassion of Peter Chamberlen". He deplored the fact that the Royal College of Physicians insisted upon a high standard in those who practised medicine, but said not one word in support of the better instruction of midwives, though he remarked with truth that "multitudes have perished because our forefathers provided no remedy". Another of Harvey's contemporaries, Percival Willoughby, who practised in Derby and whose manuscript *Observations in Midwifery* was not printed until 1863, spoke of the "incessant and violent interferences of ignorant midwives." Willoughby got out of the difficulty by instructing his daughter in midwifery. She practised as a midwife and applied to her father in difficult cases. The difficult case was made more difficult by the frequent refusal of the patient to be attended by a man. Of one experience Willoughby relates: "My daughter was much troubled and told me she feared the birth would come by the buttocks (breech). Unknown to the patient I crept into the room on my hands and knees. I found her words true and I completed the delivery."

It is greatly to the credit of the Church of England that it accepted the responsibility for the control of midwives which the Royal College of Physicians apparently repudiated. In the sixteenth century licences were granted to midwives by the Archbishop of Canterbury. One such licence to Eleanor Pead in 1567 is worded thus: "I promise I will be ready to help poor as well as rich women in labour; I will not suffer any other body's child to be brought in place of a natural child; I will not use sorcery or incantation; I will not destroy cut or pull off the head of any child and I will, in time of necessity, baptise the child with the accustomed words, using pure and clean water. I will certify to the curate of the parish every such baptism."

This is of great interest as it appears to be the first mention of compulsory notification of baptism if not of birth. (The Notification of Births Act did not become law until 1907.) A special syringe was used for the baptism before or during birth. While the Church assumed control, it did nothing to improve the education and training of midwives.

MIDWIVES AND SURGEONS

Two centuries later we find Dr Hugh Chamberlen, a later representative of the famous family, in his preface to his translation of Mauriceau's work, dated 1755, urging midwives "not to be over-confident but to seek the help of a surgeon in difficult cases", which suggests that they often practised meddlesome midwifery. At about the same time, 1769, William Buchan, who lies buried in Westminster Abbey, published his immensely popular *Domestic Medicine* of which there were numerous editions and which is in use even today. His remarks on the midwife show the low state into which her craft had fallen. "Few women think of following the employment of midwife unless they are reduced to the necessity of doing it for bread." "Not one in a hundred of them has any education or proper knowledge of her business. The mischief done by officious midwives is greater than has been imagined; this might be prevented by proper training." After the time of Smellie, the science of obstetrics assumed growing importance, but it was not until the present century, in 1902, that the Midwives Act defined the title of "Midwife" and insisted upon a certain standard of knowledge in those whose names were to be entered in the register of midwives, under the control of the Central Midwives Board. There was no longer any place for the Sarah Gamps and Betsy Prigs who had been such a reproach to British obstetrics.

In France the reform of the midwives had been accomplished at a much earlier date. There were, in Paris as well as in Holland, schools of instruction for midwives even in the seventeenth century. Midwives were appointed to attend the French Royal House. Among them was Louise Bourgeois who was present at six royal births and who wrote a textbook for midwives, which was much used in its day.

Of later date, eighteenth century, were Madame La Chapelle and Madame Boivin, each of whom was the author of a textbook of midwifery. Maria La Chapelle deserves credit for

81

simplifying the existing doctrines, as she reduced the number of presentations described by Baudeloque from ninety-four to twenty-two. Her work, which consists of three volumes, is based on an experience of over 5,000 deliveries which she personally conducted. Her pupil and successor, Marie Anne Boivin, achieved equal distinction by her treatise entitled *L'Art des Accouchements*, which appeared in 1812, and which contains the first accurate description of hydatidiform or vesicular mole. Like Smellie's treatise, this book is a medical classic which reflects great credit upon the Royal Midwife of France.

THE CAESAREAN OPERATION

Let me now refer to (1) the history of Caesarean Section, and (2) the obstetric forceps. The Caesarean operation did not derive its name from the fact that Julius Caesar was born in this manner. It was called Caesarean because the Roman or Caesarean law demanded that when a pregnant woman died, her body should not be buried until the child had been removed. It was, in fact, the legislation of post-mortem Caesarean Section, an operation still practised, although rarely. A case was reported in 1938, another in 1940. The child survived on each occasion. Caesarean Section on the living has been the subject of much controversy. Until about the end of the eighteenth century it was regarded as unjustified, so great was the risk to the mother (Plate 2). It is said that the first successful operation took place in the year 1500, when Jacob Nufer, a Swiss sow-gelder, performed it upon his own wife with a razor. The woman made a good recovery and in later years had five other children, while the baby born so sensationally grew up and lived to the age of seventy-seven.

The first successful Caesarean Section in Great Britain was performed by an Irish midwife, Mary Donally, in 1738. The patient, Alice O'Neale, a farmer's wife who had been in labour for twelve days, made a good recovery. Although other successes followed, the mortality continued to be high until antisepsis, anaesthesia and improved technique entirely altered the outlook.

INVENTION OF THE FORCEPS

One of the most important events in the history of obstetrics was the invention of the forceps by Dr Peter Chamberlen. The

Chamberlens were a remarkable family, descendants of a Huguenot refugee, William Chamberlen. In four generations there were seven medical men, including three Peters and two Hughs, and among them they retained possession of the forceps as a family secret for 125 years. Several pairs of the original instruments were found in 1818 at Woodman Mortimer Hall, Essex, which belonged to Dr Peter Chamberlen, nephew of the inventor.[1] Several of the Chamberlens acted as accoucheurs to the Royal House. Peter Chamberlen the Elder attended Queen Henrietta Maria, and Hugh Chamberlen, senior, perhaps the most distinguished of them all, was in attendance at the birth of the future Queen Anne, in 1692. In his translation of Mauriceau's treatise on obstetrics, Dr Hugh Chamberlen refers repeatedly to the fact that he and his father and brothers had long practised "a better way", but he does not divulge what the better way was. Hugh Chamberlen attempted to sell the secret on the Continent and it is said that he did eventually sell it to a Dutch obstetrician, Roonhuysen, but sold only one blade. At all events the secret gradually became known and many patterns of forceps were introduced. For example, a Belgian accoucheur, Jean Palfyn, used two steel spoons, bound or clamped parallel to each other but not jointed or crossed.

The forceps which came to the notice of William Smellie when he was still a practitioner in Lanark were devised by a French surgeon named Dusée and described in 1735 by Dr Butter of Edinburgh. This instrument was employed "when the head was lodged low in the pelvis and seemed to make no advances to birth by the throes of the mother". The blades could be hinged in two different positions, but Butter thought it best to dispense with the screw altogether.

William Giffard, in 1726, was the first, after the Chamberlens, to use the forceps, and Edmund Chapman, the first to describe and illustrate the instrument, in 1733. Chapman dispensed with the screw or so-called French lock and linked the blades by a simple groove.

Smellie, although he did not invent the forceps, was certainly one of the first to employ them. At first he used short wooden forceps in order to avoid the clinking noise of the metal blades which betrayed their existence to the patient. At a later stage he used metal forceps, having the blades covered with strips of

[1] *The Secret Instrument* by Walter Redcliffe, 1947.

leather. It was Smellie who devised the English lock by adding flanges to the groove which united the blades (Fig. 1). The pelvic curve of the forceps is an invention usually attributed to Benjamin Pugh of Chelmsford. It was not until 1877 that Jean Tarnier introduced the axis traction handles. Probably no instrument has been subjected to so many modifications and alterations as obstetric forceps.

SOME CURIOUS PATTERNS

Some of the patterns have been very curious indeed, among them the forceps of John Burton of York, for-

Fig. 1—Smellie's forceps, with English lock, pelvic curve, and blades bound with leather thongs

tunately long since obsolete. John Burton (1710–71) cuts a fantastic figure as Dr Slop in Sterne's *Tristam Shandy*. The blades of the forceps are opened and closed by screwing the handle. It is not surprising that Tristam, brought into the world by this apparatus, had a permanent deformity of the nose, and that Dr Slop lacked three of his front teeth which had been knocked out by the handle of his forceps when they slipped, as often happened. Dr Burton had a high opinion of his extractor, as he called it, and of his own ability to use it. In his New System of Midwifery, 1751, he writes: "I gave my watch to one of the midwives, desiring her to observe how long I should be in delivering the patient. In less than half a minute I had delivered the child and after-birth. How the midwives looked at each other in amazement." Burton appears to have deserved all the satire heaped upon him by Laurence Sterne.

Among other contemporaries of Smellie were Sir Fielding Ould, who wrote a *Treatise of Midwifery* in 1742 and who was one of the founders of the great Dublin School. In London, John Maubray was the first to teach midwifery in England.

PLATE I

The Tree of Hippocrates at Cos (see page 36)

Illustration from an Arabic manuscript of 1307 A.D., said to be the earliest graphic representation of Caesarean section
(see page 82)

Wilhelmina Carstairs, whom Simpson named "St. Anaesthesia", aged 17
(see page 86)

PLATE 2

[85

Starting in 1725 he gave courses of twenty lectures at his house in New Bond Street and he affirmed that "two courses may qualify any students and dutiful hopefuls to perfect themselves in our noble art of midwifery". He went too far when he stated in his book, entitled *The Female Physician*, that "the healing and obstetricious arts seem now to be arrived at their very height of perfection". He quotes "the case of Countess Margaret, spouse to the Count of Heneberg who, on Good Friday 1276, at the age of 42, brought forth at one birth 365 infants whereof 182 were males, and as many females, and the odd one an hermaphrodite. The males were baptised by the name of John, the females by that of Elizabeth, in two brazon basons which are still to be seen in the village church of Losdun near The Hague.

A few years later, Smellie altered the whole trend of midwifery. The first maternity wards in this country were established in the Parish Hospital of St James's, Westminster, in 1739, by Sir Richard Manningham.

THE "RABBIT-WOMAN"

It was Manningham who was sent by King George I in 1726 to Godalming in Surrey to investigate the case of Mary Toft who claimed to have given birth to seventeen rabbits. The Rabbit-Woman provided the sensation of London for a season, until the hoax was exposed. Her story was actually believed by many. No one would eat rabbit that year! Pamphlets were written on the case and these, some of them bound in rabbit skin, are now of great value in the rare book market.

THE TEACHING OF OBSTETRICS

I have said that Manningham was the first to establish maternity wards. The first Professor of Obstetrics at Edinburgh University was Joseph Gibson, appointed in 1726. A maternity ward with four beds, in the attic of the old Royal Infirmary, was opened in 1756 under the charge of Professor Thomas Young. The Chair was subsequently occupied by Alexander and James Hamilton, father and son respectively. James Hamilton was the last doctor in Edinburgh to make his rounds in a Sedan chair. During his tenure of office, in 1833, the study of midwifery was made compulsory for the M.D. degree. Of course the most famous of the Edinburgh obstetricians was Sir James Young Simpson,[1] who discovered the anaesthetic value of chloroform, more than a hundred years ago. He at once applied the method to obstetric practice, his first patient being the wife of a Dr Carstairs and the daughter thus born, Wilhelmina, became Mrs Barns-Graham, and died in 1910. Her photograph, at the age of seventeen, stood on Simpson's desk and he called it "Saint Anaesthesia" (Plate 2).

To return to Smellie, or rather to his immediate followers, his colleague for many years had been his fellow Scot, William Hunter, brother of the more famous John Hunter. William Hunter is remembered chiefly as an anatomist, although he had a large obstetric practice. He was very conservative and used to show to his friends his rusty forceps, as a proof that he seldom used them. Hunter outlived Smellie by twenty years, but Smellie's successor in teaching, when he left London, was his nephew by marriage, John Harvie, who, if for no other reason, deserves to be remembered as the first to show that the delivery of the placenta might be assisted by pressure of the fundus, with a hand upon the abdomen. If his advice had been followed by Sir Richard Croft, who attended the Princess Charlotte in 1817, she might not have lost her baby and died of post-partum haemorrhage, and the throne might not have passed to Queen Victoria. Great is the responsibility of the obstetrician. Two lives are in his hands, and, as Sir Halliday Croom once said in his class-room, "When a patient enters a medical ward she expects to die, but when she comes to a maternity ward she expects to recover".

This topic might be elaborated and a great deal more might be said. I have made no reference to the history of puerperal fever, nor to the history of gynaecology. Modern developments I have left entirely aside, as the historian who is not also a practising obstetrician cannot do justice to recent history. Although the work of yesterday has already passed into history, it is not easy to fix its permanent place in history when it is viewed in such short focus. For that reason I have not brought the story up to date and have halted at the safe distance of the nineteenth century. I trust, however, that I have made it clear that some knowledge of the history of obstetrics is essential to the understanding of its present day practice.

[1] See page 235.

A SCOTTISH
SYMPOSIUM

THE RISE OF MEDICAL
EDUCATION IN SCOTLAND*

IT IS INTERESTING to trace the spread of medical knowledge down the centuries, in space as well as in time, in geography as well as in history.

The progress led from Greece to Rome, then to the Moslem Empire; back again to Europe by way of Salerno, thence to Padua, Paris, and Leyden, and at last to Britain and America. As the centuries unfolded, the centre of medical education shifted from place to place, each new seat of learning contributing its quota to the accumulating mass of information. Scotland played a noteworthy part in this geographical march of medicine, and the story of Scottish Medicine since the beginning of the eighteenth century has often been told and is well known. Nevertheless the contribution of Scotland, prior to that time, is a less familiar, though no less important, chapter of medical history and for that reason it has been chosen as a subject which may be of some interest to the present distinguished company.

Medical Education has been, and may still be, regarded as one of the major activities of Scotland. Just as the Scottish marine engineer is to be found on all the Seven Seas, so has the Scottish medical man exercised his art in all quarters of the globe.

Of course, the story of systematic medical education in Scotland does not lead us back very far. The "qualified" medical man is a comparatively recent product; indeed, before the sixteenth century, the career of medicine was open to all who cared, or dared, to embark upon it, and even after regulations were framed, the standard of medical efficiency remained very uneven. After all, we must remember that the General

---

* An address delivered to The New York Academy of Medicine, Section on Historical and Cultural Medicine, on 19 April 1949.

Medical Council, which controls the practice of medicine in Britain, came into being just over a century ago. Before 1858 there was no Register of "duly qualified" practitioners of medicine.

As a background to the story of the beginnings of medical education, let me try to sketch the history of medical practice in Scotland from the earliest times.

We have very little information regarding primitive medicine among the ancient inhabitants of Scotland. There may have been a special class of Medicine Men during the Stone Age. Certainly some such persons had their place during the Bronze Age, if one may judge from such scanty evidence as is furnished by a trephined skull of that period. The healing art was probably in the hands of a priestly class, the Druids, as they were called. Medicine and Religion have always been closely interwoven among primitive races, and the earliest hospitals of which we have any record were the pagan temples of ancient Greece.

The medical practice of those ancient Scots, or so-called Picts, was influenced by various early invaders. The Roman Army possessed medical officers, and certain surgical instruments, similar to those of Pompeii, as well as memorial tablets found in Scotland, are relics of the presence there of Roman military surgeons. Another influence, of considerably later date, was that of Saxon doctors or "leeches". In one of the oldest Saxon manuscripts, the Leech Book of Bald, dating from the tenth century, there is mention of a number of Scottish herbal remedies.

Early in the Christian era, a knowledge of medicine was fostered by some of the Saints, notably by St Columba (A.D. 521–97) who had a hospital and a herb garden on the Island of Iona, and by St Cuthbert (A.D. 635–87) who wrought wonderful cures in the South of Scotland and Northumbria during the seventh century. Doubtless those monks handed on to their disciples such knowledge as they possessed, because the care of the sick and wounded formed an important part of their duties.

In still later times, indeed as late as the sixteenth century, medical practice was a hereditary accomplishment handed down from generation to generation in certain families in the Western Isles of Scotland, notably in Islay and in Skye where the Macbeths and the McConachers were the accredited medical practitioners. They possessed manuscripts of the medical classics (Hippocrates, Galen, Avicenna, etc.) translated into the Gaelic tongue, some of which are preserved in the National Library of Scotland, in Edinburgh. Certain wandering scholars added to the medical knowledge of Scotland, such as Michael Scot (1175–1232) who, in the twelfth century, studied and taught in the famous medical school of Salerno, and who brought back to his native country the current learning of the time, albeit interlarded with much magic and astrology.

Despite those praiseworthy efforts, there can be little doubt that in those early times the status of medicine was very low. In his *History of Scotland*, Tytler remarks that during the thirteenth century, "the patient who fell into the hands of those feudal practitioners must have rather been an object of pity than of hope . . . it is probable that a sick or wounded knight had a better chance of recovery from the treatment of the gentle dames and aged crones in the castles whose knowledge of simples was great, than from the ministrations inflicted upon him by the accredited leeches of the times." Such was the condition of medicine in Scotland before the foundation of the universities and the establishment of systematic medical teaching.

Although their several histories overlap to some extent, it may best serve the purpose here if one describes each in its sequence, the rise and progress of medical education in the four Scottish centres of learning.

ST ANDREWS, 1411

The first Scottish university was founded in 1411, at St Andrews, the ecclesiastical capital and a place of great importance. Although provision was made, in the original charter, for a Faculty of Medicine, there appears to have been little teaching of medicine until the eighteenth century. Medicine was merely one subject of the Arts course, and like Anatomy, was merely a part of that modicum of general knowledge regarded as essential to every well-educated man.

The most famous Scottish medical man of the fifteenth century was William Schevez (1428–97). A native of St Andrews, he had studied at Louvain, and so distinguished himself that on his return he became physician to King James III at a salary of "£20 per annum, a velvet gown and oats for two horses". Eventually, he became Primate of Scotland, in succession to Archbishop Graham whose career of self-seeking and mismanagement ended in his loss of reason, and who was treated, or virtually imprisoned in Loch Leven Castle under the medical supervision of Schevez, a difficult position for Schevez, yet his tact and skill were equal to it. Schevez bequeathed his excellent library to St Andrews University; many valuable incunabula there bear his signature.

Within the next 150 years, the three colleges of St Salvator (1458), St Leonard (1512) and St Mary (1538), were founded at St Andrews, as also were the Universities in Glasgow and Aberdeen, but there was little or no teaching in Medicine in Scotland until after the Reformation; then, John Knox laid down, in his Book of Discipline of 1560, that Glasgow should teach only Arts; Aberdeen, Law and Divinity; while St Andrews was to be the Medical School for Scotland. This plan was never put into effect, and the only result was that St Andrews continued for many a year to exercise the privilege of granting, or perhaps one should say, of selling, the degree of M.D.

Among those who took advantage of this arrangement during the eighteenth century were Jean Paul Marat and Edward Jenner. In 1772, the Duke of Chandos offered to St Andrews a sum of money to endow a chair of "eloquence". The University decided that a chair of medicine might prove more useful, and Thomas Simson was appointed. Simson and his early successors did little to adorn the chair, but the fifth Chandos professor, John Reid (1804–49), who was appointed in 1841, was a man of high attainment, whose death at the age of forty was a great loss. Another distinguished Chandos professor, after the chair had become one of Physiology, was James Bell Pettigrew (1834–1908), whose studies of motion in animals and especially of the flight of birds, was of importance in the development of aeronautics.

Other new chairs were now created, and a Medical School was gradually evolved at St Andrews University; although it did not become fully established until in 1897 it joined forces with University College, Dundee, which had been established in 1881.

ABERDEEN, 1494

And now let us turn northward to Aberdeen, the third of the Scottish Universities to be founded, but the first to institute regular medical teaching at a time when there was no other organized medical school in Britain. Aberdeen may thus claim to be "the Cradle of British Medicine". One of St Columba's disciples, St Machar, was sent on a northward journey, with instructions to build a church at a spot where a river took the form of a Bishop's crook. The river was the Don, which assumes this sinuous course near its mouth, and the church became St Machar's Cathedral, destined to be more securely founded by Bishop Dunbar some centuries later. Bishop Dunbar, in 1532, was also the founder of a hospital which, however, was rather of the nature of a home for pensioners than an institution for the sick or injured.

In the fourteenth century, Aberdeen was a centre of learning which produced the first Scottish historian, John of Fordun (*Scotichronicon*), and the first Scottish poet, John Barbour (*The Bruce*). The medical practice of that time, as already noted was largely in the hands of "skilly women", or of landowners or lairds who attended to the health of their retainers. It was in 1494 that Bishop Elphinstone secured the co-operation of King James IV of Scotland to establish the University of St Mary's, which became King's College, in Old Aberdeen. King James, it may be mentioned, took a keen interest in science and medicine. He conducted many experiments in his laboratory at Stirling, and it is on record that he actually paid several of his subjects for the privilege of extracting their teeth (see page 105).

William Elphinstone, when he became Bishop of Aberdeen in 1483, found that part of Scotland "unlettered, ignorant, and almost barbarian". As the first Principal, or President, he chose Hector Boece, or Boyis, who had studied in Paris, and who wrote a history of Scotland. The Universities of St Andrews and Glasgow had already been founded by Bishops, and Elphinstone improved upon those efforts. His University was not to be a mere sanctuary for scholars but a real centre of culture for the north of Scotland. From the very start, provision was made for the teaching of medicine by the appointment of a "Mediciner" at a salary of £12 a year with the right of salmon fishing in the River Don, a valuable perquisite. The first Mediciner was

93

James Cumyne. The third was Gilbert Skene (1556–75), author of a little book on plague, of which only one copy exists (in the National Library of Scotland). It was entitled *Ane Breve Description of the Pest* and was the first original medical work to be printed in Scotland. It is dated, Edinburgh 1568.

After the time of Gilbert Skene, the office of Mediciner at Aberdeen lapsed for a time, and the next event of importance was the establishment of a second University, in 1593. King's College did not favour the changes wrought by the Reformation and in consequence, George Keith, Earl Marischal, a zealous follower of Calvin, founded this rival University which still bears the name Marischal College. The two universities continued to work separately until their union in 1860. The students of both colleges were strictly disciplined under the watchful eyes of the "Regents" as the professors were called. Students were obliged to begin work at 6 a.m. and to be in bed by 9 p.m., although once a week they were permitted to amuse themselves on the links. From the start, Medicine was taught at Marischal College, the first professor being Patrick Chalmers, whose ledger, still preserved, showed that malaria was prevalent in his time.

In the sixteenth century, Duncan Liddell (1561–1613), a distinguished son of Aberdeen who had been educated at King's College, held for some years the Chair of Medicine and

Mathematics at the University of Helmstadt and amassed a considerable fortune, part of which, together with his library, he bequeathed to Marischal College on his death in 1613. There is a beautiful brass plaque to his memory in the Church of St Nicholas.

Fig. 2—Memorial in the Church of St. Nicholas, Aberdeen, to Duncan Liddell (1561–1613)

The next step in advance, in 1741, was the establishment of an Infirmary for "poor persons who have distemper upon their bodies and such others as meet with the misfortunes of

94

broken bones". It contained twenty beds and was the forerunner of the magnificent infirmary opened in 1936 which cost exactly one thousand times as much money to build. Medical education was furthered by the Aberdeen Medical Society, founded in 1789 by Sir James McGrigor who became Director General of the Army Medical Service and was celebrated for the excellence of his Reports on the Health of the Army. The Society was really a sort of extramural school and candidates for membership were obliged to pass an entrance examination in Osteology, Greek, and Latin.

No account of Aberdeen medicine is complete without some reference to the family of Gregory, which produced sixteen professors in various Universities. The first of them was James Gregory, Professor of Mathematics at St Andrews. His son, James, was Mediciner at King's College and was, in turn, succeeded by James the younger (son), then by John (brother). John Gregory became Professor of Medicine at Edinburgh in 1766, jointly with William Cullen, and he was the father of the James Gregory who later succeeded to the Chair, and who was the originator of the famous "Gregory's Powder" (see pages 301–2).

The teaching of Anatomy was of high standard in those early days. Andrew Moir was lecturer in 1831, when there was strong feeling against anatomists owing to the nefarious doings of Burke and Hare in Edinburgh. Moir's dissecting room was burned down yet the lecturer maintained his prestige, continuing to teach until his death from typhoid fever at the age of 38. A later anatomist of great distinction was Sir John Struthers (1823–99), while Surgery was in the capable hands of Sir Alexander Ogston, who served abroad as a surgeon in the war of 1914–18 and wrote an interesting book entitled *Memories of Three Campaigns*. Aberdeen has had many other famous graduates, among them Sir Patrick Manson (1844–1922), "the father of Tropical Medicine".

GLASGOW, 1451

Now let us glance at the third great centre of medical learning, that of Glasgow. In the sixteenth century Glasgow was a town of subsidiary importance, with a population of only four or five thousand. The University had been founded by Bishop Turnbull in 1451 but Medicine was not actively taught for a long time. Andrew Boorde, physician, monk and traveller, who

95

in 1547 wrote the first original English medical book to be printed—*A Breviarie of Health*—visited Scotland during his wanderings and spent a year at what he called a "littyle unyversite named Glasco". This would appear to indicate that there may have been some medical teaching to attract him. Certainly there was a hospital, that of St Nicholas, which had been founded by Bishop Muirhead in 1471, although very probably this was an almshouse, like Bishop Dunbar's hospital at Aberdeen. Later the Hospital of St Nicholas came to be known as Provand's Lordship and it still stands—the oldest house in Glasgow—close to the Cathedral.

There was no organized control of the practice of medicine in and around Glasgow until the Faculty of Physicians and Surgeons was founded by Peter Lowe in 1599. At that date none of the Scottish Universities granted degrees in medicine but the Faculty was empowered to examine candidates and to decide whether they might be permitted to practice. Incidentally it may be remarked that Peter Lowe was a Scottish surgeon who had served for over twenty years in the Army of France and had published in 1597 *A Discourse of the Whole Art of Chirurgerie*, the first textbook of surgery to be written in English.* Peter Lowe's aim in founding the Faculty was to regulate and control medical practice in Glasgow. It was also resolved to give free medical treatment to the poor and even today this resolution is honoured in spirit, if not in

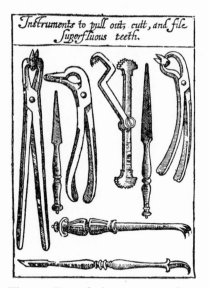

Fig. 3—Dental instruments from Peter Lowe's *Whole Art of Chirurgerie*, 1599

practice, since the Minutes of each meeting conclude with the words: "the poor were treated gratis, and the Faculty adjourned" (Fig. 3). The Faculty became a Royal College in 1962.

* In some editions entitled, *The Whole Course of Chirurgerie*.

The teaching of Medicine in Glasgow University was very desultory and ineffective until the eighteenth century. The first professor of Medicine, Robert Mayne, was appointed in 1637 but he appears to have accomplished little. The real founder of the Medical School of Glasgow was William Cullen (1710–90). Born at Hamilton in 1710, he began his career as a general practitioner in his native town, in partnership with William Hunter. In or about 1744, Hunter went to London where he became a famous anatomist and obstetrician, and where he was joined by his more famous brother John Hunter. Cullen meantime removed to Glasgow, and began his academic career as Professor of Medicine and Chemistry. With that versatility which was not uncommon at that time, he also taught Botany and Materia Medica. In 1755, Cullen was appointed Professor of Chemistry at Edinburgh, and later, as already mentioned, was transferred to the Chair of Medicine, with John Gregory as his colleague. Meanwhile, the Glasgow Chair of Chemistry passed to Cullen's assistant, Joseph Black who, famous for his discovery of "latent heat", shares with Cullen the credit of establishing the Glasgow Medical School, which was well staffed and consolidated by the end of the eighteenth century.

The Royal Infirmary of Glasgow was opened in 1794, equipped with 150 beds and "two sedan chairs to convey patients to and from their homes". The end of the eighteenth century also witnessed the establishment of a second University, in 1796, by John Anderson, a man of great ability and energy who had been Professor of Natural Philosophy since 1757. He intended to include faculties of law, theology, arts and medicine, but the medical faculty was the only one which really flourished and in the early years of the nineteenth century it became a formidable rival to Glasgow University. There were more than 700 students in 1830. Some years later the name was changed to the Anderson College of Medicine, and this institution continued to serve a useful function as an "extra-mural" school.

Meantime there were many distinguished teachers in Glasgow including Allen Thomson who taught anatomy and physiology successively at Edinburgh and Aberdeen and who eventually became Professor of Anatomy at Glasgow in 1848. His administrative ability was of great service to the University.

Of course, by far the greatest figure of the Glasgow Medical School was Joseph Lister, who went from Edinburgh in 1860 to become Professor of Surgery, and who introduced his anti-septic principle in 1865. His first paper on the subject appeared in *The Lancet* on 16 March 1867 and was entitled "A New Method of Treating Compound Fracture". Thirteen cases were described, with one death and one amputation—a remarkable result at a time when such an injury was attended by high mortality and was almost invariably treated by amputation. When Lister returned to Edinburgh as Syme's successor, the Glasgow Chair was filled by Sir George Macleod and he, in turn, was followed by Sir William Macewen (1848–1924), whose works on the treatment of brain abscess and on the growth of bone are classic accomplishments.

The Chair of Medicine, in 1862, passed into the able hands of Sir William Tennant Gairdner (1824–1907) who in the follow-ing year became Glasgow's first Medical Officer of Health. When he assumed office, one third of all deaths in the city were the result of infectious disease, principally typhus fever, but under his able control the health of the city improved greatly. There were many other great physicians and surgeons, but enough has been said to prove the importance of the Glasgow School of Medicine.

EDINBURGH

Finally, let me try to give a brief outline of the rise and early development of the Edinburgh Medical School. I have kept it to the end, as Edinburgh is the youngest of the Scottish Uni-versities, founded in 1583 (Plate 3). Nevertheless Anatomy and Surgery have been subjects of instruction at Edinburgh since the beginning of the sixteenth century. It was during the reign of King James IV of Scotland, who has already been men-tioned as a patron of medicine, that the Barber Surgeons of Edinburgh obtained their Charter from the Town Council in the year 1505. The "Seal of Cause", as it was called, em-powered the Barber Surgeons to decide, by examination, who was to practice within the Burgh. Candidates were to be able to "baith read and write" and were to be familiar with "the anatomy of man's body" and the position of the veins, vene-section being then the treatment for many ills. Furthermore, the Incorporation of Barber Surgeons, which later became the

Royal College of Surgeons of Edinburgh, was entitled to claim the body of one executed criminal each year for dissection purposes and, strangest of all regulations, was to have a monopoly of the sale of alcoholic liquor (aqua vitae). Unfortunately this monopoly has not been retained. The early meeting-place of the Barber Surgeons was a mean street called Dickson's Close. There was some intermittent teaching of anatomy during those early days, but a great impetus to learning was given in 1583, when the Town Council established the Town's, or "Tounis", College. So determined were they that their institution was to be free from what they termed "medieval papistry" that they did not apply to it the name "University". At first, there was no provision for the teaching of medicine, but an important step in advance was the foundation of the Royal College of Physicians in 1681 by Sir Robert Sibbald, who had studied at Leyden and who was the author of important works on history and geography, as well as Medicine. Sibbald and his young colleague, Dr Archibald Pitcairne, were appointed Professors of Medicine in the Town's College in 1685. They were also instrumental in establishing the Physick Garden, then an important adjunct to the teaching of medicine, on the site of the present Waverley Station. It was the precursor of the present fine Royal Botanic Garden (see page 115).

Pitcairne attained a European distinction when he was appointed Professor of Medicine at Leyden in 1692, an appointment which was then possible, as language difficulties did not exist because all teaching was conducted in Latin. Among his pupils at Leyden was Hermann Boerhaave, who succeeded him, and who became perhaps the greatest teacher of Medicine of all time.

In those days the links between Edinburgh and Leyden were numerous and strong. Firmest of all was that forged by John Monro, a surgeon in the army of William of Orange, who was so greatly impressed by the Leyden methods that he resolved that Edinburgh should have a Medical School, conducted on similar principles. Accordingly, he educated his son Alexander at Leyden with a view to having him appointed Professor of Anatomy at Edinburgh. This ambitious plan proved most successful. Alexander Monro assumed the Chair in 1720, and thus became the "Father" of the Edinburgh Medical School. He was succeeded by his son, Alexander Monro, secundus, who was followed in turn by the grandson, Alexander Monro, tertius. Monro secundus maintained the tradition of his father, indeed he was even more distinguished, but it is said that Monro tertius was content to read his grandfather's notes, over a century old, to his class, without even deleting the remark, "When I was a student at Leyden in 1719" (see page 306).

The Monros held the Chair for 128 years. But there were other noteworthy anatomists. Sir Charles Bell (1774–1842) began and ended his career in Edinburgh, but most of his great work on the nervous system was carried out in London. One of the great Edinburgh teachers of anatomy was John Barclay (1758–1826), who was obliged to deliver the same lecture twice a day in order to accommodate his large class. He was succeeded by Robert Knox (1791–1862), an admirable lecturer whose classes were very popular, and a man of high scientific attainment. Unfortunately, his career was clouded by his unwitting association with the Burke and Hare murders in 1828. One of Barclay's assistants who became a famous surgeon was Robert Liston (1794–1847). Robert Liston and James Syme (1799–1870) were closely associated as teachers of anatomy in Edinburgh until, in 1835, Liston became Professor of Surgery to University College, London, where he was the first surgeon in Britain to employ ether as a general anaesthetic.

The anaesthetic value of chloroform was discovered by the Professor of Obstetrics, Sir James Young Simpson, in 1847. Simpson was a versatile man, although his incursion into the field of surgery made him unpopular with some of his surgical colleagues. He was one of those who opposed Lister's ideas, alleging that the prevalence of septic infection was due to faulty hospital construction, or "hospitalism", as it was called.

The first medical man in Edinburgh to confine his practice to surgery was Benjamin Bell, who lived at the end of the eighteenth century, who wrote a well-known textbook of Surgery, and who was the direct ancestor of Dr Joseph Bell, the Edinburgh surgeon, the original of Sherlock Holmes (see page 289).

Benjamin Bell was one of the earliest surgeons to the Edinburgh Royal Infirmary, which was opened in 1741 and provided for 200 sick persons "each in a distinct bed". Before that day it was not uncommon for two patients to occupy the same bed. The greatest Edinburgh surgeon before the time of Lister

Old Surgeons' Hall, Edinburgh, built in 1697 in the grounds of Curryhill House, and replaced in 1832 by the present Surgeons' Hall (see page 110)

The Old Quadrangle of Edinburgh University, begun in 1789, the dome added in 1886 (see page 98)

PLATE 3

100]

The tomb of James Borthwick (1615–1675) in Greyfriars Churchyard, Edinburgh (see page 110)

Dr Francis Adams of Banchory (1796–1861); the bust in the University of Aberdeen (see page 130)

PLATE 4

[101

was Lister's father-in-law, James Syme, of whom it was said that he never wasted "a word, a drop of ink, or a drop of blood". When Syme failed to secure appointment to the Infirmary Staff he established a hospital of his own, and that hospital, Minto House, was the scene of the operation described in *Rab and his Friends* by Dr John Brown, who was Syme's house surgeon.

The wonderful work of Lister, continued at Edinburgh when he succeeded Syme in the Chair of Clinical Surgery, deserves a lecture to itself. Nor is it possible within the bounds of this outline to discuss the progress of other subjects in the medical curriculum, the contribution to medicine of William Cullen, of James Gregory and, in later times, of Sir Robert Christison (1797–1882) and many others who taught various medical subjects in the University and in the extramural School of the Royal Colleges. As time went on, and as other Medical Schools became established, Edinburgh ceased to be the main centre of medical education in Britain, although it still maintains a high standard and attracts many students, both undergraduates and post-graduates. Among them there have been many American students ever since the early years of the eighteenth century when the torch of medical learning, rekindled and strengthened by Leyden and Edinburgh, was handed on, across the Atlantic, to Philadelphia and to New York. The close friendship then established remains firmer than ever.

THE MEDICAL AND
SCIENTIFIC EXPLOITS OF
KING JAMES IV

ALTHOUGH MANY KINGS AND QUEENS have been interested in the health of the nations they governed, and have done much to promote the advance of medical science, few monarchs have themselves conducted medical or scientific investigations, and still fewer have actually participated in the practice of medicine or surgery. In ancient times there was the example of Mithridates, King of Pontus in the century before the birth of Christ, one who might almost be called a royal toxicologist, who rendered himself immune to poisons by the self-administration of small doses, and who gave his name to that most famous of antidotes, mithridatium, which, along with theriac, retained its position in nearly every pharmacopoeia until the end of the eighteenth century.

In more recent days, the practice of "the Royal Touch" in the treatment of "scrofula" or surgical tuberculosis, brought kings and queens into close contact with their afflicted subjects from the days of Edward the Confessor to those of Queen Anne, the strange ritual reaching its zenith in the time of Charles II who, it was said, "touched" more than six thousand persons in a single year (1660).

A story even stranger than that of mithridatium or of touching for "king's evil" concerns King James IV of Scotland, whose medical and scientific activities were perhaps unique in history. In his *Chronicles of Scotland* Robert Lindsay of Pitscottie writes: "This noble King James IV was well learned in the Art of Medicine, and also a cunning Chirurgener that none in his realm, that used that craft, but would take his Counsel in all their Proceedings."

THE PERSONALITY AND BACKGROUND OF JAMES IV

In order to understand his medico-scientific exploits it is essential to know something of the King's character and of the condition of Scotland during his reign.

The young prince succeeded his father, James III, under peculiar and trying circumstances. At the age of fifteen he was induced to lead a rebel army against the king, who was murdered as he fled from the battlefield of Sauchieburn, near Stirling, in 1488. It is said that he was so filled with remorse at having been partly responsible for his father's death that he wore a chain of iron round his waist for the remainder of his life. Although recorded to be "temperate in eating and drinking", James IV was a high-spirited youth, of whose various love affairs the most romantic concerned the beautiful Margaret Drummond, whom he might have married had she not been regarded as undesirable by those who favoured an English bride for the King. Accordingly, Margaret and her two sisters, Euphemia and Sybilla, were poisoned in 1501 at their father's house, Drummond Castle, and their tombs may still be seen in the choir of Dunblane Cathedral. Two years later James married Margaret Tudor, daughter of the English King Henry VII—a union of great significance to both countries, because the great-grandson of James and Margaret, James VI, became King of England, Scotland, and Ireland. The most graphic contemporary account of James IV is given by the Spanish Ambassador, Pedro de Ayala, who wrote in 1498: "The King is of noble stature and handsome complexion; he is feared by the bad, and loved and revered like a god by the good." An apt linguist, he could speak not only Latin, French, German, Italian, and Spanish, but also Gaelic, "the language of the savages of Scotland", as Ayala calls it.

SCOTLAND IN THE TIME OF JAMES IV

Scotland was a prosperous country during the reign of James IV. Among the exports were hides, sheepskins, and wool, and large quantities of river salmon. The imports included linen and silk and much wine, though ale was still the chief drink and whisky was as yet unknown, as were tea, coffee, and tobacco. Early in his reign James became aware of the need for strong armed forces. The Scots were ever fighters; indeed, Ayala said that "they spend all their time in wars, and if there is no war they fight with one another, although since the present King came to the throne they do not dare to quarrel so much."

Although they had their amusements, only those which might be turned to military advantage were favoured, and in 1491 a law was passed forbidding "futeball, golfe, or uther sik unprofitable sports", but the practice of archery was still encouraged. The entry in the Accounts, in 1503, recording the purchase of "golf-clubbes and balles to the King, 9s.", leads one to question whether the law against non-militant sports was very rigidly enforced.

It was at this time that Scotland took its place as a great naval power. The largest of the war vessels was the *Great Michael*, which was built of oak from the woods of Fife and was launched in 1511. All this military and naval activity suffered severely from the battle of Flodden, in 1513, which brought disaster to the Scottish nation and at which King James IV was among the slain. Nevertheless, his was a noteworthy reign marked by a revival of learning and the beginning of systematic medical education.

The Universities of St Andrews (1411) and Glasgow (1451) had already been founded, but in 1495 the King lent his patronage to the establishment of a university at Aberdeen, the first British university to give instruction in medicine. The individual responsible for this teaching was called the "mediciner", and his salary was £12 a year, besides the right of salmon fishing in the River Don. A few years later, in 1505, the Town Council of Edinburgh granted a "Seal of Cause", or Charter of Privileges, to the surgeons and barber-surgeons of Edinburgh, a document ratified by the King in the following year. In this manner there was established the body which became the Royal College of Surgeons of Edinburgh. Thus King James IV was closely associated with the beginnings of the teaching of medicine and surgery in Scotland.

Another noteworthy cultural event during the reign of James IV was the setting-up of a printing press at Edinburgh in 1507 by Walter Chepman and Androw Myllar, although it was not until 1568 that the first original medical work in the vernacular was printed, entitled *Ane Breve Description of the Pest*, by Gilbert Skene.

PUBLIC HEALTH LEGISLATION UNDER JAMES IV

The mention of "pest", or plague, recalls the fact that bubonic plague was widespread in Scotland at about this time. There were various laws to restrict the movements of travellers in plague-stricken areas, and the importation of English cloth was forbidden. Official scavengers were first employed in Edinburgh in 1499, and the notification of plague was made compulsory in 1505. Still more enlightened was a letter sent by the King to all burghs of Scotland in 1513, which showed that he had given considerable thought to matters of public health. His suggestions included the isolation of plague victims, the expulsion of beggars and vagrants, and the destruction of dogs, cats, and pigs in the streets. Already, in 1497, he had instituted measures for the isolation of those suffering from syphilis, the "Strange seiknes of Nappilis", which, following its dramatic appearance at Naples had spread to Scotland, where it was known as grandgore or grantgore.

Treatment was strongly discouraged, probably because the cure, at that time, was worse than the disease.

THE KING AS MEDICAL PRACTITIONER AND DENTIST

It is unfortunate that the records of the King's activities in the field of medicine are so scanty—derived mainly from the Lord High Treasurer's Accounts. One must be careful to avoid erroneous conclusions, and the fact that the King disbursed various sums to sick or blind or injured persons need not imply that he was concerned in the treatment. Many payments to doctors or "leeches" are recorded, and also to apothecaries or "pottingers", and more rarely to "surrigicos" or "barbours", as in the case of "ane man new schorne of the stane" at Coupar Angus in 1496, which would appear to have been an operation of lithotomy.

For the most part those payments seem to be merely instances of royal generosity, but there are other entries which indicate clearly that King James IV was not always content to be a mere onlooker, but determined, on occasion, to test his own skill, although he wisely limited his activities to the dressing of wounds, blood letting, and the extractions of teeth.

Of the first mentioned, this is but a single entry, dated July, 1504: "for claith to be wippes to Johne Balfouris sair leg quilk

105

the King helit, 2s." Apparently the King himself was responsible for the healing of John Balfour's leg, and paid two shillings for the surgical swabs or "wippes".

Still more interesting are those entries which suggest that the King actually paid his subjects for the privilege of allowing him to act as surgeon. Thus, an entry in 1491 is as follows: "To Domynico, to gif the King leve to lat him bluid, 28s."; and it is interesting to note that in the same year the King himself was bled by a "leech", the record stating "To a leyche that leyt the King blud, 28s". The payment, though of equal amount, is on this occasion the more usual one of patient to doctor, and not vice versa.

James IV also showed a lively interest in dentistry. In 1503 he purchased "ane turcase to tak out teith", and was himself the patient, when he paid "to the barbour that com to tak furth the Kingis tuth, 14s." Not content with this, he must needs act as dental surgeon and pay compensation to the patient, as he had done previously in blood-letting. Thus we find in 1511 an item: "To ane fallow, because the King pullit furth his teth, 14s." And in that same year we discover the strangest happening of all, when the King actually operated upon one of his own barber-surgeons, extracting two of his teeth. The entry states: "To Kynnard the barbour for twa teith drawn furth of his hed be the king, 14s." Apparently the dentist's fee of 14s. was only half of the fee paid for blood-letting, 28s.

The evidence that King James IV practised both of those activities appears to be quite definite, despite the unfortunately scanty record. One wishes that the victims of the royal favour had left some written record of their own feelings.

EXPERIMENTS IN CHEMISTRY AND IN AVIATION

Of the King's investigations in the field of science contemporary records are more informative.

King James's interest in chemistry, or rather in alchemy, coincided with the time of residence in Scotland of an Italian named John Damian, repeatedly designated in the Lord High Treasurer's Accounts as "Maister John", or as "the Franch leich" or "mediciner". He stood high in the King's estimation, and the two collaborated in many experiments. The King paid Damian well, and made him Abbot of Tungland in Galloway, although he had no ecclesiastical qualifications at all. John

Leslie in his *History of Scotland* considered Damian a complete charlatan and an "ingenious beguiler". William Dunbar (1465—1530) lampooned him in a poem as "The Feigned Friar of Tungland":

> *In pottingry he wrocht gryt pyne,*
> *He murdreist mony in medecyne . . .*
> *In leichcraft he was homicyd.*

The experiments of the King and the "friar" were concerned mainly with the transmutation of other metals into gold. Laboratories were set up at Stirling and Linlithgow, and the search for the "quintessence" was continued for some years, involving considerable expenditure for coal and wood, and for saltpetre, quicksilver, and aqua vitae. This medieval quest by the two alchemists was rudely interrupted by an accident which befell John Damian while he was conducting what must have been one of the earliest experiments in aviation, in 1507. Certainly it was a bold venture on his part to equip himself with a pair of wings made of feathers, and coupled to his shoulders, and, so equipped, to leap from the cliff on which Stirling Castle is built. Indeed, he was fortunate to escape with nothing more than a broken thigh and the loss of prestige. It is recorded that the people who had assembled to watch the experiment "were like to split of laughter", and few sympathized with the unfortunate aviator.

MAROONED CHILDREN AND UNITED TWINS

The inquiring attitude of mind so apparent in King James IV is further exemplified in his experiment in the rearing of two children in isolation, which has often been described, but nowhere so clearly as by Lindsay the historian. The King, eager to know in what tongue a child would speak if isolated from the speaking world during its early years, caused two children to be marooned with a deaf-and-dumb nurse on the island of Inchkeith. Lindsay writes: "The King gart take a dumb woman and put her into Inch Keith, and gave her two young Bairns in company with her and gart furnished them with al Necessaries . . . desiring to understand the Language thir Bairns could speak when they came of lawful age. Some say they spak guid Hebrew. But as to my self, I know not." The historian wisely

107

refrains from giving an opinion. Certainly he does not subscribe to the "Hebrew" idea.

During the reign of James IV there was born in Scotland a set of united twins, or "Siamese" twins as we now sometimes call them (after the famous Siamese couple who were born in 1811 and lived for sixty-three years). The King took a keen interest in the "monster", which had two heads and two bodies, "but from the Waste down, there was but one personage". King James caused "them" to be taught to sing two parts, "the one the Treble, and the other the Tenor, which was very sweet and melodious to hear". They also learned to speak a number of different languages, and lived to the age of twenty-eight years.

CONCLUSION

Strange as were these exploits of King James IV, there can be no doubt that he was a man of inquiring mind, with a vision ahead of his time. He retained, as few of us do throughout our lives, that gift of curiosity, so valuable as an incentive to education, which seems to be innate in childhood but which grows smaller and less compelling in adult years. James IV of Scotland may well be regarded as a royal pioneer, and not merely a royal patron, of medicine and of science. In the long line of Stuart kings, with their curious mixtures of folly and wisdom, he stands out as one whose advanced views brought enlightenment to his realm and hastened the dawn of a new age. And though his reign ended by his death on Flodden Field it heralded the approach of happier times, of more widespread culture and education, and of steady advance in medicine and science.

REFERENCES

Accounts of the Lord High Treasurer of Scotland, 1473–1513 (Edinburgh 1877–1902).
Ledger of Andrew Halyburton, 1492–1503, (London, 1867).
LINDSAY, ROBERT, of Pitscottie, *The Chronicles of Scotland, 1436–1604* (Edinburgh 1814).

SURGEON-APOTHECARIES
AND PHYSICK GARDENS

FROM THE DAWN OF HISTORY botany has been regarded as an essential part of medical education and practice. As he advanced in intellect, primitive man recognized the value of plants and ascertained which of them were foods, which were poisons, and which were remedies for disease. It took him a long time, however, to abandon the magico-religious conception of ill-health and to adopt the scientific outlook which we now take for granted. The vegetable world was the first object of his researches. Even before the value of anatomy was realized and long before chemical remedies competed with those of vegetable origin, the so-called physick garden in which medicinal plants were cultivated and studied, formed part of the equipment of many a monastery or hospice and, at a later date, of every medical school. Some of those early gardens are still preserved as relics of a past age, adjoining the universities of Montpellier, Leyden, Uppsala, and other centres of learning.

In Edinburgh, no less than the six physick gardens listed below were founded between 1656 and 1704, many years before the establishment of a complete medical school:

Surgeons' House, 1656   Heriot's Hospital, 1661
Holyrood Palace, 1670   Trinity Hospital, 1676
Town's College, 1695   College of Physicians, 1704

THE SURGEONS' GARDEN

Although the priority of this garden receives little or no emphasis in previous accounts of the physick gardens of Edinburgh, the Incorporation of Surgeons and Barber-Surgeons, founded in 1505, was the first medical institution in Edinburgh to recognize the need for a physick garden. It may seem strange that the surgeons should have decided on such a venture, but this step was a natural sequel to their acquisition of a house and grounds of their own in 1656, and to their decision to open their doors to certain apothecaries. The latter, as surgeon-apothecaries, thus acquired a professional status which must have been very acceptable to them since they had long been the buffer between surgeons and physicians.

The purchase of a permanent home by the surgeons is recorded in the Minutes of 1656 wherein it is stated that "Baillie John Jossie reported that he had made a verbal agreement to sell Curryhills House and Yards to the Surgeons, the writs to be delivered to Thomas Kincaid". Kincaid was Deacon of the Surgeons at that date, and their meetings had previously been held in his house. The acquisition of a convening house was an important advance; and this meeting place was used until 1697 when the new "Surgeons' Hall" was built on the adjacent ground (Plate 3).

Thomas Kincaid and James Borthwick were the first two apothecaries to be admitted as surgeons in 1645, when the number of surgeons in the Incorporation had fallen as low as eight members. Neither Kincaid nor Borthwick had been apprenticed to a surgeon, as the regulations demanded, but it seems that their service in the Scottish Army, which they had just relinquished, was allowed to count in lieu of apprenticeship. Each of them rose high in his profession and set a high standard for the new class of surgeon-apothecary. Of Thomas Kincaid we know little other than that he was Treasurer of the Surgeons from 1652 to 1655, and Deacon from 1655 to 1656. Our knowledge of James Borthwick is clearer, and two noteworthy relics of him are on view in Edinburgh: his portrait by an unknown artist (dated 1645), the oldest portrait in the College Hall, and his curious tombstone in Greyfriars' Churchyard depicting a dancing skeleton carrying a book and a scythe within a framework adorned by carvings of surgical instruments (Plate 4). Borthwick, who was born in 1615 and died in 1675, appears to have been appointed by the Surgeons as their first accredited teacher of anatomy directly after he became one of their number. He was twice Deacon, 1648–50 and 1659–60.

THE TEACHING OF BOTANY AND PHARMACY

Following the decision of the Surgeons to widen the scope of the instruction available for apprentices, and under the stimulus of the two surgeon-apothecaries, Kincaid and Borthwick, no time was lost in planting "medicinal plants and herbs, at an expense of £200, within the grounds of Curryhill Yards (or High School Yards)", and thus the first of the Edinburgh Physick Gardens was inaugurated. On 22 October 1656, it is on record that "the Town granted a licence to the Chirurgeons to cast twa hunder devotts in the mire for the use of their garden in Curryhill yaird", no doubt with a view to improving the soil.

The opportunity of becoming apothecaries as well as surgeons appealed to the apprentices, with the result that Kincaid and Borthwick had no lack of students when they taught "the airt of pharmacie" in the Surgeons' Garden. Examinations were held between April and September because "that season of the year is onlie proper for the tryall of entrants in the knowledge of plants, indispensable necessar to the profession of ane apothecar".

The Surgeons' Minutes of 1668 show that there was a signed agreement with the gardener, George Cathcart, who, as well as living rent-free in the basement of Curryhills House and attending to the garden, was to be at liberty "to sell drink, and to keep kyles [bowls] in the entry of the yard, providing he suffer not vulgar persons and scholars of the High School to play thereat". After Cathcart had served as gardener, and also as "Officer" to the Surgeons for over thirty years, it was decided that it might add to his prestige were he to wear a livery coat and a silver badge. This he indignantly refused to do and resigned from his office.

In 1695 the Town's College appointed James Sutherland as Professor of Botany and for a fee of one guinea per student he undertook to instruct the apprentices, not in the Surgeons' Garden but in the larger and better equipped garden of Trinity Hospital to which we shall presently refer. In the meantime, other physick gardens had been established, for example, the garden at Heriot's Hospital to which reference is made in the Records of that institution. In 1661, the gardener was instructed "to plant medicinal herbs, so that they may be studied" although who the students were to be is not stated, and appears uncertain.

THE PHYSICK GARDENS AT HOLYROOD PALACE

In 1670 Dr Robert Sibbald and Dr Andrew Balfour established a garden at Holyrood, hitherto regarded as the first of the Physick Gardens of Edinburgh. Each was a member of a well-known Fife family; each was an original Fellow of the Royal College of Physicians founded in 1681, each was knighted in the following year and each, in turn, became President of the College. In his interesting autobiography, first printed in 1932 from the manuscript in the National Library of Scotland, Sibbald tells how he and Balfour established the Physick Garden. Patrick Murray, the Laird of Livingston in West Lothian, who had a large collection of plants, was a friend of Dr Balfour and was the first to suggest "the designe of establishing the medicine garden at Edinburgh". Sibbald and Balfour rented from John Brown, "gardner of the Abbey", a plot forty feet square where they collected about 900 plants, many of them from Livingston. This small garden was placed in the care of "a youth, James Sutherland, who by his own industry had attained great knowledge of plants and of medals". Some surgeon-apothecaries opposed the idea, "fearing it might usher in a Coledge of Physitians" (as indeed it did at a later date) but Dr Balfour "made them friends to the designe". It seems not unlikely that the enmity between the surgeon-apothecaries and the physicians accounts for the neglect of any mention of the Surgeons' Garden in some of the early accounts of the physick gardens.

THE GARDEN AT TRINITY HOSPITAL

The Holyrood Garden proved too small for the purpose envisaged by Sibbald and Balfour, and they secured a 19-years' lease of the garden belonging to Trinity Hospital which had been founded by Mary of Gueldres about 1460 on a site now occupied by the Waverley Station. For this the assistance of James Sutherland was again indispensable, and he was appointed "Intendant" of this garden in 1676. It has been claimed that, with the exception of the Oxford Garden founded in 1632, the Trinity Garden was the oldest botanic garden in Britain. It was at the height of its success when James Sutherland prepared a catalogue of the plants which was published in book form in 1683 under the title *Hortus Medicus Edinburgensis*. In the preface he stated that he had acquired seeds and plants from distant countries "by correspondence and by many painful journeys in all seasons of the year". In Edinburgh University Library there is the manuscript of a Bill of Lading relating to the shipment at Rotterdam on 20 July 1694 of a cargo of plants in a ship bound for Blackness in Scotland, thence to be delivered to James Sutherland.

Sutherland's Catalogue must have been of great value to the Physicians in their preparation of an official list of drugs for the Edinburgh Pharmacopoeia which, first published in 1699, went through fourteen editions until the last, dated 1841, was superseded by the British Pharmacopoeia three years later. For the writing of the original Edinburgh Pharmacopoeia, Balfour and Sibbald were to a great extent responsible. The Physick Garden, at first independent of the University and of the College of Physicians, had been founded for the instruction of apothecaries, and Sibbald had in mind the issuing of a pharmacopoeia when he had worked for the foundation of a College of Physicians.

Trinity Garden measured 300 feet from east to west and 190 feet from north to south. It was separated from the eastern end of the Nor' Loch by a wall and mound of earth. The garden was divided into six rectangular plots, with footpaths between, and the plants were arranged systematically in accordance with genera and species. Only one of the plots was devoted to medicinal plants and, to quote from Sutherland's description, "the Dispensatory Plants or plants used in Medicine are arranged in alphabetical order, to make instructions more easy for beginners".

Trinity Hospital Garden was a botanic as well as a physick garden, however, and it was often called the Edinburgh Botanic Garden. The rarer and more fragile plants were protected by bell glasses and small frames, but as yet there were no hot houses; around the walls were many beautiful shrubs. Those walls were not very high and, as they proved ineffective in deterring trespassers—and even sheep and cattle—from invading and injuring the garden, they were repaired and heightened in 1684. A more serious calamity befell the Garden in the spring of 1689 when, during a siege of the Castle, it was thought necessary to drain the Nor' Loch. The Garden was then completely inundated for a time, and many plants were destroyed. Sutherland petitioned the Town Council to make good the loss, and he was awarded 1,000 merks. The dykes and the gardener's house were also repaired.

Almost a century later it became necessary to transfer the Trinity Garden which was "in great reputation both in England and foreign nations". The site eventually chosen was on the west side of Leith Walk, just beyond Gayfield Square. The Garden was moved thither in 1767 (the most likely of a number of dates noted in the various accounts). In Arnot's *History of Edinburgh* (1779) we read of the Leith Walk Garden that "the Botanical Garden, considered one of the ornaments of the city, consists of five acres English measure and is situated on the west side of the foot-walk to Leith. The soil is light and sandy, and in the centre of the garden is a spring of water formed into a bason. Although it is not twelve years since it was applied to botanical purposes, it is now richly stocked, and the trees are so far advanced as to afford good shelter to the small and tender plants. The conservatories form a front of 140 feet, yet they are already insufficient to contain the collection of exotic plants received from all quarters."

PHYSICK GARDEN OF THE TOWN'S COLLEGE

In 1695, James Sutherland having been formally appointed Professor of Botany, the Town's College (or University) set aside part of their garden at Kirk of Field as a Physick Garden (seen in Edgar's map, 1742). Sutherland was appointed Keeper and retained the chair and the custody of the Town Garden till 1706, when he was succeeded by Charles Preston and then George Preston. Alexander Monro primus was one of their students. The Prestons were followed by Charles Alston and he, in turn, by John Hope, father of T. C. Hope, Professor of Chemistry.

THE PHYSICIANS' GARDEN

During the latter part of the seventeenth century, then, there were five physick gardens in Edinburgh: the Surgeons', Heriot's, Holyrood, Trinity and the Town's College. There was yet another, marked in Edgar's map, near Tweeddale Court, and called "Hortus Medicus" or "Dr John Rutherford's garden".

114

Rutherford was the father of Daniel Rutherford who became Professor of Botany, and was the maternal grandfather of Sir Walter Scott. It is uncertain whether this was a private physick garden or whether it was owned by the College of Physicians, whose premises were established in 1704 at Fountain Close near at hand. Pending further information perhaps it should not be included in the official list of physick gardens.

THE ESTABLISHMENT OF THE GARDEN AT INVERLEITH

During Hope's tenure of the Chair of Botany, Materia Medica was separated from it, and the first to hold the new Chair of Materia Medica, in 1768, was Francis Home. Hope's successor as Regius Keeper and Professor was Daniel Rutherford, better known as a chemist and the discoverer of nitrogen than as a botanist. After holding the Chair for thirty-four years he was succeeded in 1820 by Robert Graham, under whose guidance the Physick Garden, now called the Royal Botanic Garden, was transferred in 1822 to its present site at Inverleith. Graham was the first President of the Botanical Society which dates from 1836. He was followed in 1845 by Hutton Balfour under whose administration the Garden was enlarged and greatly improved.

In his Presidential Address to the Botanical Society in 1874, Sir Robert Christison suggested the addition of an Arboretum for the study of forestry. A fine palm house was also erected and a museum and new class-room built.

Today the Garden is no longer a physick garden, and Botany is no longer a part of the medical curriculum. Modern drugs or materia medica are only to a small extent derived from plants; they are for the most part of chemical origin, products of the factory rather than of the garden. Yet Botany remains an important science; it has derived from Medicine quite as much as it has given to Medicine for many centuries. The disappearance of "Medical Botany" is perhaps unfortunate, but we can look back and recognize the great importance of the Physick Gardens of Edinburgh and pay thankful tribute to their medical and academic sponsors.

DR JOHN BROWN, "RAB" AND "MARJORIE"*

DR JOHN BROWN, the well-loved Edinburgh physician and writer of last century, is now remembered chiefly as the author of that immortal story, *Rab and his friends,* and of the equally attractive account of the short life of Marjorie Fleming.

These remain the best-known of his writings, but all that he wrote is still worthy of attention today, eighty years after his death. It is also worth while to recall the chief incidents of his life and work, against the background of the Victorian Age.

ANCESTRY AND EARLY LIFE

Dr John Brown came of a stock outstanding for its gifts, both intellectual and spiritual, and, as he informs us in the autobiographical essay entitled, "Letters to John Cairns, D.D.", he was the fifth John Brown to bear the name, in direct lineal descent.

The first was a weaver in the village of Carpow, near Abernethy, whose son leapt into fame in a remarkable fashion. Beginning life as a shepherd boy, he taught himself Greek, and being eager to buy a Greek Testament, he walked overnight the twenty-four miles from Abernethy to St Andrews.

"If you can read a few verses, you may have it for nothing", said a University Professor who chanced to encounter in the bookshop this rustic lad of seventeen. To his surprise, the boy acquitted himself well, and marched off as the proud possessor of the book.

In time, this second member of the dynasty became the Rev. John Brown, D.D., of Haddington, author of *The Self-interpreting Bible,* and a leading churchman and theologian.

Third in the line was another Rev. John Brown, who for

* An address delivered to the English Association (Edinburgh branch) on 9 November 1962.

fifty-five years was highly esteemed as minister of the Secession Church at Whitburn, West Lothian. His son, the fourth to bear the name, who also entered the Church, was minister at Biggar, and there the fifth John Brown, with whom we are concerned at present, was born in 1810. At the manse in Biggar, John Brown grew up, and for the first twelve years of his life had no other teacher but his father. He was only six years old when his mother died. Taking her place as well as he could, his father encouraged that love of learning which was innate in the boy, so that, when he entered the Royal High School of Edinburgh, he was able to take his place alongside others of his own age.

It was in 1822 that Rev. John Brown of Biggar was called to Edinburgh, where, at first, he ministered in Rose Street Church. Later, when the Secession and Relief Churches joined to form the United Presbyterian Church in 1847 he became minister of Broughton Place Church, where "Jeems the door-keeper" was the beadle.

The young John Brown was fortunate in his school friends, many of whom remained life-long associates, among them Lord President Inglis, Sir Theodore Martin, Sir Douglas Maclagan and others, but perhaps his closest friend, who became his colleague and his neighbour when they both practised as medical men in Rutland Street, was Alexander Peddie. Dr Peddie was President of the Royal College of Physicians in 1877, and his Harveian Oration in 1890 was the basis of the book entitled *Recollections of Dr John Brown*, published three years later. Alexander Peddie and John Brown, both the sons of Ministers, first became acquainted when they sat together on the pulpit steps of the crowded church during the Induction Ceremony of the latter's father at Rose Street. Some years later, they were again closely associated when both were apprenticed to the famous surgeon James Syme.

INFLUENCE OF JAMES SYME

John Brown might have carried on the family tradition as a minister, but his father's friend, Rev. James Belfrage of Slateford (then a village, near Edinburgh), strongly advised him to choose medicine. Belfrage himself was an M.D., and ministered to the bodily, as well as to the spiritual needs of his people. He introduced John to James Syme who, undaunted by his failure to secure an appointment to the Staff of the Royal

Infirmary, had taken a lease of a near-by mansion house, Minto House, and had converted it into a surgical hospital with twenty-four beds.

This venture was a great success, and the hospital lacked neither patients nor students. Syme's classroom, accommodating about 250, was always crowded, and the number of those apprenticed to him at high fees was quite unusual. John Brown was third on the Roll, and Alexander Peddie, who sketched the well-known portrait of Syme as he sat and taught, was number thirteen.

John Brown used to boast proudly that his fee for apprenticeship bought Syme's first carriage, a gig with C-springs and large yellow wheels. Pupil and master had the first drive in it together, over Corstorphine Hill, Syme remarking before they started, "I make one rule, John; there will be no talk".

John Brown began his work with Syme in 1829, and in December 1830 there took place the events recorded twenty-eight years later, in *Rab and his friends*.

In 1833, Syme, on being appointed Professor of Clinical Surgery, assumed charge of wards in the Royal Infirmary, but he did not abandon Minto House, which continued, for a time, to function as a hospital and dispensary. Eventually it was demolished to make way for the buildings which now constitute Chambers Street.

ASSISTANTSHIP AT CHATHAM

When the term of his indenture with Syme came to an end in 1831, John Brown journeyed south by steamboat to act as assistant to another Scottish doctor, Dr Martin, who practised at Chatham in Kent. Writing home to his sister Isabella, John mentions some of his expenses: "Leeches for a poor miserable child, 3s., Dinner (very dear and exorbitant), 2s., Whatley's Logic (a good book, though perhaps I should not have bought it), 12s., Pair of leather braces, 4s."

The young assistant was very busy at Chatham, especially during an outbreak of cholera in 1832.

Early one morning a sailor called to row him down the river to a village where cholera had broken out with great violence. As they neared the place they could see many people waiting, all clamouring and shouting for the doctor. Before the boat reached the shore, an elderly, but powerfully built man plunged into the water, seized John Brown with one arm like a child, and, fending off the crowd with the other arm, carried him into a cottage close by.

It was "Big Joe", determined that his grandson "Little Joe", smitten by cholera, should be the first patient to be seen by the doctor. The boy recovered, but "Big Joe", already ill when he carried the doctor ashore, died that night.

In another of his letters, John Brown speaks of cholera raging on one of the convict ships moored near Chatham. He writes, "900 sleep in one ship, their hammocks huddled between decks. They work twelve hours a day, and are broken down by dissipation." It is not surprising that the mortality was high.

MEDICAL PRACTICE IN EDINBURGH

John Brown returned to Edinburgh in 1833, and at once began to practise from his father's house. In the same year he graduated M.D. and resolved that he would be a physician rather than a surgeon. At that time specialism did not extend beyond these two main categories.

It is a mistake to suppose that Dr John Brown was a doctor whose main activity lay in the field of literature. Actually, he had two professions, and he pursued each of them with energy and success. His medical practice was not large, but his advice was highly regarded, and it is not surprising that one whose manner was so sympathetic was beloved by his patients. John Brown was, indeed, what the French call, "un homme très spirituel".

He owed much of his success, both in medicine and literature, to his devoted wife, Catherine Scott McKay, whom he married in 1840. They had three children, two daughters who died young, and a son, John Brown, who, along with D. W. Forrest, edited the collection of his father's letters, *Letters of Dr John Brown*, published in 1909. Mrs Brown died in 1864, after a prolonged illness, and after her death it is not surprising that the tinge of melancholy and depression which sometimes clouded the happy outlook and good humour so obvious to all his friends, became accentuated and even caused him occasionally to withdraw from society.

It was at that time that his sister Isabella, who had for some years kept house for their father at Arthur Lodge, Dalkeith Road, came to stay with him. She outlived her brother, until 1888.

Miss E. T. M'Laren, a close family friend, known to them as Cecy, has given a charming account of those days in her book, entitled *Dr John Brown and his sisters Isabella and Jane*. Jane married Rev. J. S. Wilson of New Abbey, near Dumfries, in 1863, and died in 1894.

No reference to the family is complete without some mention of Dr John's half-brother, Alexander Crum Brown, Professor of Chemistry at Edinburgh University for thirty-nine years, a man of profound learning who was said to be an expert even in Chinese. Although "Crummie's" class was often riotous, he bore the students no ill-will, and for many years his hospitable house in Belgrave Crescent was frequented by numerous students.

Dr John Brown resided in Albany Street at the time of his marriage, but as his practice and family grew, he and his wife removed to Rutland Street, which was then the Harley Street of Edinburgh. Rutland Street is now a dull little street overshadowed by the Caledonian Station and Hotel, but at that time the station entrance was in Lothian Road, and the new buildings were not completed until 1903.

NEIGHBOURS AND COLLEAGUES

Professor James Syme had his consulting rooms at No. 3 Rutland Street; Lister, when he came to Edinburgh in 1854, resided at No. 11 after he married Syme's daughter Agnes and before he went to Glasgow in 1860; and Alexander Peddie occupied No. 15. On the wall at 23 Rutland Street is engraved the legend: Dr John Brown, Author of *Rab and his friends*, lived in this house, 1850 to 1882. Lister, having made his great discovery in Glasgow, returned to Edinburgh as Syme's successor in 1869. In 1877, at the age of fifty and at the height of his fame, he decided to go to London, where his antiseptic doctrine had made little headway. The result was eventually a great success, but only after a hard struggle. Dr John Brown wrote in a letter at the time of Lister's departure: "I am very sorry about Lister, and fear he is sorry himself. I wish he had the moral courage to say, 'Get thee behind me, London', and gone on his way here rejoicing, and sending his multitudes of antiseptors all over the world."

Besides his immediate neighbours, John Brown had many friends in Edinburgh, where he was a well-known figure, living as he did in the very heart of the new town quarter. Among the prominent medical men of the time were Sir James Young Simpson, Sir Robert Christison and Sir Douglas MacLagan.

Revolutionary changes were in progress; the discoveries of anaesthesia in 1846–47, and of the antiseptic method in 1865, completely altered the outlook in surgery. In 1858, Virchow's work destroyed at a blow the old-fashioned doctrine of the "humours" which had survived for so many centuries. The Age of Bacteriology was still to come, as also was the discovery of X-rays, the transmission of disease by mosquitoes, and many other wonders. Methods of medical education were changing also, and John Brown held strong views on this subject. He stressed the importance of a liberal education in medicine, but he also held that there should be no State licensing and that the average patient would have enough sense to avoid consulting quacks.

When he became a Fellow of the Royal College of Physicians in 1847, the controversy which ended in compulsory registration (1858) was at its height, but John disliked argument and took no active part in the battle. He served the College faithfully and helpfully as Librarian from 1848 to 1858. Although he wielded so able a pen, he never shone as a public speaker, and he took little part in the business of the College.

CLASSICS AND LITERATURE

In the field of Art, his chief friend was Sir George Harvey, who drew some of the pictures of Rab, while in Literature he greatly admired Thackeray whom he considered had been unjustly treated by the public. Among his correspondents were Ruskin and Carlyle, also Mark Twain, who visited him in Edinburgh, and Oliver Wendell Holmes, whom he never met, but with whom he had much in common. Much of his interest in the classics he owed to the versatile Professor Blackie. "Latin and Greek are not dead", John Brown affirmed, "although the present age is doing its best to kill them."

Dr John Brown's allegiance to Latin led him to adopt for his books of essays the title, *Horae Subsecivae*, a title unattractive to many readers. Indeed, he confessed that it had been a mistake, and that he ought to have called them plainly, Odd Hours or Spare Hours, though not, as one wag suggested, Brown Studies. A lady reader, on one occasion, is said to have asked a bookseller for Dr Brown's "Horrors of Society".

Professor David Masson, who assumed the Chair of English Literature in 1865, and who knew John Brown well, has given an able analysis of his writings in his *Edinburgh Sketches and Memories* published in 1892. He tells us how Dr John Brown had come to be called "The Charles Lamb of Scotland", because he and Lamb had much in common. Both had explored many odd corners, and in the works of both there is to be found a mixture of humour and pathos.

Lamb, however, was entirely devoted to literature, while Brown ever remained the doctor. In the life of the latter, there was no transition from practice to authorship. He did attempt to retire about the year 1874, and sent out circulars to that effect, but his patients would not hear of it; they would have no other doctor than the dear and trusted Doctor John.

The kindly understanding which pervades all his writings showed itself to a much greater extent during his lifetime towards those who were honoured by his friendship. Children immediately accepted him and loved him; they never seemed to be shy, as they were with other strangers. He loved young people and understood them. As for dogs, they were a passion with John Brown. In so "doggy" a city as Edinburgh was then, and still is, he greeted them in the street, and was greeted by them in turn. Once, when driving with his sister, he stopped talking and looked round eagerly. "Is it someone you know?" she asked. "No," he replied, "it's a dog I don't know."

John Brown was the recipient of many tributes and honours. In 1859 he was admitted a Fellow of the Royal Society of Edinburgh; in 1861 he was made an Honorary Member of the Royal Medical Society; and in 1874 he became an LL.D. of Edinburgh University.

Dr John Brown's first serious entry into literature came about in a curious fashion. It was in 1846, before which date he had made occasional contributions to *The Scotsman* and other papers, dealing mostly with the amenities of Edinburgh, under the assumed name "Randolph".

JOHN BROWN AS ART CRITIC

One morning he received from the editor of *The Witness* newspaper, Hugh Miller, who later became so eminent a geologist, a letter along with four five-pound notes, requesting him to write a notice of the paintings of the year, on view in the Royal

Scottish Academy. His first impulse was to decline, as he did not fancy himself as an art critic, but his wife prevailed on him to accept. The result was his "Notes on Art", in the Second Series of *Horae Subsecivae*. His introductory remarks show that he was well fitted for the task, and that he had given much thought to the subject of art in general. To this theme he returned later in his essay on John Leech, to be found in the Third Series of the *Horae*, one of the longest, and most entertaining essays. He wrote: "There is more good sense, good drawing and beauty in John Leech's *Punch* pictures than in all the Art Union illustrations put together. It is not what a man has learned from others, but what he sees and feels, that makes him a painter."

John Brown was clever with his pen, not only as author, but as artist, though he had no pretensions in this direction and never used colour. Amusing pen and ink sketches of quaint little men and, more often, of dogs, adorn many of his letters, while, in writing to a child, he makes use of large double-lined capitals, adding, on one occasion, "it is tiresome to go on making these clumsy fellows of letters", and lapsing into ordinary script, though returning to capitals at the end in order to sign, as was often his wont, JEYE BEE.

He must have enjoyed writing, "Our Dogs", which begins, "I was bitten severely by a little dog when with my mother at Moffat Wells, being then three years of age, and I have remained 'bitten' ever since in the matter of dogs."

RAB AND HIS FRIENDS

John Brown's analysis of the characters of Wasp, Toby, Crab, John Pym, Dick and other dogs shows him to be a remarkable exponent of canine psychology. And, of course, there was the famous Rab, so closely linked with the name of Dr John Brown that many people imagine that he wrote nothing but *Rab and his friends* (Plate 5)!

It is true that he was essentially an essayist, and that no major book came from his pen. Certainly "Rab" was John Brown at his best, and has had millions of readers. Originally printed as a sixpenny pamphlet in 1858, the circulation had risen to fifty thousand within four years.

As explained in the first illustrated edition, it was at first a lecture, entitled "The Howgate Carrier, his Wife, and his Dog

Rab". The Preface begins: "My uncle, the Rev. Dr Smith of Biggar, asked me to give a lecture in my native village, the shrewd little capital of the Upper Ward. I never lectured before; I have no turn for it; but I had an odd sort of desire to say something to these people, who were boys and girls when I left them. I could think of nothing to give them. At last I said to myself, 'I'll tell them Ailie's story'. I had often told it to myself; indeed, it came on me at intervals almost painfully, almost demanding to be told. . . . I sat down about twelve and rose at four, having finished it. I slunk off to bed satisfied and cold." Thus, although R. L. S. wrote of J. B.,

> *Ye didnae fash yersel' to think,*
> *Ye stapped your pen into the ink,*
> *An' there was Rab!*

"Rab" had really demanded much thought during the twenty-eight years which had elapsed since the events took place. "Rab and his friends" is included in the Second Series of *Horae Subsecivae* (1861), in good company with "Our Dogs", "Notes on Art", and "Letter to John Cairns, D.D.".

In the same volume may be found a link with Sir Walter Scott, the paper on "The Black Dwarf's Bones" which Dr John Brown originally communicated to the Anatomical Society of Edinburgh in 1836. It is a clever mixture of anatomy and literature.

The first volume of *Horae Subsecivae*, or first series, as it is usually called, has a distinctly medical flavour. The original edition is dated 1858, but to later editions have been added the delightful account of his old teacher Mr Syme, and the obituary notice of Sir Robert Christison. Of Syme he said that "he never wasted a word, a drop of ink or a drop of blood". There is also an Appendix called "Plain Words on Health", and the remarks on "The Doctor, our duties to him, and his duties to you" might well be followed in modern medical practice.

Dr John Brown did not welcome the intrusion of science into medicine which was already gathering impetus in his time. In the paper comparing the views of "Locke and Sydenham", and still more strongly in the essay entitled "Art and Science", he deplores the fact that Medicine is becoming more and more of a Science and less and less of an Art. He held that the microscope and stethoscope and other instrumental aids to diagnosis could never take the place of sheer, unaided observation. Of course he would have been the first to welcome the immense advances of scientific medicine such as we witness today, just as during his own lifetime he acclaimed the introduction of chloroform and of antisepsis. Yet he emphasized the humanistic aspect, the subtle knowledge which comes from experience, and which can hardly be communicated to others. Perhaps the best part of a doctor's knowledge is the part which dies with him.

Many of John Brown's remarks could not be applied to the Medicine of today, but as an antidote to present-day extremes of specialism, and excess of physical tests, his views are still worthy of consideration. They bring the patient more definitely into the picture.

The Third Series of *Horae Subsecivae*, which was first printed as a collection in 1882, just before the author's death, contains such noteworthy descriptions of scenery as "Minchmoor" and "The Enterkin", and we wish there had been more essays of this kind, so eloquent and so inspiring.

MARJORY FLEMING

Included in the Third Series of *Horae* is the tale which has attracted almost as much comment as "Rab and his friends", namely the essay entitled "Marjorie Fleming". The work of this remarkable child, "the youngest immortal in the world of letters", who died at the age of nine, came to light in a curious manner half a century after her death.

Although she was never known as Pet Marjorie during her short lifetime, and her name was Marjory, and not Marjorie, the title Pet Marjorie was used by her first biographer, Mr Henry Brougham Farnie, a journalist who discovered and publicized her writings in 1858, forty-seven years after her death.

Marjory Fleming was born at Kirkcaldy, Fife, on 15 January 1803, and she died on 19 December 1811. A lovely statuette, the work of Mr C. d'O. Pilkington Jackson, marks her grave in Abbotshall Churchyard (Frontispiece).

Mr Farnie's account of her life and journals appeared in *The Fife Herald*, published in Kirkcaldy, and was reprinted as a sixpenny booklet, entitled, *Pet Marjorie, a Story of Child Life fifty years ago.* The little work strongly appealed to Dr John Brown when he reviewed it for *The North British Review* in 1863, and added, as some reviewers still do, his own comments, and further information which he obtained from Marjory's sister Elizabeth (born 1809). Elizabeth Fleming told Dr Brown that she remembered seeing (though it had since disappeared), a book by Miss Maria Edgeworth, inscribed, "A gift to Marjory from Walter Scott". On this slender evidence, Dr John Brown introduced into his review, and later, into his famous essay, the dramatic opening scene, with Scott as the central figure, to which reference will be made presently.

On seeing the review, Mr Farnie hastened to re-write his booklet, incorporating, with due acknowledgement, the new information revealed in the review. Thereupon Dr John Brown, probably feeling that his thunder was being stolen, wrote the full-length essay which introduced Marjory to a world-wide circle of admirers.

Originally published as a separate booklet, it was called, *Marjorie Fleming, a Sketch, being the paper entitled Pet Marjorie, a Story of Child Life fifty years ago*, by John Brown, Author of "Rab and his friends", 1864. In the Third Series of *Horae Subsecivae*, published in 1882, the title was simply "Marjorie Fleming". In all fairness it must be granted that John Brown's approach to the subject was quite different from that adopted by Mr Farnie, whom he far excelled as an author.

In particular, Dr John Brown's introduction of Sir Walter Scott into the tale was welcomed by many a reader. Sir Walter had died only thirty years previously, and there were many still living who had seen or known him. Those familiar with the story will recall how Dr John Brown, fairly carried away by the sentimental aspect of his theme, reports Scott as saying to himself, in 1810, "I can make nothing of *Waverley* today, I'll awa' to Marjory", and how, with his deerhound Maida gambolling beside him, he strode across from Castle Street to Mrs Keith's house in North Charlotte Street, of which he possessed a key. "Marjorie", he shouted as he entered. "Where are ye, my bonnie wee croodlin' doo?" Then he carried back to his own house his "warm, rosy, little wifie", wrapped in his plaid.

There is nothing of Scott in this language; it is all Brown's own imagination. Scott's friendship with Marjory was at least possible, and it may be that John Brown felt himself quite entitled to include an element of fiction in order to make a good story. Certainly the majority of his readers have accepted as historical truth all that he wrote on Marjory Fleming. Nevertheless modern commentators, for the most part, have felt rather sceptical regarding this aspect of the story, and it would seem that those who desire the whole truth should not take Dr John Brown's version too literally.

In the *Scottish Historical Review* of October 1947, Mr Frank Gent, in an illuminating article on "Marjory Fleming and her Biographers" commenting on the "on-ding o' snaw" in John Brown's *Marjorie Fleming*, writes, "There was no snow in Edinburgh during November 1810", and he goes on to say that Maida the deerhound did not then exist, and that the manuscript of *Waverley*, mislaid by the author in 1805, was not rediscovered until 1813, and not in 1810, as Dr Brown seems to state.

Furthermore, the alleged friendship between Scott and Marjory receives no corroboration from the writings of either of them.

There is no reference to Marjory either in Scott's *Journal* or Lockhart's biography of Scott, and Marjory herself mentions Scott only once, as the author of her favourite poem, *Helvellyn*.

All this is difficult to reconcile with Dr John Brown's statement that Scott said of Marjory, "She's the most extraordinary creature I ever met with".

Unfortunately Dr Brown made a number of errors in his transcription of Marjory's writings, and these errors were copied by Mr Lachlan Macbean of Kirkcaldy, who was the next commentator, and who, when he entered the field in 1904, had not the advantage of access to the original manuscripts. Dr Brown had died in 1885, and Marjory's sister Elizabeth, in 1881, and Mr Macbean therefore borrowed from Dr Brown's son his father's copy, with all its errors and omissions. From this, and from local sources of information, Macbean compiled his book which he called *The Story of Pet Marjorie*. It is attractively written, and is indispensable to all who care to follow the fascinating quest for the real Marjory Fleming.

The manuscripts had not been lost, but had been consigned by Elizabeth Fleming in 1880, a year before her death, to the care of an old friend, the Rev. Dr Macgregor of St Cuthbert's, Edinburgh. In 1914, they passed into the custody of the Rev. Dr Archibald Fleming of St Columba's Church of Scotland, London, a namesake, but no relation of Marjory's. In 1930,

Dr Fleming's heirs handed them over to the National Library of Scotland, Edinburgh, and there they remain.

It was only at this point that their full significance was realized, and a Collotype Facsimile Edition, edited by Mr Arundell Esdaile of the British Museum, was published in 1934.

In an introductory note, Mr Esdaile deplores "the fog of sentimentality" which has surrounded the writings of Marjory Fleming. The book is handsomely produced, and bears the title: *The Journals, Letters and Verses of Marjory Fleming.*

For the benefit of those who prefer to read Marjory in ordinary print rather than in script, there was prepared in the same year, by Frank Sedgwick, a handy little book of 208 pages, entitled *The Complete Marjory Fleming*, with an index and notes which explain and reproduce the original writings as accurately as possible. All that Marjory wrote retains its fascination, especially, perhaps, her life of Mary, Queen of Scots, and her comments on the four King James's, both to be found in Journal Number 3. In the second Journal, we find the oft-quoted remark on her dislike of multiplication: "The most Devilish thing is 8 times 8 and 7 times 7 it is what nature itselfe cant endure".

We can never be grateful enough to Dr John Brown for his service in making Marjory known to the world by his charming essay, which is a gem of literature, in spite of its errors and inaccuracies.

In the *Dictionary of National Biography*, Sir Leslie Stephen wrote of "the extraordinary precocity of Margaret Fleming, called Pet Margarie or Marjorie", remarking that "no more fascinating infantile author has ever appeared".

CONCLUSION

Many were the tributes to Dr John Brown at the time of his death in 1882, and his work has stood the test of time.

Swinburne did well to link his name with his two principal characters, when he wrote of

> *"Some happier isle in the Elysian Sea*
> *Where Rab may lick the hand of Marjorie."*

Looking back over nearly a century, it is difficult to reconstruct a picture of Dr John Brown, but it may be appropriate to conclude one's remarks by quoting from the Harveian Oration of 1890, delivered by his closest friend Dr Alexander Peddie, who said, "His sweetness of nature, so apparent in his writings, was doubly felt by his friends from his looks, words and actions. To know him was to love him."

DR FRANCIS ADAMS OF
BANCHORY*

A CENTURY HAS PASSED since Dr John Brown, author of the immortal "Rab and his Friends", wrote for *The Scotsman* an obituary notice of his colleague in medicine and in literature, Dr Francis Adams of Banchory, and it seems only fitting that on the present occasion a further tribute should be paid to that very remarkable doctor and scholar (Plate 4).

Few visitors to Banchory pause to inspect the granite obelisk to his memory which stands close to the garden wall of his house in Dee Street. In any case, few could decipher the Latin inscription which records his faithful devotion to Medicine and to the Muses.

Nevertheless, in his day he was well known and highly esteemed not only as an efficient country doctor but also as a brilliant man of letters whose translations of early Greek medical classics remain as a permanent contribution to our literature.

Although such works are no longer used as guides to medical practice, they are of great historical value. In the days of Francis Adams they were still in use as text books, and an essential part of the M.D. examination was the writing of a commentary on one of the Aphorisms of Hippocrates.

Born on the Island of Cos in 460 B.C. Hippocrates is regarded and revered as "The Father of Medicine". He it was who showed disease was not a punishment sent by the gods, but that it arose from natural causes, and that Nature was the great healer. "Our natures", he wrote, "are the physicians of our diseases."

Hippocrates thus transferred Medicine from the realm of magic to that of common sense: he also gave it a noble code

* From "The Scotsman", 25th February 1961, on the centenary of the death of Dr Francis Adams.

of conduct, the Hippocratic Oath, which still forms an important item in the Medical Graduation ceremony at every Scottish university.

The English translation of Hippocrates, Adams's best-known work, was published in 1849, and it was followed four years later by a translation of the writings of Aretaeus the Cappadocian. Aretaeus, who lived at Alexandria in the second century A.D. was the first to describe many diseases still known to us today.

Neither of these translations, however, cost Adams the effort necessary for his first great book, a translation from Paul of Aegina.

About A.D. 650, Paul, the last of the "Byzantine Compilers", collected and wrote down all that was known of Greek medicine, for the benefit of succeeding centuries, and his work was highly prized by the Arab doctors who were the next custodians of medical learning for six centuries.

So much for the books he translated: what of the man himself?

Francis Adams was of humble birth, the son of a farm labourer or gardener in the Parish of Lumphanan in Aberdeenshire.

Of his early youth little is known and it would appear that for the most part he was self-taught. He entered King's College, Aberdeen, with a bursary in 1809, and four years later, at the age of seventeen, he became M.A. By that time his interest in classics had become a passion.

In later life he wrote: "I began by devoting 17 hours a day to the study of Virgil and Horace, and then having mastered the difficulties of Latin, I naturally turned my attention to Greek. It was the late Dr Kerr of Aberdeen who drew my attention to the Greek Literature of Medicine, and at his death, I purchased the collection of Greek authors which he had made."

Francis Adams next studied medicine, probably as an apprentice or extramural student in Edinburgh, and in the autumn of 1815 he went to London and there passed his examinations as a Member of the Royal College of Surgeons. Returning to Scotland, he settled at Banchory-Ternan, where he spent the remainder of his busy and useful life. His home, formerly the Old Manse, was demolished in 1893, when a modern house was erected on the site by his son-in-law and successor, Dr McHardy.

131

Banchory-Ternan, as it was called then, derives its names from words denoting the great choir of St Ternan, Ternan being one of the missionaries sent north from Candida Casa in Wigtownshire by St Ninian. The same derivation gives us Bangor and Bangour.

In Adams's day, Banchory was, and still is, the centre of a wide agricultural district, and he conducted his practice on horseback, riding twenty or thirty miles on his daily professional round.

Despite his extraordinary zeal for literary work, he never neglected his medical duties, but combined the two aspects of his work without detriment to either.

Discovering that he required little sleep, he exploited this peculiarity to the utmost. As he tells us himself, "I sat up late and rose early, and snatched every minute I could from the duties of my profession. My practice, though not lucrative, was extensive, especially in the obstetric line; I arranged, however, to work at my translation ten hours a day."

He must have been a man of good physique, but even so, the achievement was truly marvellous. It does not surprise us to learn that he often fell asleep, or at least fell into a reverie, while on his rounds. His faithful horse (so faithful that a wag remarked that the authors of the translations were Adams and Dobbin) was not slow to take advantage of the situation and would stop to graze by the roadside, while his master, absentmindedly or half-asleep continued to bob up and down in the saddle.

DOCTOR'S ANTICS

This pantomime often delighted the local schoolboys, who gladly risked a caning for being late for school as they watched the doctor's antics. Little did they realize how strenuous was his life; his books and his patients were ever in his thoughts.

Dr John Brown once paid a surprise visit to Adams at Banchory and has told how he found his friend "at breakfast, ready to ride up the Feugh, and amusing himself with pencilling down a translation of an Ode of Horace into Greek verse".

Soon he became known in the wider world, and counted among his friends not only John Brown but also Sir William Hamilton, the philosopher; Sir William Jardine, the naturalist; Jones Quain, the anatomist; and William Sharpey, the physiologist. Yet he esteemed quite as highly the confidence of his humble patients, and it is significant that when he was offered the Chair of Greek at Aberdeen University he declined to accept it, preferring to continue his work as a country practitioner.

He well deserved the LL.D. of Glasgow and the Hon. M.D. of Aberdeen, which were among his other honours.

For many years he was president of the Aberdeen Medical Society, and even on winter evenings would ride the seventeen miles to and from the city to attend the meetings.

Not content to confine his attention to Greek translations, Francis Adams published a number of articles in various medical journals, including contributions on such topics as dislocation of the knee-joint, poisoning by arsenic, obstetric emergencies, and "case of a woman stung by an adder".

The width of his interests is further shown by the fact that when the British Association met in Aberdeen in 1857 he contributed, along with his son, Dr A. Leith Adams, a distinguished Army surgeon who afterwards became a Fellow of the Royal Society, a paper entitled, "Ornithology as a Branch of Liberal Education, with notes of all the wild birds which have been discovered in Banchory-Ternan, and remarks on such of them as have been found in India".

DEESIDE AND KASHMIR

In this paper the father and son compared the birds of Deeside with those of distant Kashmir. Francis Adams's energy and enthusiasm never deserted him. Only a few weeks before his death there was published an article by him in the *Medical Times and Gazette*, discussing the question, "Is the Turkish Bath the same as the ancient Roman Bath?"

The manner of his passing was characteristic. After a visit to a distant patient on a wintry night, he contracted pneumonia and died within a few days, on 26 February 1861.

Pneumonia was a deadly disease before the days of antibiotics. Antiseptics and anæsthetics were also unknown at that time: Adams was among the last to practise medicine under the old Hippocratic conditions.

Great-hearted and generous, he never regretted having remained at Banchory and never felt any lack of scope for his talents. His wife died young and to his heavy tasks there were added the responsibility for the care of their six children. Some of their descendants are still alive; the writer met one of them, a great-granddaughter, in New Zealand a few years ago.

A century after his death we salute the memory of good Dr Francis Adams, he whose ideals are embodied in the first Aphorism of Hippocrates, who revered the art of medicine when he wrote: "Life is short, and the Art long; opportunity fleeting; experiment dangerous, and judgement difficult. The physician must be prepared, not only to do what is right himself, but also to make the patient, the attendants and external circumstances co-operate."

THE GEOGRAPHICAL
OUTLOOK

JANUS IN THE DOORWAY*

LET ME BEGIN BY thanking the Osler Club most cordially for their kind invitation to deliver this address. It is indeed a high honour, not only to me, but to the Medical School of Edinburgh which I represent.

Although my main thesis concerns three early medical travellers, it is only fitting that any Oslerian Oration should begin, and end, with Osler, and I propose to follow this rule.

I do not know what Sir William Osler would say if he knew that one who has so long since passed Anthony Trollope's "Fixed Period" in the number of his years, had been chosen for this duty, although, really, it was that wicked attendant spirit Dr Egerton Yorrick Davis, and not Osler at all, who spoke of "the uselessness of men over sixty years of age". One need not remind Oslerians that the fictitious Egerton Y. Davis gave William Osler and his friends a lot of trouble.

THE OSLER LIBRARY

Three weeks ago it was my good fortune to compose this Oration while seated in the Osler Library at McGill University, Montreal, that shrine which contains, as Osler himself directed, the urn with his ashes. Although this urn is not "on the mantelpiece" as he suggested, and is not even on public view, it is there none the less, as also is the feeling of his presence.

Osler's prophecy seems to have come true. His words were: "My astral self can peek at the books I have loved, and share the delight with which kindred souls still in the flesh may handle them."

Oliver Wendell Holmes once said, "Happy is the child who has tumbled about in a library". As a young man, Osler had this advantage in the library of his friend and teacher, Dr James Bovell, whose name, throughout his life, he would often scribble down to promote his thoughts. Osler was ever the

---

* The Oslerian Oration to The Osler Club of London, 12 July 1961, originally entitled "The traveller looks both ways".

bibliophile, and it is pleasant to find that, at the last, he came to rest among his beloved books in Montreal.

He had been appointed Professor there at the age of twenty-five, and ten years later he set out from that city on the second stage of his glorious pilgrimage. Of that period he wrote: "I left Montreal a rich man, not in this world's goods, but rich in the treasures of friendship and good fellowship. There was nothing but cobwebs in my pocket, but plenty of capital in my brain-pan."

William Osler was born at Bond Head, some forty-five miles north of Toronto. The house has long since disappeared but the Medico-historical Society of Toronto has built a Cairn to mark the site, and it is of interest to us assembled here, to know that the Cairn is being dedicated in distant Canada at this very hour allowing for the time differences.

Dr Linell is to tell the story of how the idea of the Cairn arose, and Professor Farrar is to contribute personal recollections of Osler.

OSLER AND EDINBURGH

I do not propose to relate again the well-known details of Osler's life-work, but perhaps I may be forgiven if I interpolate a few words regarding his associations with Edinburgh. We nearly secured Osler for the Chair of Medicine when it became vacant in 1900, but, alas, we failed. Recalling fifteen years later, this landmark in his life, he wrote: "In the depression associated with influenza, I cabled withdrawing my name. I wonder what would have become of me in Edinburgh—Whisky or John Knox? It was a disappointment to me, as I feel I could have been very happy in Edinburgh, and could have got on with the men, as I have always liked the Scots."

The cable was worded, APPLICATION WITHDRAWN—LOCAL PRESSURE TOO STRONG—SO SORRY—OSLER.

Influenza was not the only restraining factor, nor, indeed, was local pressure. If Edinburgh had invited him to come, instead of inviting him to become a candidate, we might have been more fortunate, and he would have had no trouble from either Whisky, or John Knox, strong forces though they were then, and still are.

Eight years later, our students attempted to make amends by choosing Osler as the only non-political candidate for the post of Lord Rector. The other candidates were, George Wyndham for the Conservatives and Winston Churchill for the Liberals.

Politics determined the issue, although Osler came within about 200 votes of victory, and Wyndham beat Churchill by a mere hundred (the actual figures were Wyndham—826, Churchill—727, Osler—614). A record of that great fight in 1908 still exists on a stone wall in Lindsay Place, close to the University, which bears the legend VOTE FOR OSLER, in large white letters.

OSLER THE TRAVELLER

Osler had by that time made Oxford his home, but he spent many holidays in Scotland. During two successive years he visited the lovely and lonely Island of Colonsay, which will not surprise anyone who knows that enchanting Isle. A few years later he explored the Guy Mannering and Crockett country, the wilds of Galloway of which he wrote, "I did not know that the Highlands came so far south in Scotland" (Plate 6).

One need not trace in detail Osler's other journeyings. Ever a traveller, always on the move, the slippered and cushioned ease of the arm-chair scholar was foreign to his nature. Montreal, Philadelphia, Baltimore and Oxford were his homes in fairly rapid succession.

He lived during a period of much significance for Medicine; he saw the end of the Victorian Age and he witnessed the birth of Bacteriology, of X-rays and of other astounding changes.

THE WIDER OUTLOOK

Like the Roman God of doorways, Janus, from whom the first month of the year takes its name, he looked both backward and forward, an outlook essential to everyone who uses a door. The policy of facing both ways is needful for progress. It is true that Osler, in addressing his students on what he called "A Way of Life", advised them to live in what he called "day-tight compartments" and to concentrate on the work in hand. He knew how the student is apt to regret the past and to dream of the future, neglecting meantime the task of today. Osler was the personification of Janus, and none knew better than he, that one's range of observation should be wide, and that concentration had its disadvantages. He was fond of recalling the fate of the scholar Casaubon in George Eliot's

Middlemarch, who became so immersed in a sea of facts that he reached no conclusions in his research. Rooted to his desk, he saw nothing beyond it.

How different was Osler; he imposed no limits on his mental adventures in space and time.

SOME MEDICAL JANUSES

There have been many other medical Januses, and I would like to recall a few of them in this talk, which I have entitled "The Traveller Looks Both Ways" or "Janus in the Doorway".

One of the earliest on record was Hippocrates who, in Osler's words, "made observation the warp and woof of our Art". He opened the door to the new world of Nature, and said goodbye to Medicine based upon magic and superstition. Hippocrates ranged far and wide throughout Greece, and is said to have died at Larissa, though his tomb has long since vanished.

Five hundred years later, Galen inaugurated an epoch as wonderful as that of Hippocrates, and he, too, was a wanderer. Pergamos, Alexandria, Rome and again Pergamos were the scenes of his manifold activities and his dogmatic writings.

During that long period of reform and revolution in learning which some call "The Renaissance", many door-keepers played their parts, including Vesalius in Anatomy and Paré in Surgery, as well as the mystic and misunderstood Paracelsus. No visitor to the grave of Paracelsus at Salzburg can remain unmoved on reading the epitaph, *Vitam cum morte mutavit, 24 September 1541.* He exchanged life for death: or death for life, interpret it as you choose. He was barely 48 years old, and his career had been one of strife. In his view, mobility was essential in Medicine. "Every doctor should be a traveller", he wrote. "Sicknesses wander here and there, and if a man would understand them, he must wander too". Osler called Paracelsus, "that strange compound of charlatan and philosopher", and historians are still arguing about him.

Next century there appeared a very different kind of Janus, William Harvey, who journeyed to the Continent on at least three occasions to "search out the secrets of Nature" with such care.

Later, Britain began to cater for her own medical students. Scholars did not travel so widely, and it is interesting to recall that Sir Benjamin Brodie (1783–1862), President of the Royal Society and Chairman of the General Medical Council, paid his first visit to the Continent at the age of fifty-one, having previously taken no holiday for many years.

On the other hand, his contemporary, Sir Henry Holland (1788–1873), tells us in his *Recollections of Past Life*, written when he was over eighty, that each year, for half a century, he spent two months abroad. He visited every European capital and was eight times in the U.S.A.

I have mentioned at random a few medical travellers of former times, but let us now look a little more closely at three others, each one of them a keen traveller, and each a "Janus" in his own way.

Andrew Boorde, Jerome Cardan and Pieter Camper may not be very familiar figures in the history of Medicine; nevertheless they are well worthy of our attention. Boorde was the only Englishman of the trio, Cardan was Italian and Camper was Dutch.

THE ADVENTURES OF ANDREW BOORDE

Andrew Boorde, sometimes written Borde, or Bored (indeed he called himself Andreas Perforatus), was born in 1490 at Cuck-field in Sussex, where a house still bears his name.

At an early age he became a Carthusian monk, but, finding the discipline too irksome, he wrote to his Superior stating that he was "not able to byde the rigourosity" of such a religion and begging to be relieved of his vows.

What the answer was, we do not know, but he continued to sign himself "Andrew Boorde, Priest", and he went back to live at Charterhouse on his return from Montpellier where he had studied Medicine for a year. At this stage, he had the good fortune to attend the Duke of Norfolk, whose nieces Katharine Howard and Anne Boleyn became, in turn, Queens of England.

This gained for him the friendship of Thomas Cromwell, who employed him more than once as an ambassador, or rather, as a spy, in the course of his Continental wanderings. Indeed, it is from his Reports to Secretary Cromwell that we derive such knowledge as is available regarding Andrew Boorde's travels. His desire to see the world was strong, and we next find him at the University of Orleans.

While crossing the bridge there one day, he fell in with a

party of nine English and Scottish pilgrims who were making their way to St James's of Compostella in Spain. He told them that they would do better to die in England, saying that he would rather go five times to Rome than once to Compostella. They remained unconvinced, however, and he thereupon resolved to go with them. After great privations they reached their destination, but on the return journey they all died, one by one, the result of eating fruit and drinking water. Boorde, who had been more abstemious, found himself the sole survivor, and when he reached France, he "did kiss the ground for joy".

Hardly had he set foot in England, than he was off again; this time to ascertain, for Cromwell, the Continental opinion regarding the matrimonial affairs of King Henry VIII. It did not take him long to report that the King had few friends across the Channel.

Our next news of Boorde is contained in a letter from Scotland, dated 1 April 1536. He writes, "I am now in Scotland and at a little town named Glasco, where I study, and practise physick for the sustentation of my living." Boorde had a poor opinion of the Scots, and he regarded them as thieves and liars. "I, Being there, was hated, but my physick did keep me in favour, and I did learn their secrets."

Boorde made yet another Continental journey which took him as far north as Denmark and as far east as Jerusalem, and then he settled for a time at Montpellier to write the books which are his chief memorial. Later he practised at Winchester, but somehow fell from grace and found himself in the Fleet Prison, and there he died from jail fever (as typhus was called), about 1599.

Boorde's "Breviary" and other writings

Andrew Boorde's principal work is his *Breviary of Health*, the first book by a medical man to be written and printed in the English language. In his "Preface to Physicians" he advises the cultivation of three assets, "Logic to define truth from falsehood, Geometry to weigh and measure drugs, and, above all, an eloquent tongue to convince one's patients".

A second Preface, for the non-medical reader, insists that a work on physick "should not be too manifest", because, Boorde adds, "if I should write all my mind, every bungler would practise upon my book". The "breviary" is a sort of household dictionary from A to Z. It begins with the word Abstinence, and continues through Memory, Mirth and Music, discussing more than three hundred aspects of medical practice. A sequel to this book was the *Dietary of Health*, and in it Boorde tells us that "a good cook is half a physician, wherefore the physician and the cook must consult together".

Besides his medical works, Boorde wrote an account of his travels which he quaintly entitled, *The First Boke of the Intro-duction of Knowledge*. This guide-book describes no beauty spots or places of interest, but concentrates on the lives and habits of the people of many lands, with interesting notes on languages, coinage, food and clothing.

In Cornwall, for instance, "the people can speak only Corn-ish. There is plenty of fish and tin, but the beer is beastly."

France, he found very pleasant, with well-dressed folk who delight in song and dance. Spain, on the other hand, was very poor.

For the benefit of pilgrims to the Holy Land, some hints are given. The traveller should first go overland to Venice:

"At Venice, you should buy a bed, and a chest with a lock and key, and then bargain with a Captain to take you to Jaffa, whence you can go on foot to Jerusalem, unless you are sick."

The remarks of so versatile and observant a wayfarer as Andrew Boorde are still worth reading.

THE CAREER OF JEROME CARDAN

The second of our trio of Janus-like wanderers, Jerome Cardan, though ten years younger than Andrew Boorde, was a very different person, reflecting to a greater extent the mystical and superstitious age from which the civilised world was then emerging.

Jerome Cardan is usually regarded as a medieval physician; nevertheless he did look ahead in a very remarkable fashion. His name survives, or did so until recently, in the Cardan shaft of motor engineers, Cardan's rule in algebra and Cardan's well in the county of Fife. He is mentioned in few histories of medicine; perhaps he was overshadowed by greater giants of his time. Nevertheless he sounded new depths on many sciences, and his Collected Works fill ten large folios.

His unhappy childhood, his early struggle with poverty and

attempt to live by gambling, his astonishing rise to fame as Professor of Medicine at Bologna and Pavia, his pathetic old age after his son had been executed as a murderer, and finally his death in Rome as a pensioner of the Pope—these are the headlines of this unusual career.

Cardan's studies range from Algebra to the subject he called Metoposcopy, the study of lines and wrinkles on the face and forehead, after the fashion of palmistry or phrenology.

His writings entitled *De Subtilitate* and *De Varietate*, at one time in wide popular demand, deal with such matters as the raising of sunken ships, the making of linen, the origin of mountains, the twinkling of stars, how to catch mice and how to make ink—besides a long dissertation on dreams and omens. The book on algebra is perhaps his best work. Medicine and Mathematics were often combined then, as they are today.

Cardan seems to have placed science before art in medicine. "The doctor's calling', he wrote, "is completely servile, and so full of toil that I do not marvel that it used to be peculiar to slaves."

A Famous Consultation

In spite of this rather unorthodox attitude towards the healing art, Cardan became one of the leading physicians of his time, and he was the very embodiment of the peripatetic physician. This was clearly shown when he was summoned from Milan to Edinburgh in 1552, to attend Archbishop Hamilton, Primate of Scotland, and virtually the ruler during the minority of Mary, Queen of Scots. The Archbishop suffered from asthma, and his medical attendant, a Spaniard named Cassanate, wrote to inform Cardan, "He is worried night and day, and can hardly breathe, and eagerly desires your services".

Cardan hoped that the patient might meet him at Lyons, and there he awaited his arrival, and many persons flocked to consult him. At last a message came, to the effect that, as State Affairs made it impossible for the Archbishop to leave Scotland, Cardan must needs come all the way, for which journey he would be amply recompensed. In Paris he met Sylvius the anatomist and also Jean Fernel, and eventually he reached Edinburgh early in June, and proceeded to the Archbishop's country palace at Monimail, near St Andrews, the tower of which may still be seen.

Being a wise physician, Cardan resolved to study the case for some days before expressing an opinion. Eventually he drew up a number of rules regarding baths, diet, exercise and mode of life. The patient was advised to cough at certain hours with his head lower than his heels, a procedure which, many years later, came to be known as "postural coughing". The pillow and mattress were to be stuffed with straw and on no account with feathers.

All this has quite a modern flavour, but Cardan had not forsaken astrology, as he showed when he drew the horoscope predicting for the Archbishop a stormy future, but a long life. Cardan could not have foreseen that his patient would be hanged for treason, twenty years later.

He visited Gessner at Zurich on his way home, and was given an enthusiastic welcome on his arrival at Milan. Although he looked both ways and reflected the opinions of two different schools of thought, Jerome Cardan deserves a place among the medical immortals.

PIETER CAMPER: ARTIST AND OBSTETRICIAN

The third of the Janus-like travellers whose deeds I have chosen to record did not make his appearance on the stage of history until two centuries after the time of Boorde and Cardan. Pieter Camper, who was born at Leyden in 1722, came to London to study under William Smellie, at a time when midwifery was becoming a science. Being a clever artist, he drew some of the Plates for Smellie's famous Treatise.

When Camper became his pupil, Smellie had already been established in London for ten years, having begun his career by practising for sixteen years in his native town of Lanark. After the publication of his book in 1752, he became the acknowledged leader of British Midwifery. To prepare the drawings for his work, Smellie employed Rymsdyk, who was also the artist employed by William Hunter, but he also made use of his student Pieter Camper.

In his *Travel Journals*, reprinted in 1939, Camper has left an interesting record of his three visits to England. He had heard of Smellie from a Scottish student at Leyden, and he came to London to study Art as well as Midwifery. Arriving at Harwich on 16 December 1748, after a stormy passage of sixty hours, he continued by coach to London.

On 2 January 1749, Camper writes: "I was accepted as a Member of the Painters' Academy in London" and, three days later, "I enrolled in Dr Smellie's course in Midwifery".

A month later, to quote again from the Diary, "I was taken to see Sir Hans Sloane, 87 years old, and hard of hearing, but well preserved. He lives at Chelsea, and has a famous collection".

On 7 May, "Botanized at Primrose Hill with two other doctors", and on 10 May, "Sought herbs at Sydenham, a pretty village". Later he visited Oxford and Cambridge, as well as Bath, where, he wrote, "The Baths are very bad".

In 1752, Camper made a second journey to England. He was then Professor at Franeker, and could travel only during the vacation. The object of this visit was to make more drawings for Smellie.

He met Dr Donald Monro, who told him that his father, Alexander Monro primus, had torn his tendo Achillis while dancing, and that Professor Plummer had also torn his. He had several interviews with William Hunter and with John Fothergill, and discussed matters of mutual interest.

Many years passed before Pieter Camper visited England for the third and last time. He now had a high reputation, having been appointed Professor of Anatomy and Surgery at Amsterdam in 1775. There he wrote his well-known work on the application of Anatomy to Art. His later years were spent at The Hague, where he died in 1789. The last journey to England was made four years before his death. He desired to ascertain the attitude towards the operation of symphysiotomy, which he had practised with success in six cases. Smellie and Hunter had both died, and had been succeeded by Denman and Osborne, both of whom regarded symphysiotomy as "unwarrantable, though less dangerous than that most fatal operation, Caesarian Section".

On this visit, Camper spent much time at the British Museum, which he described as "a vast collection covered with dust".

He met John Hunter, who discussed with him the anatomy of the elephant; and Dr Herschel, who took him to Windsor to see his large telescope. He travelled to Birmingham to see the engines of James Watt, and there he also visited Dr Withering.

On 8 November 1785, Camper was admitted to the Fellowship of the Royal Society, when Sir Joseph Banks was President.

At this point, the Diary breaks off rather abruptly, as diaries sometimes do.

CONCLUSION

I have recalled to you the lives and wanderings of three very different travellers, not merely as a tribute to the memory of each of them, but also as a stimulus to their successors today.

We are all travellers, in time if not in space, and it may be our good fortune, as we journey through life, to promote human happiness, to add to human knowledge, or, at least, to supply one little stone or brick which may be useful to someone who is building on a larger scale. Slow though our progress may be we must ever push onward; the great thing is, to keep moving.

"For my part", wrote Robert Louis Stevenson, "for my part I travel, not to go anywhere, but to go."

Whether our journey is purposeful or not, it is always helpful to reflect upon the travels of our medical ancestors. As we do so, we instinctively range ourselves alongside them, and we find that their ideals are much the same as our own, although the environment has become so very different.

BACK TO OSLER

Today, we are all thinking of Sir William Osler, as we pay to him our annual tribute, this time on the 112th anniversary of his birth. He is a living force still, 42 years after his death. Few of us can recall him personally, but many who know him only through his writings revere him as an inspiring teacher, and, above all, as a teacher of youth. Osler loved young people and children, and there was much of the child in his gay optimism and his keen sense of humour.

His was indeed "a nature sloping towards the southern side". Throughout his life, he remained "strange to the familiar", retaining the priceless gift of curiosity, which is innate in children, but often sadly faded in adult life—that gift of wonderment at things which are usually just "taken for granted".

To this optimism and curiosity there was added, in Osler, that most valuable asset which he called Aequanimitas; that steady and solid trait so essential to the successful practice of Medicine. Equanimity implies not only a calm imperturbability when faced with some serious emergency; it also signifies a helpful attitude towards the unloveable, intolerant, and even aggressive patient who sometimes crosses our threshold.

In his textbook of surgery, published by Peter Lowe in 1597, there is a version of the Oath of Hippocrates which concludes with the words, "I shall patiently sustain the injuries, reproaches, and loathsomeness of sick men, and all other base railings". Equanimity should always include tolerance, an effort to like the unlikeable folk and to put one's self in the position of the sufferer.

Sir Thomas Browne phrased this ideal neatly when he wrote, "Let me be sick myself, if sometimes the malady of my patient be not a disease unto me", and Osler himself once said that his creed had been "to like and sympathize with everyone".

Optimism, Curiosity, Equanimity; what a stable tripod upon which to base one's medical life and outlook; what a happy assemblage of attributes for any traveller to carry in his haversack.

And so, Fellow-Oslerians, we who do ourselves stand like Janus in the doorway, travellers looking both ways, back upon the past with thankfulness, and forward to the future with confidence—we have every reason to give thanks for our heritage, for all that was done for us by the pioneers, and most of all for the noble ideals so well emphasized by William Osler.

PLATE 5
(see page 123)

The new version of "Rab", drawn by Edwin Douglas for the title page of *Rab and his friends*, second illustrated edition

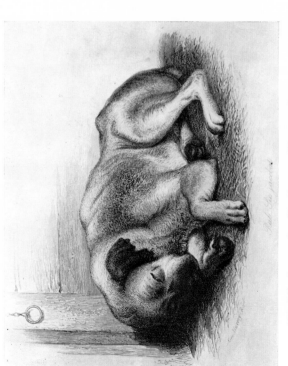

"Rab", drawn by Sir George Harvey for the first illustrated edition of *Rab and his friends*, and criticised by Dr John Brown as "not Rab, too leggy and gentlemanly"

Sir William Osler and his son Revere at Oxford in 1916
(see page 139)
(Photograph in the Osler Library, McGill University, Montreal)

PLATE 6

[149

"CORYAT'S CRUDITIES"

A Continental Tour in 1608

"OF ALL THE PLEASURES IN THE WORLD, travel is in my opinion the sweetest and most delightful." Thus wrote the optimistic Tom Coryat on his return from a journey of many hardships, so charmingly described in his book which was widely read and accepted for many years as the last word on Continental travel. It was not the earliest guide to Europe, for that had been written fifty years before by Dr Andrew Boorde. Entitled *The First Boke of the Introduction of Knowledge*, it is full of interest, though almost tantalizing in its brevity. Coryat, on the other hand, gives full measure in his *Crudities* and, as we have no reason to doubt his veracity, his is a valuable record of the "sights" of the Continent 350-odd years ago.

A commendable precision of description is shown in the full title of this precursor of Baedeker: *Coryat's Crudities, hastily gobled up in five Moneths travells in France, Savoy, Italy, Rhetia commonly called the Grisons country Helvetia* alias *Switzerland, some parts of high Germany and the Netherlands; Newly digested in the hungry aire of Odcombe in the County of Somerset, and now dispersed to the nourishment of the travelling Members of this Kingdome.*

The original edition of 1611 is a book-lover's treasure of rare vintage; a copy was sold in Edinburgh for a large sum, several years ago. Fortunately it has been reprinted more than once, and for those who desire a further draught of Coryat than can be given in this outline, the edition beautifully produced in 1905 by James Maclehose of Glasgow may be commended. There is also a three-volume edition dated 1776.

THE LIFE AND TRAVELS OF THOMAS CORYAT

Before dipping into the *Crudities*, let us glance at the biography of this prince and pioneer among tourists. The known facts of his life are meagre. Thomas Coryat (or Coryate), son of George

Coryat, Rector of Odcombe in Somerset, was born in 1577. Three years at Oxford gave him some knowledge of languages and logic, but did not guide him into a learned profession. It is said that his wit earned for him a position as a sort of Court Jester to Prince Henry, elder brother of Charles I, and it is probable that he was misunderstood and derided by the scholars of his day, who could scarcely regard as wholly sane one whose chief passion was for travel.

At all events, he set out on his wanderings in 1608, eventually reached Venice, and then walked all the way back to Flushing, about a thousand miles, with one pair of shoes, which he hung up in the church of his native village of Odcombe just before he departed on that longer and more ambitious tour to Asia, from which he never returned. It was in 1612 that he left for the East, by way of Constantinople, "Troy", Jerusalem, Ispahan, Agra and Ajmere.

He had planned to travel for seven years, but death claimed him before five of those years were spent, and his work remained unfinished. He died of dysentery at Surat in December 1617. The famous and well-worn shoes remained in Odcombe church until the eighteenth century. A more lasting monument is the guide-book.

THE FIRST EDITION OF THE "CRUDITIES"

There was no great thirst for travel literature in those days, and its authors were regarded for the most part as writers of fiction, following the lead of the fourteenth-century Sir John Mandeville, himself a fictitious character. So Tom Coryat found it necessary to secure some sponsors before any printer would accept his work. He appears to have gone to no end of trouble; indeed, when the book was eventually published in 1611 (the year of publication of the Authorized Version of the Bible), it was prefaced by more than sixty sets of "Panegyrick Verses" by all the leading poets of the time, including even Ben Jonson and John Donne. Most of them are in English, but a few are in Latin, French and even Greek.

While the symposium of poetry doubtless promoted the sale of the book, it cannot be said that the writers were entirely complimentary in their remarks on Coryat. Very few then took him seriously, and his description of the wonders of the cities of Europe left them cold. They preferred to poke fun at the traveller who lived on twopence a day and slept in stables, comparing him ironically to Ulysses and generally regarding him as a fool. Almost without exception they refer to the industry of his quill pen and, above all, to the one pair of shoes which brought reflected glory to the village of Odcombe.

> *One payre of shoes has done Odcombe the grace*
> *To make her name known past the Alpine hills,*
> *And home return'd has worne out many Quils.*

Another "poet" wrote of Coryat:

> *How he did go at least nine hundred mile*
> *With one poore paire of shoes, saving alone-a*
> *He onely once did sole them at Verona.*
> *So that it grew a Question whether*
> *Thy shoes or feete were of more lasting leather.*

One more variation of the theme will suffice:

> *Home in one paire of shoes did trample,*
> *A fearfull and a strange example.*

Not content merely to embellish his work with the versified remarks of his friends and patrons, Coryat dedicates it to Prince Henry, and adds an Epistle to the Reader in which he extols the advantages of travel, showing how it enables one to meet and converse with scholars of other countries, to visit the shrines of the saints and the scenes of "divers famous battels", as well as to acquire a "knowledge of forraine languages, an ornament the most precious and excellent that can be incident to a Gentleman". Finally, after asking the reader to "joyne with me in thy best wishes for happy successe in my future travels", he signs himself, "Thy benevolent and itinerating friend, T. C., The Odcombian Legge-stretcher".

CONTINENTAL TRAVEL IN 1608

Now let us judge for ourselves the interest and value of this quaint volume of *Crudities*.

We are off on our tour with Coryat from the very first sentence. "I was imbarked at Dover, about tenne of the clocke in the morning, the fourteenth of May, being Saturday and Whitsun-eve, Anno 1608, and arrived in Calais about five in the afternoone, after I had varnished the exterior parts of the ship with the excremental ebullitions of my tumultuous stomach."

A seven-hour Channel crossing must indeed have been a trying experience!

In accordance with the law he and his fellow-travellers were brought before the Governor of the town, who "asked many questions, as about the King and the newes of Ireland" before dismissing them to their lodgings. Coryat gives a little history of the town, and then with a "Thus much for Calais" he takes us to Boulogne. There he saw the great castle on the hill, and at a greater height the watch-tower "which our English do call the old man of Boulogne". What interested him most, however, was the place of execution, "at the toppe whereof is a wheel whereon the bodies of murderers are broken in pieces with yron instruments", and there was also "a Gallowes, consisting of two goodly faire pillers of free stone".

Amiens he greatly admired, the Cathedral there "being the very Queene of al the Churches in France and the fairest that ever I saw until then". It contained many beautiful pictures of kings and queens and saints, "a marveilous rich Pulpit", and "a Globe or Spheare of the World, very cunningly made in brasse".

"The principallest relique that is kept in this Church is the forepart of St John Baptist's head, enclosed in a piece of gold that is beset with precious stones. . . . It is never shewed but at sixe of the clocke in the morning, in a little Chappell, consecrated to that purpose."

Paris was the next objective, "a Citie exceeding great, very populous, and full of goodly buildings". The bridges over the Seine, the University and the Palace of the Tuileries are well described, as also is Notre Dame Cathedral, although the "pompous papistical ceremonies" offended the "Godly Protestant" in Coryat. At the Church of St Denis, four miles from Paris, he saw the tombs and monuments of many kings of France, and among the treasures "an Unicornes horne valued at one hundred thousand crownes, being about three yardes high". Doubtless this was the same Unicorn's horn as had been described by Jerome Cardan of Milan, who saw it as he passed through Paris in 1552 on his way to attend Archbishop Hamilton of St Andrews. In Cardan's view this horn was "more pleasing than all the statuary and architecture of that Church".

The palace and gardens of "Fountaine Beleau" also claimed the traveller's admiration. He writes of the fountain, of the ponds stocked with great carp, and of the huge beech trees. There were many pheasants and storks, and several ostriches, "birds that will eate yron, as a key, or a horse shoe".

Coryat now turned his steps southward. "At Lyons our billes of health began; without the which we could not be received into any of those cities that lay in our way towards Italy. For the Italians are so scrupulous that they will admit no stranger within the wals of their citie, except he bringeth a bill of health from the last citie he came from, to testifie that he was free from all manner of contagious sicknesse."

From Lyons he proceeded to Savoy, noting, as he went, numerous red snails of great size, abundance of chestnut trees and vast fields of barley. Usually on foot, but sometimes on horseback, and at one place carried in a chair up the mountain-side by "certaine poore fellowes which get their living thus", Coryat continued his journey. Now, as he entered the Alps, the going was more difficult or, to quote him again, "the wayes were exceeding harde and steepe, and so uneven that a man could scarce find any sure footing". Nevertheless Savoy, with its high mountains and abundant springs, was to Coryat "the best place that I ever saw in my life". Yet the people were poor and beggars were numerous. A certain Duke of Savoy when asked "whether he had any hounds to hunt with", told his questioners to return next day, "when he shewed them a multitude of beggars sitting at meat in his house. These, he said, are my hounds that I feede every day and with whom I hope to hunt for the glory and joys of heaven."

Coryat noted many things in Savoy: the swift rivers dashing over stony courses with "horrible and hideous noyses", the wooden bridges, the "admirable abundance of butterflies", the quaint attire of the women, with high "wastes" near to their shoulders and voluminous "linnen caps". The beds in this country were "so high that a man could hardly get into his bedde without some kind of climbing". Goitre was very pre-valent, "many men and women having great bunches or swellings in their throates, some as bigge as an foote-ball", and this was attributed to "the common drinking of snow water".

From Savoy he began the long descent towards Italy by way of Mount Cenis. "The waies were exceeding uneasie, stony, and full of windings and intricate turnings, and I continually descended headlong."

FORKS, FANS AND UMBRELLAS

Our traveller was greatly attracted by Italy. For him, it was "the garden of the world, beautified with goodly rivers, pleasant meadowes, and fruitfull vineyardes, fat pastures, orchards, woodes, and what not, so that the first view thereof did even refocillate my spirits and tickle my senses with inward joy." He fell ill from drinking the sweet wine of Piedmont, and he advises all travellers to "mingle it well with water". Nor did he favour the habit of "sprinkling the best meats with cheese"; this he loved "not so well as the Welchmen doe".

There was, however, one Italian food custom which greatly intrigued Coryat; indeed he may have been the first to introduce into England the use of the forke. "The Italians", he wrote, "do alwaies at their meales use a little forke when they eat their meate. For while with their knife they cut the meate, they fasten their forke, which they hold in the other hand, upon the same dish. This form of feeding is used in all places in Italy, their forkes being of yron and steele, and some of silver, but those are used only by Gentlemen. The Italian cannot by any means indure to have his dish touched with the fingers, seeing all men's fingers are not alike cleane. Thereupon I my selfe thought good to imitate the Italian fashion by this forked cutting of meate not only while in Italy but in England since I came home."

Turin, Milan, Cremona and Padua were visited in turn. The Cathedral of Milan was "as faire if not fairer than the Cathedral of Amiens", while in the Church of St Ambrose there were two wonderful objects, "the brasen serpent which Moses erected in the wildernesse", and "a rich Tapistry of needlework that presents a goodly picture of Moses".

The more modern aspect of Milan was revealed in the "Citadell of an incomparable strength", with stout bulwarks and many "huge pieces of Ordinance". "Among the rest was one exceeding great, a culverin made of brasse and about twenty foote long, which was said to carry a bullet at the least eight miles."

The population of Milan at the time of Coryat's visit was "not so few as three hundred thousand soules". It was then midsummer, and the heat was countered by fans and by parasols. "Both men and women do carry fannes to coole themselves withall, by the often fanning of their faces. Also many of them doe carry things they call umbrellaes that minister shelter against the scorching heate of the Sunne. These are made of leather in the forme of a little cannopy extended upon wooden hoopes, and they are used especially by horsemen when they ride."

CORYAT IN VENICE

At last Coryat reached Venice, his most distant objective on this tour. He estimated that, by the route he had taken "the total summe of miles betwixt Odcombe and Venice was 952". Yet the long journey was worth while. Venice eclipsed all other cities in beauty. This "richest Paragon and Queene of Christendome", so peerless, incomparable, and glorious, "doth amaze and drive into admiration all strangers upon their first arrivall".

"The Grand Canal and its branches runne through the city as the veynes doe through the body of a man, with sumptuous marble palaces on both sides, making a glorious and beautifull shew." Lovely bridges, more than 400 in number, added to the beauty of the scene; "the Rialto bridge, with rowes of shops, is the fairest that I ever saw, read, or heard of." All transport was by water. The statement, by a certain traveller, that he rode through Venice, is stigmatized by Coryat as "a fiction as grosse and palpable as ever was coyned". There are "certain little boates, which they call Gondolas", bearing at each end "a crooked thing in the form of a Dolphin's tayle", and "the watermen alwaies stand when rowing". The fairest place in the whole city is the Piazza of St Mark. There you may find a cosmopolitan crowd of "Polonians, Slavonians, Persians, Grecians, Turkes, Jews, and Christians, each distinguished from the other by their proper and peculiar habits".

Coryat noted some peculiar traits in the Venetians. At a playhouse, for instance, he "saw women act, and they performed with as good a grace, action, and gesture as any masculine actor". In the market he observed "great Senators coming to buy things for the maintenance of their family, a practice I commend to the English Gentleman who scorneth to buy his own victuals but employeth his Cooke about those sordid affaires".

The women of Venice wore long veils, and a more curious fashion was the wearing of "chapineys" under their shoes, worn in order to make them appear tall. "These chapineys are of wood covered with leather of sundry colors, redde, yellow or gilt and many are even half a yard high. I have heard that the nobler a woman is, the higher are her Chapineys." "All the Gentlewomen are assisted and supported when they walke abroad, to the end they may not fall by reason of such frivolous and ridiculous instruments. I my selfe have often laughed at them for their vaine Chapineys."

Coryat left Venice with genuine regret, for he would not exchange the sight of it for "foure of the richest mannors of Somersetshire wherein I was borne".

HIGHWAY ADVENTURES

Now he began his long walk homeward, by way of Germany and the Low Countries. In Baden, as in many other German cities, he observed "the heads of wilde boares nailed upon the dores of dwelling houses" because "it is the custome when they have killed any boare in hunting to cut off his head and erect it in that manner".

It was near Baden that Coryat escaped from thieves by a clever ruse. He met "two clownes in ragged cloathes, armed with weapons, who strooke no small terrour into mee". Fearing that he would be attacked and robbed, he "undertook a politike and subtile action. For I put off my hat and very humbly begged money of them, in Latin and by gestures", with the surprising result that "they gave me so much as paid for my supper that night in Baden, even foure pence halfe-peny".

Another adventure befell the wayfarer as he approached the town of Worms. "I stept aside into a vineyard by the high waie to taste of the grapes, as I did often in Lombardie without any controalement. But there came a German Boore (for so are the clownes of the county called) who looked fiercely upon me and swaggered insolently with Allemanne wordes which I understood not, threatening me with his halbert so that I was in deadly fear. At length I took heart and discharged a whole volley of Greeke and Latin shot into him, hoping to show him that I had learning. . . . After many bickerings had passed betwist us, three or foure good fellowes came by, and asked what the quarrell was. One of their company could speak Latin and he told me that the Germanes were wont to fine any that they catch in their vineyards without leave. So the controversie was compounded for a small price which was twelve of their little

coynes called fennics. I would counsell the gentle reader to beware of going into vineyards without leave or thou mayest pay
a farre deerer price for thy grapes than I did."

TIME AND WINE

Two great sights deeply impressed Coryat in Germany, the
Clock of Strasbourg and the Tun of Heidelberg. Not only does
he fully describe them, but his book contains a "true figure or
representation" of each.

The astronomical clock of Strasbourg Cathedral, completed
in 1574 by Conrad Dasypod, the Archimedes of Strasbourg, is
"the Phœnix of al the clocks of Christendome". It is "decorated
with a great company of mathematicall conceits which doe
decipher the obstruse and secret mysteries of Astronomy". "At
the toppe is a most excellent effigies of a Cocke, and it croweth
at certaine houres . . . yielding a sound very neere the true
voyce of that bird." Also "Certaine artificial men doe come
forth at every quarter of an houre with a delightfull grace,
holding hammers wherewith they strike little bels, each with a
pretty decorum."

Coryat concludes his description of the Strasbourg Clock by
expressing the hope that his words may be read by some wealthy
citizen who might thereby be "encouraged to erect the like in
Paules Church of London".

As for the Great Tun of Heidelberg, this was, to Coryat, "a
kind of monstrous miracle", one of the wonders of the world.
The drawing of it, bought in Frankfurt, is one of the most attractive illustrations in the book. It had a capacity of 500 hogshead,
took three years to build and was completed in 1591. "Each
ende is sixteen foote high, and the belly eighteene. . . . When the
Cellarer draweth wine out of the tun, he ascendeth several
degrees of wooden staires and so goeth to the toppe. . . . I advise
thee Gentle Reader that intends to travell into Germany and
dost happen to ascend to taste of the wine, that thou dost drink
moderately", otherwise "such a giddinesse will benumme thy
braine, that thou will scarce descend the steepe ladder without
a very dangerous precipitation".

"Thus much of Heidelberg", and there is more of Mayence
and Frankfurt, Bingen and Bonn, Düsseldorf and Dordrecht,
then with "a prosperous gale of wind all the way betwixt
Flushing and London", whence Coryat tramped home to Od-

combe. Between Venice and Odcombe he had walked 1023 miles, and during his five-months' tour he had seen five and forty cities.

SIC EXIT CORYATUS

Here we must leave Coryat, for there is little else to record of his travels and adventures. His only other published work is a little volume of letters from India, to various friends and patrons and to his mother. Most of them are dated 1615, and they appeared in print under the title "Thomas Coryate: Traveller for the English Wits: Greeting. From the Court of the Great Mogul (1616)", with a frontispiece showing the writer riding upon an elephant.

Perhaps the most interesting letters are those addressed to his mother, in which he tells of his long journey of 2700 miles from Jerusalem to Ajmere "in the company of Caravans from place to place", occupying "fifteene months and odde days" and "all this tedious way afoote, with no smalle toile of bodye". He had already spent a year in Ajmere, learning Persian, Turkish and Arabic to such good purpose that he had made an Oration in Persian to the Great Mogul, requesting a passport to the city of Samarkand.

He announced his intention of returning by way of Babylon, Mount Ararat, Aleppo and Egypt, of spending two more years in Italy and Germany, and then, his seven-year plan accomplished, "with all expedition into England, and to see you with as great joy as ever did any Travailer his mother". As his final message he writes: "I pray you mother, expect no more letters from me till my arrivall in Chrystendome for it will be a farre greater comfort to you to hear that I have accomplished my travells. . . . Have patience for a time, and from Turky or from Venice I will dutifully remember you again. Your loving dutiful and obedient Sonne, now a desolate pilgrim in the World, Thomas Coryat."

There can be little doubt that, had Coryat lived to complete his travels, an account of them would have been well worth reading. Unfortunately, he left no manuscript, and the slight notices of his work by contemporary writers add little to the information contained in the letters.

During his long absence a rumour reached England that he had been drowned near Constantinople, and this drew from

John Taylor, the "Water-poet", a lament or epitaph in verse, to be followed very soon by further doggerel, to commemorate his "reviving", when the rumour was contradicted. From this it may be inferred that since the publication of the *Crudities*, the author had become a popular figure.

Some notice of Coryat's travels is also to be found in that lengthy postscript to Hakluyt's *Voyages*, by Samuel Purchas, entitled "Purchas His Pilgrimes, contayning a History of the World, in Sea Voyages and Lande Travells" (1625).

An account of Coryat's last days was given in 1655 by the Rev. Edward Terry, Chaplain of the Lord Ambassador to the Court of the Great Mogul. Terry, who met Coryat in India, tells us that, had he lived to write his last travels "they must needs have swoln into many huge volumns" . . . "for he was a very particular and faithful Relator of things he saw". The Ambassador, Sir Thomas Rowe, pressed Coryat to stay longer at Ajmere. "But he thankfully refused and turned his face presently towards Surat, about three hundred miles distant." There, he was overkindly used by the English, who gave him Sack. Though Coryat was a very temperate man, the drinking of it increased his Flux which he had then, and hastened his end within a few days. Terry writes: "*Sic exit Coryatus*. Hence he went off the stage and so must all after him. For if one should go to the extremest part of the world East, another West, another North, and another South, they must all meet at last in the Field of Bones, wherein our Traveller hath now taken up his lodging, and where we leave him."

IN QUEST OF THE
WITCH DOCTOR*

I HESITATED WHEN I WAS FIRST ASKED to address this Meeting, as I did not think that such account as I could give of a recent visit to Africa, would be suitable for this learned Society. But I accepted after I had been assured that the paper given at this Annual Meeting is never taken very seriously and is simply a means of attracting Fellows to participate in the business part of the Meeting.

I had never been in Africa before this year. I had surveyed mankind in China, also in Peru, but Africa remained the Dark Continent, strange and mysterious, waiting to be visited.

One might find something new there, for did not Pliny tell us many centuries ago that there was "always something new out of Africa?" Certainly so far as actual exploration went, the nineteenth century produced a succession of geographical thrills, and new features were added to the map at home as they were revealed in Africa by Speke and Baker, Mungo Park, David Livingstone and a host of others. My father was a junior teacher in Alexander Buchan's school in Dunblane, before Buchan went to Edinburgh in 1860 to accomplish his great work for meteorology. My father told me that a large map of Africa adorned the schoolroom wall and that Buchan would delight to add to it the new discoveries as these became known. There had been a time when cartographers added fictions of their own to fill the gaps—a whole series of lakes on the site of Lake Victoria, and of course the Mountains of the Moon, sometimes shown as a great range, extending right across the continent. But now there was no need to draw upon the imagination, and gradually the blank spaces became filled and the field for further exploration became narrowed.

---

* An address delivered to the Royal Society of Edinburgh, at the request of the Council, 22 October 1951.

More recently the interest in Africa has become political and educational rather than geographical, and has centred in the problem of rapidly developing civilizations.

FIRST IMPRESSIONS

Sometimes I am asked what impressed me most during my African journey. Was it the native life or the big game, the strange exotic birds and flowers, or those gigantic physical features such as the Victoria Falls, the Great Rift Valley or the seemingly endless River Nile which I followed along its entire course? Those impressions were doubtless vivid, but Africa gave one something more, something moving and appealing, something almost spiritual, intangible and difficult to express in words, a sort of soulfulness which made one feel transported into another world. It hardly existed in South Africa or Rhodesia, but one began to sense it in Kenya and its spell became stronger in Uganda and still stronger in the Sudan. It was weird and uncanny, but in no way terrifying. It was in fact quite friendly and helpful, the sort of feeling which comes to those who are receptive when they visit lovely places, even in Scotland, such as the Hebrides. The whole background of Africa is conducive to strange happenings; one is not surprised to find it a land of magic and of witchcraft. I welcomed the mental process which made me so conscious of the supernatural in Africa. One of the main objects of my tour was to acquire some information regarding native African medicine. As my title implies, I was in quest of the witch doctor, although the quest was not fully rewarded, for reasons which I shall presently explain.

A second motive for my tour was a series of lectures which I undertook to deliver at various universities and medical societies; but of this I shall say little, as it does not reveal the true Africa. It may interest you to know, however, that the Faculty of Medicine at Cape Town University, founded in 1918, was modelled upon that of Edinburgh and staffed, as it still largely is, by Edinburgh graduates.

No one can say that Johannesburg is a beautiful city, its leading features being a series of sky-scraper buildings, and those great mounds of yellow earth from which gold has been extracted and which are now being investigated anew in the hope that they may yield uranium. Johannesburg is the New

York of South Africa; Pretoria, only thirty-five miles distant, is the Washington—a colourful city with fine buildings. South Africa was, however, merely my gateway to the more remote interior.

VICTORIA FALLS OF THE ZAMBESI

I left Johannesburg early one morning, flew over the great salt marshes of Bechuanaland and within four hours was looking down upon the Victoria Falls. It is said that this is a scene which never disappoints. For me it far exceeded expectations. A dense white cloud of spray is visible many miles away and the dull roar of the water is audible. The River Zambesi, a mile wide, flows tranquilly along and gathers speed only some yards above the point at which it hurtles into a great chasm, and then follows a zigzag canyon for the next forty miles. I had not realized how closely one may approach the fall; therein lies its unique charm. One stands on the dry edge of the chasm, while in front, within a stone's throw, the water roars over the opposite edge. Yet the dry edge is far from dry, indeed one is drenched in the volume of rising spray which causes the top of the cliff on which the visitor stands to be known as The Rain Forest.

"Have you the smoke that sounds, in your country?" the old Chief asked Livingstone on that morning of 17 November 1855. And Livingstone recalled, rather pathetically, the Falls of Clyde in his native Lanarkshire. He landed in a canoe on one of the islands which literally overhang the fall, and from that point he first peered over, into the abyss. One cannot identify the five columns which Livingstone described, rising like smoke to mingle with the clouds, but as one watches the succession of rainbows moving slowly along in the spray, as the sun sinks low in the afternoon, one may fitly recall Livingstone's remark: "Scenes like these must have been gazed upon by angels in their flight."

At the closed western end of the cleft is the fall named Devil's Cataract, and near the edge stands the bronze statue, inscribed simply—Livingstone, 1813–73. Missionary. Explorer. Liberator. Huge blue and yellow butterflies flit about in the sunlight, and gay birds add to the loveliness of the scene. The opposite end is called the Boiling Pot; here the churned mass of water seems to be confused by its fall, but it can find outlet only into the next canyon, far below (650 feet) the road and railway bridge which has spanned the gap since 1905. I spent three days at the Falls and would fain have stayed longer.

THE GRAVE OF CECIL RHODES

But I still had a long way to go, and after a very rough overnight journey by rail I found myself in the broad street of Bulawayo, and from that centre I visited Cecil Rhodes's grave in the Matoppos and, 300 miles to the West, the ruins of Zimbabue. It is strange to stand beside Rhodes's grave in the solid rock, to think of the short but eventful life of the Empire builder, and to fancy what his thoughts may have been as he gazed often on the seemingly endless ranges of rocky hills now called The World's View. The bronze plaque is simply engraved, "Here lie the remains of Cecil John Rhodes", with no dates. At Shabani I stayed with the doctor, an Aberdeen graduate, and saw this asbestos-mining town which employs 6,000 Matabele workers. The output of ore is 4,000 tons a month, and the work of crushing, extraction of fibre by suction, grading and packing, continues night and day. Farther on, seventeen miles beyond Fort Victoria, are the curious brick ruins of Zimbabue, reputed source of the gold of Ophir, and a subject of endless argument among archaeologists. The date of building still remains uncertain.

In Bulawayo, the Director of the Museum presented me with a witch doctor's outfit—the sticks used for divination, the zebra-tail switch, and various horns and shells containing medicine, now on view in the Royal College of Surgeons, but of the witch doctor himself I had seen nothing. It was at Bulawayo that I first made the acquaintance of the witch doctor, though not at first hand, I must confess. Like so many other travellers in Africa, I saw neither a lion nor a witch doctor.[1] This was most disappointing. Nevertheless I did learn a great deal from those who were well acquainted with both, and of my informants the most illuminating were various African medical assistants whom it was my pleasure to meet.

PRIMITIVE MEDICINE ANALYSED

Native African medicine cannot be placed alongside modern scientific medicine and compared with it. The two are utterly

[1] I did meet a witch doctor during a second visit to Kenya in the following year (Plate 7).

different and are based upon entirely different beliefs. The African, like primitive man elsewhere, does not admit that disease can arise from what we call "natural causes". For him, it is a magical or magico-religious phenomenon, of supernatural origin. Living as he does in a world of spirits, holding inter-course with them in dreams, taking care to remain on friendly terms with the god of rain or the god of fire, can we wonder that he regards disease as the work of an evil spirit, the ven-geance of an enemy, or the wrath of an offended god? Where this doctrine of disease holds sway there is little room for logical treatment by drugs or diet. A supernatural disease must be treated by supernatural methods. But there are exceptions to this belief. Some diseases such as colds, constipation, or malaria, are so common that they are accepted as a normal part of life and not as diseases at all. At all events those common maladies are treated by domestic remedies which have been discovered by the trial-and-error method. Certain herbs are known to be purgatives, others will reduce fevers, and so on. Bodily injuries, such as wounds or fractures, have a cause so obvious that there is no need to regard them as supernatural. Surgery is probably a more ancient art than medicine. And so it comes about that in Africa two systems of medicine co-exist side by side. The first is domestic medicine, or folk medicine, known to everyone and used for minor illness, as indeed it is used even in civilized communities today. It has a close affinity with modern medicine, and science has learned much from it.

WITCHCRAFT IN MEDICINE

The second system of medicine, that of the so-called witch doctor, is in an entirely different category. Sometimes vegetable remedies are used, but for the most part the treatment consists of incantations and spells, and the invoking of the supernatural. Even civilized man has a fondness for mascots; this is carried to extremes by the witch doctor. The witch doctor, be it noted, is not a witch but is rather the enemy of the witch. He is essenti-ally a diviner or prophet. He is concerned with rain making, fertility, the recovery of stolen goods, the imputation of guilt. Medical treatment is only one of his many activities. His methods are akin to those of the psychoanalyst. He draws no distinction between the material and the spiritual; he treats body and soul alike. The pebbles or sticks are cast upon the ground,

The Chief and the witch doctor, Kenya 1952
From the gourd which he holds the "doctor" has poured out
the seven heaps of little pebbles on which his verdict
depends (see page 165)

PLATE 7

PLATE 8

William Harvey demonstrating his researches to Charles I (see page 79)

(The painting by R. Hannah in the Royal College of Physicians, London)

and the pattern which they assume is interpreted (Plate 7). The guilt for disaster or disease may be attributed to some innocent person who may be punished by death. Rain-making is innocent enough, but witch-hunting may lead to the murder of innocent persons. Is the witch doctor to be regarded as a murderer? He may be acting, in all good faith, in the interests of the tribe. To the British way of thinking, witchcraft is just so much nonsense and superstition. The fact that the witch doctor, should he himself fall ill, submits to be treated by another witch doctor, is evidence of his genuine belief in his own art. But if this leads to murder, as sometimes happens, the murderer must be tried and punished in the usual way. The Witchcraft Suppression Ordinance of 1896 was the first legal attempt to stamp out the evil of the witch doctor. Legislation of this sort shows a lack of insight into the African way of thinking. To view witch-doctoring as a crime was surely unwise, and the result of the law has simply been to drive the practice underground. It is still very widespread, and it may take generations to eliminate the evils of witchcraft. The cure is not to be found in legislation but rather in education. Scientific medicine can learn little or nothing from the witch doctor, but a study of his ways is essential to the administrator. The continents of Europe and Africa can never understand each other unless they meet on the common ground of anthropology. It may be imagined that modern medicine might borrow valuable knowledge from the other system of native medicine, the folk medicine of Africa. Nevertheless little is to be gained from this research. The vast majority of native vegetable remedies have no action at all. Some are purgatives, some allay fever, but of the hundreds which have been tested by pharmacologists, very few have proved to be of value. It is rather a sterile field for research. I was interested to find in Medical Schools for Africans at Makerere College in Uganda and at the Kitchener Medical School in Khartoum that the students were keenly interested in the indigenous medicine of their countries and were proud of their heritage. The Uganda students were prepared to defend some of the methods of the witch doctor; the Sudanese, on the other hand, claimed their descent from the great Arabian physicians of medieval times. This line of study deserves encouragement; it may provide a sound basis for medical study and a foundation for a good ethical standard.

A TRIBAL DANCE

I have mentioned the importance of anthropology, and it was a pleasure for me to meet, in Nairobi, a Cambridge graduate who was conducting an anthropological survey of the Kikuyu people of the Kenya Highlands. We examined one of the hollow logs which the Africans place in trees or on sticks, to attract wild bees. I was to see those hives later in Uganda, where they are equipped with a little roof. We made an excursion into the Aberdare Mountains, with scenery very like that of Perthshire. At a place called Tuso one could imagine oneself in the Trossachs. In passing a village on the way we were fortunate to find some fifty women, clad in brown tunics, with numerous earrings and necklaces, who had arranged themselves in a circle and were performing a tribal dance in order to bring rain. There was much rhythmical clapping of hands and stamping of feet and the wailing of a curious melody, if melody it could be called. The dancers did not notice us, we drew nearer, and the dance continued for a long time. But suddenly it ceased, and when they saw us they became very excited and even menacing. We made a move towards the car, but it was not easy to escape in a graceful and dignified way. Then I felt in my pocket several packets of sweets, so I solemnly presented one to each lady and we withdrew as they made up their minds whether the gift was an ornament or something to eat.

It may interest you to hear of my further journey north through Africa. My next objective was Nyeri, a little town which stands at an elevation of about 9,000 feet, near to Mount Kenya. The hotel is called the Outspan, and, during his later years, it was the home of Lord Baden Powell, Chief Scout of the World. I often sat on his verandah, then occupied by Colonel Jim Corbett (author of *The Maneaters of Kumaon*), who would tell me the names of the birds which came for food—the black and yellow weaver birds whose nests are such common objects in the African landscape, the glossy blue starling with its burnished steel appearance, the little waxbills, the sunbirds with their curved bills, and many others. A constant visitor was the East African squirrel, striped black and brown. Mount Kenya (17,000 feet) was seldom clearly visible and was difficult to photograph. But when it did appear, especially by moonlight, it looked majestic, the great sweep of hillside, then the rocky

166

summit with the Lewis Glacier to one side, all looking curiously out of place on the equator which is said to pass right through the summit.

WILD LIFE FROM TREE-TOPS

One evening we set out to watch for big game in the Tree Tops Hotel, probably the strangest hotel in the world, which later became so widely known, after the Royal Visit. It is miles from any other habitation, close to a clearing in the forest, and is built among the branches of a large fig tree forty feet from the ground. The white hunter marched along in front of us with his gun at the alert, and he pointed out the rope ladders on various trees, providing for our escape should any dangerous animal appear. But we reached the tree without incident, climbed up, and drew the ladder after us. It was almost dark, and the moon would not be up for some time. Meantime we partook of an excellent dinner, and then to each of us was allotted a berth. Most of our party of eight decided to snatch a little sleep. We were told we must keep very quiet, and I lay awake for a time, fearing that I might snore and scare away the big game. But I must have slept, as I was beginning to dream of quite impossible beasts when I heard someone whisper "There is a rhinoceros below". As I shook off my slumber I recollected that the hotel advertisement stated that "all charges for the night's lodging and entertainment will be remitted if buffalo, or elephant or rhinoceros are not seen". I had gambled on the chance of seeing nothing but it was once in a lifetime and, like the other guests, I slipped on a dressing gown and tip-toed out to the balcony. Two ghostly forms were prowling about below us in the moonlight, sniffing and snorting, but never thinking of looking up to see us in the tree. For a long time we watched, in the warm tropic night. Presently the bushes at one side of the clearing parted. A pair of large tusks appeared, and then the head and great flapping ears of an elephant. Probably he noticed that the rhinos were in full possession of the stage; at all events he came no farther and soon departed altogether. The two rhinos were then joined by a mother rhino with a calf, and the childish antics of the baby were quite amusing in a beast of such bulk. But after two hours or so I decided that the exhibition did not justify further loss of sleep, and although a few ardent watchers remained on the balcony all night, they saw nothing more. I looked out again as dawn was breaking, just in time to see two graceful bush-buck trot across the clearing.

One obvious disadvantage of observing big game in this fashion is that photography is not possible. But even in more favourable circumstances, as for example the Nairobi Game Park, it is not easy to approach near enough and the result is usually a tiny animal in a vast background. Commonest of the antelopes are Thompson's Gazelles, or Tommies, as they are called locally. The ugly wildebeeste with its strange antics is also common, familiar in crossword puzzles as the gnu; and there are bush buck and water buck and the pretty little creature called the dik-dik.

FROM NYERI TO THE RIFT VALLEY

All too soon I left Nyeri, and bumped along the rough road back to Nairobi (" three hours for a reckless driver, four hours for a careful driver", as the hotel notepaper states), raising clouds of that thick, penetrating, brick-red dust so character-istic of Kenya. Sitting directly behind the driver one noticed several large holes in each ear, and that the ear lobe, stretched into a long loop, had been neatly knotted to render it less obtrusive since he had abandoned the use of ear-rings. It was a striking commentary on the African's keen desire for rapid civilization. Education becomes most enlightened in Africa when it lays stress on Social Service and seeks to develop the existing art and music. This is being done in many schools. In the Secondary School at Kagumo, the most favoured subjects are carpentry and water-colour painting.

The way from Kenya, very attractive as seen from the motor bus, lay across the Rift Valley, and, as far as Nakuru, it was a modern highway constructed by Italian prisoners during the last war. This great cleft in the face of Africa extends through the Dead Sea and the Red Sea, then splits into two, the western branch following Lake Albert and the line of small lakes, the eastern branch passing through Lake Rudolf and down through Kenya. According to Gregory, it was caused by the subsidence of a strip of the earth's crust between two parallel faults. On either side of the valley which is, here, about 6,000 feet above sea level and about 60 miles in width, there is a steep bank or escarpment, actually a cliff in places, some 2,000 feet in height. The floor of the valley is intersected by a number of lakes which have been drying up in recent years. Lake Naivasha appeared pink as we approached, and then we saw that the colour was due to a huge flock of flamingoes. Lake Nakuru had obviously shrunk considerably, leaving a great expanse of soda which was whirled into a number of miniature tornadoes by the wind. There was also a number of volcanoes in the valley; Mount Longonot (9,000 feet), and Mount Meningai with a crater ten miles in diameter. The commonest tree is a flat-topped acacia, popularly called the umbrella thorn. The remainder of the road passed over the Mau summit, through wild and lovely scenery. As we rounded a corner, a leopard dashed across the road with a bird in his mouth.

TEA IN AFRICA

The vegetation became more profuse and of a brighter green as we descended to approach Lake Victoria, passing the town of Kericho which is in the centre of Brooke Bond's great tea gardens. One is apt to forget that tea is an important product of Africa; the annual export reaches ten million pounds weight of tea. There were some rubber trees but this industry has been much less successful. A night in the hotel at Kisumu was very hot and sticky and it was a relief to embark next morning on the curiously long steamer *Usoga*, which takes a week to sail round Lake Victoria. Hundreds of Africans were waiting to embark. They are great travellers and many of them spend their lives in moving about. There was many a traffic jam on the gangway and women and children were the last to come aboard. Fortunately the lake was calm and on the following evening Entebbe was reached, only five hours late.

Although it is only three miles north of the Equator, Entebbe is a very pleasant place. Between the hotel and the lake is a little golf course and a local rule states that a ball which has lodged in the hoofprint of a hippopotamus may be lifted and re-played without penalty. There are many hippos here, also crocodiles, but they are seldom seen on land. The birds were interesting— that useful enemy of snakes, the tall secretary bird, like a hawk on stilts, crested cranes, white-headed eagles, hornbills, shrikes, and the familiar Uganda crow with its white collar and breast, looking like a negro in a surplice, and of course the common weaver bird. There were no mosquitoes at Entebbe; indeed, I met very few in Africa. The tiny "lake fly" (chironomus) is

169

extremely abundant but fortunately does not bite. It occurs in such dense clouds that it obscures windows, and wind-screens of cars. The natives mix the bodies of these gnats with oil and press them into cakes, which are sold as a sweetmeat in the market. As a rule the African carries luggage, medicine bottles and even lawn mowers, cleverly balanced on the top of the head, another common sight in the market-place.

TOWARDS THE CONGO

I discovered that a motor bus ran occasionally from Kampala to Lake Kivu in the Belgian Congo, 300 miles distant, and although the doors of the bus were held in position by string, the windows would neither open nor shut, and a large hole in the floor revealed the machinery, I determined to risk the journey. But first I was obliged to secure a Certificât de Moralité, stating that I had not been in prison within the past few years, and a Health Certificate affirming that I was not suffering from any of the thirty-two named diseases in a list which included plague, mumps, mania and rabies. In the end all this proved needless as I did not cross the frontier. The bus reached Kabale many hours late, and I discovered not only a delightful little White Horse Inn (Austria in Africa), but I met the Inspector of Agriculture who made a hobby of collecting native plant-remedies and who had exactly the information I sought.

The Bahima tribe of this district, like some other African tribes, live largely on blood and milk, and they carefully tend the long-horned cattle so characteristic of Uganda. The interest of the road made the long journey to Kabale well worth while. The birds seemed to be very tame; even eagles continued to sit on the fence-posts as we passed. As we came down again to the level of Lake Victoria, I crossed the equator for the eighth time, and the driver's wife posed for me with one foot in each hemisphere.

A VOYAGE DOWN THE NILE

The time had now come for me to set out on the last stage of the journey, following the Nile from the Ripon Falls where the river leaves Lake Victoria, through the shallow Lake Kioga with its masses of blue water lilies, and on across Lake Albert, then down the White Nile through the Sudd to Khartoum. The tour involved eight changes of conveyance, which included four steamers, two railway trains, and two motor buses. Most of this journey was accomplished by stern-wheeler steamers of very shallow draft, although the craft on Lake Albert is a miniature liner, the *Robert Coryndon*. Near the point at which the White Nile leaves the lake we were sailing close to the shore, when we noticed a herd of thirty or forty elephants coming towards the water and waving their trunks above the long grass like a field of snakes. We saw their flapping ears and their shining white tusks, but soon they sensed us, turned and made off with a rapid graceful movement which seemed remarkable for such bulky animals. A little later we had a good view of a small group of buffalo, and as for crocodile and hippos, those were almost constantly visible during the greater part of our three weeks' journey. The native life was also fascinating. Our first halt was Rhino Camp, where the Bari people predominate. They are simple, friendly people. The women's dress consists merely of a bunch of leaves which is renewed daily. Their scanty curly hair is plastered with red mud, which gives a strange appearance. In the market place a girl was amusing herself and her friends by using as castanets two small gourds filled with seeds. I tried to buy this instrument with an East African shilling, but money meant nothing to her. Then I produced from my pocket a number of large safety pins which I carried as first aid for torn clothing; very useful in that land of thorn bushes. The girl seemed impervious to my dumb-show efforts at barter, but her bolder friend seized the pins and pushed the castanets into my hand.

At Nimule we left the steamer and travelled by car to Juba, in order to avoid a series of cataracts. Then we joined another stern-wheeler which was to be our home for the next two weeks. It was not merely a steamer. A barge as large as the steamer itself was tied to either side and we pushed two other barges in front of us. Thus a perfect village of five boats tied together made its way down the Nile. Besides the Sudanese crew there were aboard about 200 Africans and 12 European passengers. I shared a cabin with a Belgian consul going home on leave from the Congo.

IN THE DINKA COUNTRY

Our navigation was very curious. The river varied greatly in width and there were many shifting sandbanks. When we came to a bend in the river the captain deliberately ran aground, then waited for the current to swing the stern right round and so release us, and thus, performing a complete turn, we resumed our course; the manoeuvre was something like figure skating. Often we bumped the bank, sometimes the side barge mounted the bank and slid along on the mud, and at one place we remained firmly aground for about twenty hours while numerous natives on the bank tugged this way and that until at last we were afloat. There were frequent opportunities of going ashore, at Shambe and elsewhere, and of viewing at close quarters those curious Nilotic people, the Dinkas and the Shilluks. The Dinkas are very tall, some even seven feet in height, and they have a curious habit of standing on one leg. The women are not good looking so far as features are concerned, but they walk most gracefully. They wear little or no clothing; like Kipling's Gunga Din "The uniform he wore was nothing much before, And rather less than half of that behind". The Dinka covering is limited to a necklace or a bracelet, and some are daubed over with wood ash, which, it is said, helps to keep off mosquitoes. They seem to be nomads, bringing their goats and cattle down to the Nile in the dry season and building temporary conical grass huts on the bank. We saw some of them fishing from dugout canoes but the only fish I saw caught was a very tiny one. Farther down the river, the Dinkas gave place to the Shilluks, whose hair is done up in strange fashion and whose faces are marked by a series of scars like a chaplet of beads.

NAVIGATING THE SUDD

We now entered that peculiar region known as the Sudd, where the river almost loses itself in a vast marsh covered with miles and miles of papyrus in every direction. Until the present century the Nile actually was lost and it is easy to see why the discovery of its source was so long delayed. Baker wrote of the Sudd, in 1870, "The entire river became a marsh through which the water oozed by innumerable channels; the White Nile had disappeared". Now, the channel is kept open by steady dredging but there is an immense loss of water by seeping away and by evaporation. Many suggestions have been made for a greater control, and something may yet be done, after the great Nile dam at Jinja is completed. Some travellers find the journey through the Sudd rather boring; the channel is narrow and is limited on either side by a wall of papyrus some twenty feet in height. But the bird life is fascinating. Pelicans and ibises are numerous, also the big marabou stork, the largest bird that flies, and there are the little plovers which attend the crocodiles and keep them free from insect pests. Lovely kingfishers brought flashes of colour and we also saw that strange beast with the enormous beak, the whale-headed stork. In fact one was quite sorry to leave the Sudd and to see the river widen until at Malakal it was about quarter of a mile across. The banks now became grassy and a few trees appeared.

LIFE IN KHARTOUM

But from here to the great bridge of Kosti, where we left the boat and took train to Khartoum, the scene was much tamer and less interesting. There were no more Nilotics, only Arabs in white robes and for the first time one heard that awful word baksheesh. Of Khartoum I could say a great deal, although it was a new world and hardly seemed to belong to Africa. Although the heat is fairly intense (110° or so) there are no mosquitoes and it is very pleasant to sleep on the roof and to be awakened by the song of a bulbul perched on the end of one's bed.

One cannot be in Khartoum without being conscious of the Gordon tradition, and without recalling the dreadful days of the Mahdi. Although the Mahdi's tomb was totally destroyed by Kitchener after the battle of Omdurman in 1898, it was rebuilt by the Mahdi's son Sir Sayed Ahmed Rahman in 1948. It is an ornate garish building with some very ugly stained glass and gilt furniture. In one corner is a grandfather clock which belonged to Gordon, and in the Khalifa's house, which stands close by, one may see the first motor car brought to the Sudan by Sir Reginald Wingate, and also the famous warning letter from the Khalifa to Queen Victoria, recalling to her the fate of Hicks Pasha, and advising her to accept the Moslem religion.

There was something strangely Biblical about Khartoum— the white-gowned, turbanned men, the veiled women, the camels and donkeys, the habit of speaking in parables. It was a very suitable conclusion to an African pilgrimage.

The African dream was about to fade; I would go to sleep in shadowy, mystic Africa, and awake in a Europe of stern reality.

But something would remain. I could recall the rainbows of the Victoria Falls, the glaciers of Mount Kenya, the elephants and the giraffes, the Kikuyu children and the tall Dinkas, but above all, a warmth of welcome and an atmosphere of friendliness which, I am sure, could be surpassed nowhere.

HARVEY IN SPACE AND TIME*

SINCE ANDREW DUNCAN DELIVERED THE FIRST OF THE EDINBURGH HARVEIAN ORATIONS in April, 1778, on the 200th anniversary of the birth of William Harvey, there have been many memorable orations on a great variety of subjects. Only about one-fifth of the orations deal directly with Harvey and his work, because the Laws of the Society, very wisely, impose no restriction upon the choice of a topic. Each orator is faced with a problem which becomes steadily more difficult each year.

Every aspect of Harvey's life and doctrine has been subjected to the most detailed scrutiny, not once but many times. Notwithstanding all this, the oft-repeated tale may still prove stimulating to a new generation of "neophytes", as well as refreshing to mature and seasoned Harveians. I have therefore decided to stick to Harvey, and to delineate him against a background of geography and history, space and time. Under the first heading, some account is given of Harvey's three Continental journeys, and, in the second place, an attempt is made to trace the history of his discovery of the circulation and to explain the long delay in its acceptance.

During the past year I have made various pilgrimages in pursuit of Harvey; to his birthplace at Folkestone; his school at Canterbury: Caius College, Cambridge; St Bartholomew's Hospital; and the Royal College of Physicians of London (though Harvey would scarce recognize any of those scenes today); to Oxford, where in the last stages of the Civil War he continued his studies in embryology, using the eggs of a hen which his friend George Bathurst obligingly accommodated in his rooms; and, finally, to Harvey's last resting-place in the little village church of Hempstead in Essex, now perhaps better known as the birthplace of Dick Turpin, the highwayman, than as the burial-place of William Harvey.

* Oration to the Harveian Society of Edinburgh, met in the Royal College of Physicians of Edinburgh on 15 June 1956.

How vastly the British scene of Harvey's labours has changed. Abroad, he seems more clearly to fit the picture, especially in Padua, where, though the city is sadly scarred by bombing, one may still see the anatomical theatre where Harvey followed the demonstrations of Fabricius; and the pulpit used by Galileo. Almost certainly Harvey attended the lectures of Galileo, who did for science what Harvey did for medicine, replacing vague argument by accurate measurement.

Let me give you a brief account of Harvey's three visits to the Continent, as the influence of foreign travel upon his lifework is not always fully recognized.

I suppose Scotland at that time (as occasionally today) was regarded by the English as a foreign land. Harvey was with the Court when his Royal employer, Charles I, was crowned at Holyrood in 1633, and he came north again in 1634 and 1641.

But these Scottish journeys were so well described by Sir Henry Wade in a recent Harveian Oration[1] that I shall concentrate on the Continental wanderings, so significant in the colourful life of William Harvey.

STUDENT DAYS AT PADUA

The wandering physician is a familiar figure in history. Hippocrates, Galen, Paracelsus, and others were never very long in one place. The founders of the Edinburgh Medical School drew their inspiration from Leyden; and Sir William Osler, himself a mobile professor, was wont to say that permanence of residence, good for the pocket, was bad for the brain.

Harvey was fully aware of the advantages of study abroad, and it was fortunate for him that after he had taken his degree at Cambridge his father was eager to send him to the Continent and could well afford to finance such a venture. The choice of Padua as his postgraduate school was probably influenced by the fact that John Caius had studied there. To Padua, then, at the age of nineteen, William Harvey went, taking his degree in 1602, and, as representative of the English "nation", leaving his "stemma" or coat of arms, which was discovered by Professor George Darwin in 1892, in the cloister surrounding the old quadrangle of the University.

Unfortunately Harvey kept no diary, or, if he did, it has long since disappeared. Accordingly, in order to reconstruct for

[1] 'Harvey in Scotland', *Edinb. med. J.*, 1938, **45**, 761.

ourselves the Padua of that day we must refer to the records of contemporary travellers.

BOORDE, LITHGOW, AND CORYAT

Half a century before Harvey, the agile and versatile Dr Andrew Boorde (or Borde), he who wrote the first medical book in English to be printed in England, *The Breviarie of Health*, in 1547, had journeyed far and wide, and had written *The First Boke of the Introduction of Knowledge* (1542), which may be regarded as the first Continental guide-book, a lively and informative account which is still well worth reading (see page 141).

Another early traveller, not a medical man, was the Lanark-born William Lithgow, "lugless Willie", whose ears had been cut off because of a youthful misdemeanour. His book entitled *Rare Adventures and Painful Peregrinations*, 1632,[2] was very widely read in its many editions, although his information is not always accurate or credible.

More interesting than either of those, and more close to the time of Harvey, was Tom Coryat, son of the Rector of Odcombe, in Somerset. His was one of the most fascinating books of travel, under the title *Coryat's Crudities, hastily gobled up in five moneths travells*,[3] etc., and dated 1611, nine years after Harvey left Padua.

Coryat's description of Padua is interesting although of course he had no special interest in the medical school. Venice he regarded as the most beautiful of all cities, "The richest Paragon and Queene of Christendome", he called it. From there he walked all the way home, about a thousand miles, in one pair of shoes, which he hung up in his father's church, and there they remained for over a century. Coryat, whose exploits are recorded in detail in my earlier essay (page 149), mentions the Bills of Health, which, as we shall see, caused Harvey so much annoyance, and he may have been the first to introduce into England forks and umbrellas.[4] He wrote: "The

[2] The full title is: "The Totall Discourse, of the Rare Adventures, and painefull Peregrinations of long nineteene Yeares Travayles, from Scotland to the most Famous Kingdomes in Europe, Asia, and Africa."

[3] "Coryat's Crudities, hastily gobled up in five moneths travells in France, Savoy, Italy, Rhetia commonly called the Grisons country Helvetia *alias* Switzerland, some parts of high Germany and the Netherlands; Newly digested in the hungry aire of Odcombe in the County of Somerset, and now dispersed to the nourishment of the travelling Members of this Kingdome."

[4] See p. 154 of this volume.

177

Italians cannot endure to have their food touched with the fingers, and do always use a little fork, of iron or steel or sometimes if they are gentlemen, of silver. Many do carry things they call umbrellas that minister shelter against the scorching sun." But let us return to Harvey.

There can be no doubt that the years in Padua had a profound influence upon his career. His teacher, Fabricius of Aquapendente, was a worthy successor of Vesalius, Colombo, and Fallopius. The work of Fabricius on the valves of the veins may well have initiated in the mind of young Harvey that train of thought which led to so spectacular a discovery.[5]

During the twenty-five years or so following his return from Padua, Harvey was busily engaged in London, as physician to St Bartholomew's Hospital (1609), and in private practice, as Physician to the King, and as Lumleian Lecturer to the College of Physicians (1615). His title, be it noted, was that of Professor of Anatomy and Surgery. This period culminated in the publication of his book in 1628.

THE SECOND AND THIRD CONTINENTAL JOURNEYS

Harvey's second Continental journey took place in 1630, when he was chosen to accompany a wealthy young nobleman, the Duke of Lennox, on a grand tour of France and Spain. It was hoped to include Italy, but the visit was cancelled on account of plague. Of this tour there exists only the scanty detail contained in a letter from Harvey to Lord Dorchester. He writes from Spain, in a letter which reveals his inquiring mind: "We could scarce see a dog, crow, kite or raven or any other bird or anything to anatomize; only some few miserable people the relics of war and plague where famine had made anatomies before I came."

A few years later, in 1636, Harvey had the good fortune to make his third Continental journey, and of this tour we have a clearer record, revealed in a number of letters which came to light in 1911: letters from Harvey to Basil Fielding, afterwards Earl of Denbigh, who was, at the time, English Ambassador at Venice.

After he performed the famous post-mortem examination of

---

[5] The Hon. Robert Boyle had an interview with Harvey in later years, and was told that this was so. It is mentioned in one of the rarest of Boyle's works—*Disquisition about final causes of natural things*, 1688, p. 159.

Thomas Parr, the old countryman aged, or said to be aged, 152 years, who was brought from Shropshire to London by the Earl of Arundel, Harvey was invited by the Earl to accompany him on a political mission to Vienna, ostensibly an embassy, but also an expedition to acquire art treasures for the King. Harvey, a patron of the arts, and an expert critic, readily assented.[6][7] The party left England on April 7 1636, sailing from Margate in the ship *Happy Entrance*, and landing in Holland. They proceeded up the Rhine, then up the River Main "in a boat drawn by nine horses". It was a leisurely journey, and Harvey had plenty of time to make observations on strange trees and plants, and would often wander so far that the Ambassador was angry with him, as there was real danger from thieves and wild beasts. Coryat, who had travelled by the same route, records the prevalence of robbers, and advises all travellers to carry a stout stick. At length they reached Frankfurt on 3 May, and then Nuremberg 11–22 May, where Harvey demonstrated the circulation of the blood to the Professor of Anatomy, Caspar Hoffmann, who had been his fellowstudent at Padua, but who was among those who misunderstood the discovery, saying that it was "contrary to the wisdom of Nature". "I beg you to observe", Harvey had written, "and to see the thing with your own eyes." Nevertheless Hoffmann remained unconvinced, and asked such stupid questions that eventually Harvey laid down his knife and left the theatre.[8]

HARVEY IN QUARANTINE

The second misfortune of this tour was of an entirely different nature. On the return journey from Vienna, Harvey had left the main party at Augsburg with the intention of travelling to Italy. He went by way of Munich and Innsbruck, then over the

[6] The journey is described by William Crowne, a member of the expedition, in a little book of seventy pages which is now rather rare. It is entitled "A true relation of all the remarkable places and passages observed in the travels of the Rt. Hon. Thomas Lord Howard, Earl of Arundel and Surrey, Premier Earl and Earl Marshall of England, Ambassador Extraordinary, etc. (1637).

[7] A more modern and extensive account is given in *The Life, Correspondence, and Collections of Thomas Howard, Earl of Arundel*, by Mary S. Hervey (1921), Ch. XXVI, pp. 357–95, which describes "The Great Embassy to Germany".

[8] The most significant reference of recent date to this journey is the paper by Sir D'Arcy Power on "A Revised Chapter in the Life of Dr. William Harvey, 1636," in *Proceedings of the Royal Society of Medicine*, Sect. Hist., 1917, x, 33. Sir D'Arcy suggests that the demonstration to Hoffmann may have taken place on the homeward journey, when Nuremberg was again visited, from 10–13 November.

Brenner Pass, and on to Treviso on 3 August, where, he writes, "I have received a very unjust affront". It was alleged that he had passed through a plague-stricken area without having his Bill of Health or "sede", the all-important passport, duly countersigned and cleared. Harvey, detained for this reason, writes to Lord Fielding, who expects him at Venice, "I am fallen into the hands of a base and evil people, and while they delight to exercise their tyranny, I am to lie in the open fields for God knows how long, and I fear it will do hurt to my health".

As a result of this letter Harvey was offered a roof and a bed, but this he declined, as he said "such offers were unreasonable, like physick when a man was dead"; and his next letter, on 16 August, to Lord Fielding is even more doleful. "Their manners and cruelty have been shameful and I now have a sciatica that maketh me lame. I have never longed for anything so much as to be gone from this base place." It is difficult to understand why Harvey, then aged fifty-eight, a medical man, and a person of importance, should have been singled out and virtually imprisoned in quarantine for about a month. England was not held in high esteem on the Continent at that time. Perhaps the delay explains why Harvey did not return to visit his old friends at Padua. Besides, the thirty-five years which had elapsed since his student days must have brought many changes, and it is often very depressing to revisit the old scenes of one's youth.[9]

Eventually set free, he did reach Venice, where his reception was very different, as the next letter, dated from Florence on 7 September, states "I can never forget your many favours and your kind entertainment at Venice". He was joined at Rome by his friend Dr George Ent in October, and although we have little knowledge of the homeward journey, we are told that Harvey visited the School of Anatomy at Leyden, that he had a rough crossing from Rotterdam, and that he landed at Deal on 27 December 1636.

Aubrey, who is at best a gossipy biographer, states that

[9] *Eleven Letters of William Harvey to Lord Fielding, June 9–Nov. 15, 1636.* Purchased from the Earl of Denbigh and presented to the Royal College of Physicians by Sir Thomas Barlow, Bt., President: 18 October, 1912.

Comments upon the letters are given in a chronicle of the family of Lord Fielding called "Royalist Father and Roundhead Son, being the memoirs of the first and second Earls of Denbigh, 1600–1675," by Cecilia, Countess of Denbigh (1915). Chapter VI, pp. 111–21, deals with "The Tribulations of Doctor Harvey".

Harvey made a fourth journey to the Continent in 1649, but of this we have no certain knowledge.

THE SLOW ACCEPTANCE OF HARVEY'S DISCOVERY

Now let us turn to another aspect of Harvey's activity—namely, his work on the circulation of the blood, and the events which followed its publication. The foregoing references to Harvey as a traveller may be regarded as a fitting introduction to the adventures of his famous book and to the curiously tardy acceptance of his great discovery.

I do not propose to refer in detail to his second work, *De Generatione*, 1651, dealing with those researches which arose quite naturally as a sequel to his work on the circulation, which occupied many years. It was eventually published in 1651 at the urgent request of Harvey's friend Sir George Ent. This work advanced embryology as far as that science could have gone without the aid of the microscope. Harvey, who laid great stress upon comparative anatomy, tells us that he used "a magnifying glass" to study the prototype of the heart in insects, shrimps, and other creatures, but he was not familiar with the microscope. It was left to Malpighi in 1661, and to Leeuwenhoek in 1674, to supply proof of the existence of the capillaries which Harvey presumed to exist as "pores in the solid parts, permeable to the blood, connecting the arteries with the veins" (*De Motu*, Ch. XI).

Harvey's masterpiece, the *Anatomical Disquisition on the Motion of the Heart and Blood in Animals*, often called for short, *De Motu Cordis*,[10] published at Frankfurt in 1628, was printed on poor paper and was full of printers' errors. As an example of book production it ranks very low, but as a clear, brief, and logical account of the author's researches it is beyond praise.

The first English translation appeared in 1653 and the first Dutch edition in 1650. Other translations were much later products—German 1878, French 1879, Russian 1927, Danish 1929, and Spanish 1936.[11]

You will recollect how Harvey begins his "Disquisition" with a concise review of the existing knowledge, although, as he tells us in the preface, he has no intention of making a large volume. "I teach anatomy", he writes, "not from books but from dis-

[10] *Exercitatio anatomica de motu cordis et sanguinis in animalibus.*
[11] Italian translation was published by Professor Premuda of Padua in 1957.

sections: not from the positions of philosophers but from the fabric of nature." Then he proceeds to defend the three propositions of his thesis, and to develop and expound the argument which you all, as Harveians, know so well.

As we read this little classic, the most important medical book ever written, we find the discovery so plainly set forth that we marvel why it was not immediately accepted. The philosopher Thomas Hobbes said that Harvey was one of the few pioneers who saw his discovery universally accepted during his lifetime; but this is hardly true. Indeed, the real significance of Harvey's work in the practice of medicine was not apparent for at least two centuries, and it took about fifty years before those best qualified to judge, the anatomists and scientists, appreciated its significance.

DELAY IN PUBLICATION

Why this long delay in the acceptance of a truth so obvious? For the first part of the delay the discoverer himself was responsible. Harvey had not rushed into print. Darwin waited twenty years, Jenner eighteen years, and Lister eight years before publishing their results. Their work was not fully appreciated for many more years. Lind's recommendations for the prevention of scurvy were ignored by the Royal Navy for forty-three years.

Harvey, from the first, made no secret of his discovery. He lectured on the circulation, as Lumleian Professor to the College of Physicians, for twelve years before stating his views in print. Thus when the book did appear some of his pupils and friends were ready to accept the new teaching, but others regarded Harvey as a crank. As Aubrey remarks, " 'Twas believed by the vulgar that he was crack-brained and he fell mightily in his practice" (see page 196).

It is sometimes said that Harvey's discovery was a mere accident, that all the evidence was there, awaiting the genius who would grasp the opportunity of assembling the facts.[12] There could be no greater error. Since student days at Padua, and perhaps even then, Harvey had been continuously at work building up his argument and confirming each step by observa-

[12] The full story is admirably discussed in a series of papers by the late Dr H. P. Bayon, entitled *William Harvey, physician and biologist: his precursors, opponents and successors,"* in *Annals of Science*, 1938–9.

tion and experiment. His novel methods of investigation, so revolutionary in his day, and so different from the bookish methods of his predecessors, were in themselves deterrents to the acceptance of his results. It cannot be too strongly stated that Harvey had not only discovered the circulation of the blood, he had proved the efficiency of the scientific method in medical research, a proof which was to be stated even more clearly by Claude Bernard more than two centuries later. The discovery of a principle is always more important than the discovery of a fact, as it leads to further advances. Ehrlich's discovery of chemotherapy outshone his introduction of salvarsan as the remedy for syphilis. Lister's use of the antiseptic method was much more outstanding than was his use of carbolic acid, because here was a new principle, not just a new remedy. That is one reason for the long delay in belief in the circulation of the blood.

TENACITY OF THE OLD IDEA

And there is this further point—not only did the new discovery arise from the application of new methods of research; it could be accepted only by those who were prepared to discard the old beliefs. Before the new idea could be approved it was necessary to disprove the old. And at that time the dead hand of Galen still lay heavy upon medical science, if indeed it could be called "science". Prior to Harvey's day it was known that the blood moved, but with an ebb-and-flow motion in the veins, like the tides of the sea. The heart was not regarded as a pump; it drew to itself the blood as it dilated; in other words, diastole, not systole, was the important movement. The liver, not the heart, was the central organ concerned in the production and movement of the blood. It was thought that there were two kinds of blood—the dark variety, which originated in the liver and carried nourishment to the body, and the brighter-coloured blood, which came from the heart and supplied heat. The blood conveyed three kinds of spirit—natural, animal, and vital. The ideas were all very obscure and very hypothetical. It is to the credit of Servetus, the only real predecessor of Harvey, that he discovered that natural spirit and animal spirit were one, and that they became transformed into vital spirit in passing through the lungs.

Harvey himself stated that the cause of the change of colour was that the blood was "strained" as it passed through the lungs, just as earlier anatomists thought that the blood was strained, and thus altered in some way, as it oozed through the pores between the right and left ventricle of the heart. The foetal circulation was also ill understood, and Botallo (of Paris) in 1565 had added to the confusion by describing as a normal appearance a persistent foramen ovale which he found in an adult body.[13] It is true that Vesalius had shown that the septum between the ventricles was not porous; but the new anatomy of Vesalius had not been entirely accepted, and ancient textbooks with the Galenic descriptions were still in use. Many contemporary anatomists—Alexander Read at Barber Surgeons' Hall, Crooke and Collins at Cambridge, and Winston at Gresham College[14]—simply ignored Harvey's doctrine, and continued to teach along the well-worn lines, refusing to abandon the old ideas. Others were actively opposed to the new explanation, for various reasons, and often for very little reason at all.

For example, there were the clinicians, the so-called "practical" folk, who asked what was to be the *use* of this teaching. Did it really matter which way the blood moved? Had the so-called discovery saved any lives? According to the loquacious Dean, Gui Patin, of Paris, it was simply "an ingenious piece of fiction". This demand for a clinical outcome of his discovery was anticipated by Harvey when he wrote: "Many questions in medicine, physiology, pathology, and therapeutics can be answered by the truth we have declared, on which I might expatiate, but my whole life would not suffice for the completion of the work." More than once he refers to his "Medical Anatomy, or Anatomy in its application to Medicine". Perhaps this manuscript, like his notes on the Generation of Insects, was lost when the College library was destroyed by fire or when his

[13] Castiglioni, A., *A History of Medicine* (Eng. trans.), New York, 1941, p. 428; Willius, F. A., and Dry, T. J., *A History of the Heart and Circulation*, Philadelphia, 1948, p. 45. (A pioneer in the anatomy of the foetus was Giulio Cesare Aranzio (1530–89) of Bologna.)

[14] *The Reception of Harvey's Doctrine of the Circulation of the Blood in England as exhibited in the writings of two contemporaries*, by Sir Humphry Rolleston, in *Essays on the History of Medicine*, Sudhoff 70th Birthday Volume (1924). The two contemporaries are Winston and Power, and they illustrate the two extreme points of view. Thomas Winston, 1575–1655, repeats the description of pores in the septum which "cannot be seen in dead bodies because they fall together," but which serve to "strain" the blood. Henry Power, 1623–68, on the other hand, repeated and confirmed Harvey's experiments, and showed that "the partition wall is firm and compact, and absolutely devoid of any perforations."

rooms in Westminster were raided by a mob during the Civil War: "Rapacious hands stripped my house of its furniture, and, a subject of far greater regret to me, my enemies abstracted from my museum the fruits of many years of toil." Those were calamities which he greatly deplored.

Thus was the propagation of Harvey's doctrine delayed, a very different state of affairs from that which obtains today, when the discovery of a new antibiotic reaches the practitioner almost in advance of its time and with a speed which may even be dangerous.

EARLY PRINTED CRITICISMS

One of the earliest critics of Harvey to state his views in print was James Primerose (Primrosius), a physician of Hull who had studied under Riolan in Paris, and who evidently wrote for the sake of writing, upholding the older views in a work printed in 1630.[15] He would probably have attracted little attention had he not been answered in a thesis at Leyden, De circulatione, by Roger Drake, a Cambridge student who upheld Harvey's views. Drake was supported by one of his teachers, Hendryk du Roy (Henricius Regius), of Utrecht, who entitled his work "A sponge to wash away the dirt of Primrosius",[16] which called forth from Primerose a reply headed, "An antidote to the poisonous sponge of Henricius".[17] Both are dated 1640.

Another antagonist of Harvey was Emilio Parigiano (Parisianius), of Venice, who was answered with more dignity by Dr George Ent, Harvey's lifelong friend, in his work, An Apology for the Circulation of the Blood, 1641. Harvey took no part in those controversies, well knowing that none of the critics had taken the trouble to really understand his views, and that they based all their arguments on the old conception. The only critic who received a detailed reply from Harvey (a reply printed in English editions of De Motu Cordis) was Jean Riolan, of Paris, who had been his fellow-student in Padua. When Riolan remained unconvinced Harvey wrote a second letter in rather stronger terms. The duel of words ended in 1690, when Pierre

[15] Flourens, P., Histoire de la Découverte de la Circulation du Sang, 1854.
[16] Regius Henricius, Spongia pro eluendis sordibus animadversionum J. Primrossii, Leyden, 1640.
[17] Primrosius, Jacobus, Antidotum adversus spongium venatum Henrici Regii, Leyden, 1640.

Dionis, a supporter of Harvey and a teacher of his doctrine, assumed the Chair of Anatomy in Paris.

The famous anatomist Thomas Bartholin, 1616–80, was the first to introduce the knowledge of the circulation into Denmark,[18] but he did not do so wholeheartedly, as he described in his textbook, *Institutiones Anatomicae*, 1641, both the old and the new view, apparently leaving the reader to form his own judgement. Harvey's views are contained in a Supplement by Jan de Wale (Walaeus), of Leyden.

Spain was one of the last countries to accept the new knowledge. It has been said that Harvey's work was banned by the Inquisition, but I have been unable to discover the source of this statement. Even in the eighteenth century, Galenic anatomy was still taught in Spain, and Professor Izquierdo, who in 1936 undertook the first translation of *De Motu* into Spanish, tells us that while Sobremonte, in 1649, and Morello, in 1678, accepted and wrote upon the Harveian view, Piquer, of Valencia,[19] as late as 1751, was antagonistic, and still taught the older idea. Izquierdo also states that the first book on physiology written and printed in the New World in 1727 was the *Cursus Medicus Mexicanus*, by Salgado, of Los Angeles.[20] It gave "a confused idea of the circulation", and probably the author had never seen Harvey's treatise. Nevertheless, Salgado's work was still used as a textbook at the end of the eighteenth century.

HARVEY'S FIRST SUPPORTERS

From those critics, most of them slaves of the age-long teaching, and sworn Galenists, it is a relief to turn to those who were ready to free themselves from the influence of Galen, and to accept the new view regarding the circulation, or at least to ascertain for themselves by experimental methods whether it could be true. Of those supporters, one of the first was Robert Fludd, a man four years younger than Harvey, who was a leader of the so-called Rosicrucians, and whose mystical works were printed in Frankfurt by William Fitzer, who also published Harvey's masterpiece.[21] In his *Integrum Morbium*, of 1631,

[18] Gotfredsen, E., *The Reception of Harvey's Doctrine in Denmark*, Acta med. scand., 1952, **142**.

[19] Piquer, Don Andres, *Institutiones Medicae*, Madrid, 1751.

[20] Izquierdo, J. J., *Harvey, iniciador del methodo Experimentale*, Mexico City, 1936.

[21] Weil, E., "William Fitzer, the publisher of Harvey's De motu cordis"; *Library*, 1944, **24**, 142.

Fludd makes a favourable reference to the discovery of the circulation.

René Descartes, in his *Discours de la Méthode*, 1637, accepted Harvey's principles, and so did Francis Glisson, whose classic work on the liver, *Anatomia Hepatis*, 1654, reinstated the liver in correct perspective. As early as 1639 the renowned Francis de la Boe (Franciscus Sylvius) was giving demonstrations of the circulation, in dogs, to his class at Leyden.

Werner Rolfinck, of Jena, was a well-known anatomist who in 1641 believed and taught that the blood circulated, while Nathaniel Highmore introduced the new discovery into his book on anatomy, dedicated to Harvey, which gives one of the earliest descriptions of the circulation.[22]

Sir Thomas Browne, whose view must have carried weight, said that he regarded Harvey's discovery as better than the discovery of America, and few today would disagree with that opinion.

Of course the most helpful of the critics were those who took the trouble to repeat Harvey's experiments rather than merely argue about them. Such a one was Hermann Corning, of Helmstadt, whose book, *De Sanguinis Circulatione*, 1643, brought strong support to the doctrine, as also did the work of Henry Power, one of the first to use the microscope, whose experiments are described in his *Microscopical Observations on the Lamprey*, 1664. This, surely, was the only true method of appraising Harvey's work, by repeating his experiments, thus applying to his results the method which he himself used to secure them.[23]

No reference to Harvey's discovery is complete without some mention of the controversy regarding priority which continues unabated to this day, especially, perhaps, in Italy. All manner of absurd claims have been made, often on very slender evidence: that the circulation was known to the ancients—to the early Chinese and to Hippocrates, to Arabian physicians and to a numerous band of anatomists, mainly of Italian birth, who lived shortly before the time of Harvey. The confusion of ideas

---

[22] Highmore, Nathaniel, *Corpus humani disquisitio anatomica in qua sanguinis circulationem . . . prosequutus est,* 1651.

[23] There is an unpublished manuscript (Sloane MS., 1543) in the British Museum dated 1652 in which Henry Power describes experiments to demonstrate the circulation, performed by Harvey in 1614, two years before the usually accepted date of the discovery.

was increased by frequent misinterpretation of the word "circulation", which at first simply denoted movement. Everyone who has driven a car in France must be familiar with the policeman swinging his baton and urging the traffic to move on. "Circulez, circulez", is his order.

LATE CLAIMS FOR PRIORITY

It is sometimes forgotten that nothing was said of other claims to the discovery until Harvey's view was beginning to meet with general acceptance, about 1650. Not one of the earlier critics claimed that the circulation of the blood was already known, or had been discovered by someone else before Harvey.[24] The claim of Cesalpino was mentioned for the first time in 1655 by Nardi. There is a statue of Cesalpino in Rome, proclaiming him to be the discoverer of the circulation of the blood. This claim was followed by allegations that the discovery was made before the time of Harvey by Colombo, Ruini, Servetus, and others. It is true that Servetus had discovered the lesser circulation, as also had Colombo and the thirteenth-century Arab physician Ibn Nafis, whose work has come to light recently. But both Servetus and Colombo adhered to the pre-Vesalian anatomy: they believed that the blood was prepared in the liver, and then flowed through the heart to the veins.

The interest of Servetus in the blood stream arose from his desire to find a habitat for the soul. The physiological work of Servetus was first quoted by William Wotton in 1694;[25] it had attracted no attention until then. The trend of Servetus was to theology rather to physiology, and it was on account of his Unitarian views that he suffered martyrdom in 1551. Edinburgh University, possessing one of the three surviving copies of his *Restitutio Christianismi*, has a peculiar interest in Servetus. Further discussion of those claims for priority of discovery, which continue to this day, would carry us far from the present theme—namely, the reasons for the long delay in the acceptance of the circulation of the blood.

[24] Johannes Antonides Van der Linden, 1609–64, a famous Dutch physician, did all he could to discredit Harvey, and stated that it was George Heriot, 1563–1624, jeweller to James VI of Scotland, who first suggested to Harvey the idea of the circulation of the blood.

[25] Wotton, William, *Reflections upon Ancient and Modern Learning*, 1694.

CONCLUSIONS

An attempt has been made to explain this delay, which arose from a variety of causes. These may be summarized in conclusion as follows:

1. The so-called "practical" physicians of Harvey's time, who demanded that every new discovery should be immediately applicable as a life-saving or health-restoring measure, regarded the circulation of the blood as a matter of academic importance only.[26]

2. The refusal to abandon the fixed age-long traditions, dating even from the days of Galen, prevented many from accepting, or even from studying for themselves, a conception so contrary to current opinion.

3. The new doctrine of the circulation involved not only a change of view regarding the motion of the heart and blood but also a revolutionary change in methods of investigation; a completely new outlook; the replacement of scholastic argument by direct observation and experiment. The change was so staggering that it could hope to gain acceptance only by slow degrees.

The delay in the acknowledgement of the circulation of the blood was a phenomenon peculiar to the age in which Harvey lived.

Few were prepared to write, as Abraham Cowley did:

> *Thus Harvey sought for Truth in Truth's own book*
> *The Creatures which by God himself was writ*
> *And wisely thought 'twas fit*
> *Not to read Comments only upon it*
> *But on th' Original itself to look.*

The experimental method of investigation, as novel to Harvey's critics, is now familiar to the most junior medical student. It has long since ceased to be a matter for argument. Moreover, increased facilities of transport and communication have made it possible for a new discovery to be known throughout the world in a matter of hours. Within a few weeks, or months at most, each addition to the existing knowledge is

---

[26] At first Harvey's doctrine exercised a more profound effect upon biology than upon medicine; it formed a starting-point for a vast number of further biological investigations.

examined and assessed at its true value. Indeed, the speed of integration of new discoveries and new ideas has become almost terrifying. Thus, it is not only right and proper, but even salutary, for us to turn back the pages of history, to recall Harvey's experience, to assess his achievement, at this Festival when we are met to honour his memory.

RESEARCHES
AND DISCOVERIES

THE WAY OF THE
INVESTIGATOR*

.

IN THE MAYO FOUNDATION HOUSE at Rochester, Minnesota, at one time the home of Dr W. J. Mayo, and now a meeting place for the many medical pilgrims who visit the Mayo Clinic, there is a remarkable stained glass window, dedicated to the memory of those who made the greatest contributions to medical progress from the earliest times to the present day.

The window consists of a triple series of panels, which illustrate advances in each of the three fields of medical activity —Education, Practice and Research. The third of those great lines of progress, that of research, might appear to be the most important, so far as medical progress is concerned, although of course all three overlap and intermingle. Despite the modern trend of specialization, the teacher of medicine conducts researches, and the path of research may be followed even by the busy general practitioner.

A DEFINITION OF "RESEARCH"

One should not define too narrowly this word "research". The careful, persistent, repeated quest for new knowledge is really one of the oldest of man's activities.

Research is the principal occupation of childhood, that inquisitive period so tantalizing to many parents, who are obliged to answer, or attempt to answer, numerous questionings of "how" and "why". As the child grows up, his attention becomes focused and less diffuse, and he is indeed fortunate if he retains in adult life his simple curiosity, the desire to know, the questioning attitude towards the most ordinary facts and objects. The inquisitive child, or student, may be a nuisance

---

* Inaugural Address to the Section of the History of Medicine, Royal Academy of Medicine in Ireland, delivered by invitation, 19 January 1956.

to his parent or teacher, but the ultimate result of his researches may be of great significance.

As Cicero remarked: "We should strive to render ourselves strange to the familiar." In other words, we should preserve an attitude of mind which sees something new and fresh and strange in the most ordinary sight.

This questing spirit, or state of continual wondering, is the most valued possession of the investigator, a far more important asset than the elaborate apparatus of the best laboratory.

RESEARCH AND DISCOVERY

Research does not always lead to discovery, although it proceeds in that direction, always hoping to produce results, however insignificant.

Every discovery is building upon foundations laid by others, often upon ideas and results which never appeared in print. Unrecorded work has its value, and innumerable discoverers who might have achieved fame remain unknown. Perhaps the time was not ripe for their discovery. Acceptance came only when the climate of opinion was favourable. There have been other discoverers, who did not grasp the significance of their own work, and it was left to others to explain and to apply at some later date.

As Sir Thomas Browne said: "Who knows whether the best of men be known, or whether there be not more remarkable persons forgot than any that stand remembered in the known account of time." When we praise famous men, let us also think of the unknown pioneers who "have no memorial, who are perished as though they had never been". In any case, discoveries are merely the peaks in the chart of progress, made possible by the spade work of many obscure and forgotten researchers. The research is more important than the discovery. Furthermore, we should remember that the pursuit of research was at one time difficult and even dangerous.

EARLY OBSTACLES TO RESEARCH

In early times the quest for knowledge was strictly limited by superstition and by magic. Nature had hardly a chance. It has been stated that medical advance was retarded by the early Christian Church, which discouraged the study of all natural phenomena, despising the natural in an endeavour to exalt

194

the supernatural. Of course this view reacted unfavourably upon the progress of medicine.

In the Roman Empire, research was discountenanced unless it yielded results of practical value. The so-called "practical man" has always been the enemy of progress, and insistence upon utility is still a deterrent in various lines of research.

A third barrier to progress in early times was a slavish adherence to Aristotle's deductive logic. Men preferred to argue rather than to observe or to experiment. This trend is rather surprising in our day, when the experimental method is the possession of every child, and logic is often, perhaps too often, left to the philosophers.

Galileo, early in the seventeenth century, encouraged men to solve scientific problems by the simple use of accurate measurement. At about the same time, Francis Bacon opposed the old scholastic view, urging men to think for themselves, to acquire and to verify knowledge by making experiments, and to argue from experience and not from authority.

The Renaissance, while it brought greater freedom to science, brought new difficulties which have continued to the present day. For a time the way seemed clear. It was possible for one man to study many subjects. The papers read before Royal Societies and Academies could be understood by any intelligent person. As the sciences multiplied, each speaking its own language, a time was reached when each special branch, be it of science or of medicine, became intelligible only to the few. A paradoxical state has now been reached in which science was never before so free, and yet, at the same time, never so restricted. In consequence, one of the greatest needs of the present time is for interpreters who can make plain to those in other fields, even in adjacent fields, and also to some extent to the average citizen, the progress achieved by the investigators and the specialists. Having mentioned the difficulties attending the work of research, let us examine the methods by which fresh investigations should be conducted.

THE QUALIFICATIONS NEEDED FOR RESEARCH

Let us look at the man, before we discuss his methods. The successful investigator is rather a rare individual. Brain alone is not enough: an honours degree is only a small part of the necessary endowment. Teaching, practice and research, the three essentials, do not always march hand in hand. Ability to teach is more common than ability to seek out new knowledge. Indeed, the man of original mind is seldom a good teacher. Few students attended the lectures of John Hunter or those of Joseph Lister a century later, because each of these great surgeons taught new ideas which were ill understood and not fully appreciated, even by their colleagues. Naturally enough, the students felt that as the new work was at variance with the accepted truths it might even prove a disadvantage at examinations. It is still recognized that the best teacher is he who bases his instructions upon the accepted statements of the textbooks, although he may, and often does, awaken in his students the critical faculty and the desire to know more. Nevertheless, capacity for knowledge is not always linked with capacity for research, either in teacher or student.

As for the third leg in the tripod of medical activity, that of practice, it is hardly to be expected that the best physician will be the best original investigator, although there have been notable exceptions. From its very nature the practice of medicine, with its constant change of problem involved in the treatment of different diseases, may be actually antagonistic to the sustained logical thought and to the deliberated pondering on one particular problem, or one special disease, which the work of research demands.

Research, in fact, may actually conflict with practice. It is well known that Dr William Harvey, just after he published his discovery of the circulation of the blood, "fell mightily in his practice and 'twas thought he was crack-brained". The mental attitude of the physician is very different from that of the investigator. The medical practioner, with his quick, self-confident decisions, is quite unlike the medical scientist whose approach to each problem is slow, diffident and critical.

The former is concerned with known and established facts, the latter deals with unsolved questions and the exploration of the unknown. Indeed, it would appear that research is a calling, a vocation, which comes only to the few, but which must be answered, like the call which impels the preacher or the reformer in the religious sphere.

A life of research may involve considerable sacrifice. Seldom is it possible to combine such a calling with the establishment of a comfortable home or the cultivation of a taste for music,

196

drama or literature. The research worker must be a superman indeed. Infinite patience and sound health are only two of the many assets essential to success in such a career.

Most of those difficulties are now fully recognized, and the way of the investigator has become smoother and more attractive in recent years.

HOW DISCOVERIES ARE MADE

Having discussed the physical and mental equipment of the investigator, we may now note how he proceeds to attack his problems and, if possible, to make new discoveries.

Whatever the method, and however simple or however complicated the apparatus or means of investigation, there must be first of all a plan, some end or object of attainment, however vague. It was Claude Bernard who, in his little book, *Introduction à l'Étude de la Médecine Expérimentale,* published in 1865, showed so beautifully that the essential basis or starting point to the solution of every problem is a theory or premiss, an assumption, a hypothesis—call it what you will. A hypothesis is to science what inspiration is to art. Every physician uses it in establishing a diagnosis. Experience has taught him that the disease may be this or that, and he proceeds to observe, if necessary to experiment, by various tests and special examinations, and then to select from the various possibilities. In like manner the investigator begins his work after having formulated his hypothesis, which of course is only a scaffolding or framework, to be altered or even discarded as the work of construction proceeds.

All the experiments are designed to confirm or to refute the hypothesis. There should be no hesitation to alter the plan, if the hypothesis is no longer serviceable. As Huxley said, "the tragedy of all enquiry is that a beautiful hypothesis may be slain by an ugly fact". Nevertheless, the observer notes what he sees, not what he expects to see or what he would like to see. The unusual and the unexpected may be of great importance. Sir Patrick Manson, whose discovery of the transmission of filaria embryos by the mosquito was the first direct proof that many diseases were carried by insects, used to tell his students: "The thing you cannot classify may be pointing the way to a discovery."

Having completed his observations for the day, the investigator puts on his thinking cap and uses his imagination. Imagination is to be avoided during the process of observation. As Claude Bernard said, imagination should be shed, like one's overcoat, on entering the laboratory, but should be put on again, like a coat, on leaving it. Imagination assists towards an acceptance or rejection or modification of the hypothesis; and so, the work of the next day proceeds. The result of an investigation may be the discovery of an error in the accepted knowledge. This may be quite as valuable as a new discovery. Lister once wrote: "Next to the promulgation of truth, the best thing a man can do is the recantation of error." At this stage, it may be well to refer to researches which are so often undertaken today by a team of workers rather than by one individual. This plan has much in its favour, and there is a stimulus in the team spirit which may be of great value.

On the other hand, the solitary investigator has greater freedom when he has only his own work to consider.

Some problems may actually demand a team of experts, each contributing work from his own special field. Clearly there can be no hard-and-fast ruling in this matter.

THE ALPHA AND OMEGA OF RESEARCH

Two further important aspects of research concern the beginning and the ending of any original investigation. "Nothing so difficult as a beginning in poesy, unless perhaps the end", wrote Byron, and the sentiment applies to much else besides poesy. It is essential to know what has been accomplished already. Too frequently, an investigator sets out on a promising journey only to find that the land had been explored long since by someone else. Disappointments of this sort can be avoided by a preliminary exploration of the literature, or even by a talk with some experienced authority. Of course, too much reliance should not be placed upon previous work. It may be necessary to repeat and to check earlier results before beginning a search, or re-search, of one's own. In any case the foundation should be carefully laid or tested.

Research is just as difficult to end as it is to begin. At what point should the "finalising" process start? It is most important to know just when and where to stop and sum up; otherwise, one may go on accumulating data, as did Casaubon, with his "Key to all the Mythologies", in George Eliot's revealing medical novel, *Middlemarch*, until one is overwhelmed and drowned in a mass of facts regarding which no conclusion has been reached. Mere knowledge is not enough; a commentary or application is essential. Even an interpretation may be necessary, to bring new facts into line with existing knowledge.

Sometimes there has been a long delay in making public a noteworthy discovery. William Harvey discovered the circulation of the blood twelve years before he felt justified in describing it in print, and Charles Darwin continued his work for twenty-two years before he published his *Origin of Species*. Such delays would be very unusual today, when transport and communications are so rapid that every new discovery becomes immediately known throughout the civilized world; known, very often, before the fresh knowledge has been fully tested and corroborated. In the past many discoveries were made known "before their time", that is, before the world was ready to accept them, but in these modern days the world is prepared to accept any new contribution sponsored by "Science". The fact that even science has its limitations is only just beginning to dawn upon our bewildered minds, so mesmerized are we by the amazing advances of the twentieth century.

ACCIDENTAL OR UNINTENTIONAL DISCOVERIES

A discovery may be quite fortuitous. The researcher may be led into some side issue which he finds to be more important than the original object of his quest. Everyone has had the experience of looking for a lost article and finding something else. Columbus had set out to find a route to the Indies when he discovered America. Galvani (or was it Galvani's wife?) saw, in the larder, the twitching of frog's legs, suspended on a copper wire, as they swung in the breeze against an iron railing, and he realized the significance of the phenomenon. Many persons before them had seen an apple fall from a tree, or a kettle-lid moved by the power of steam, but only the genius of an Isaac Newton or a James Watt could realize the importance of such everyday events. These men alone had the genius to interpret what they saw. Discovery does not result merely from "a happy chance".

As Pasteur was wont to say: "Chance favours only the mind that is prepared." Simple observation is of no value unless imagination is also used to reveal the full support of what is observed. The instinct of the born investigator shows itself under such circumstances. Sherlock Holmes remarked to the naïve Dr Watson: "You see, but you do not observe."

The fact that immunity to smallpox was conferred by an attack of cowpox was well known to the dairymaids of Gloucestershire for many years before Jenner, in 1796, made use of this knowledge and introduced vaccination. Foxglove tea was used by the country folk of Shropshire as a cure for dropsy long before Withering introduced it into medical practice as digitalis, and indicated both is value and its dangers in his *Account of the Foxglove*, in 1785. The successful researches of these two country practitioners serve to show how medicine may draw knowledge from "unqualified" sources.

The countryman is often a more accurate weather-prophet than the meteorologist. Aristotle learned much of his natural history from the fishermen of Greece, and we may still learn much from the gardener, the shepherd, the instrument maker, the laboratory technician, and the nurse. Especially the nurse: every wise doctor is ready to listen to her views. After all, she sees the patient all the time, while the doctor makes his observations during a limited period.

THE DISCOVERY OF A PRINCIPLE

Perhaps the most important and far-reaching discovery of all is the discovery of a principle. It is much more significant than the revelation of a new fact. A new fact may be added to existing knowledge, but a new principle has a wider influence and leads inevitably to more and more discoveries. Nevertheless, mankind is singularly slow to accept new principles, though quite ready to accept facts. The new principle may involve the discontinuance or discarding of knowledge which for long, even for centuries, has been accepted with apparently unshakable belief.

Often the principle is twisted so that it may later appear only as a fact. That is why surgeons misunderstood Lister, and imagined that he had discovered the antiseptic value of carbolic acid. In reality carbolic acid was only one means of utilizing his great principle, that of preventing the entry of germs into a wound, the principle which has made modern surgery possible.

Hippocrates was probably the greatest medical discoverer of all time. Not only did he show that disease arose from natural causes and was not the work of a demon or a god, but he gave to medicine, in the Hippocratic Oath, a charter of conduct which has formed the basis of all codes of medical ethics during the centuries which followed this "discovery".

William Harvey when he published, in 1628, his treatise on the circulation of the blood, was stating, not merely a new fact in physiology, but a principle which was thenceforth to alter and to control the entire fabric of medical knowledge.

Louis Pasteur (1822–95), a chemist and not a medical man, conducted an astonishing series of investigations, all of which yielded spectacular results. Pasteur's researches seem to follow an evolutionary scale. He began by proving that the fermentation of wine was a biological and not a chemical process. Having discovered the cause of diseases of wine, he next turned his attention to a disease of silkworms which had threatened to wreck the silk industry. Chicken cholera provided the next problem, then anthrax in sheep and cattle, but his crowning achievement was the prevention of rabies in man by the inoculation of an attenuated virus. Thus did Pasteur demonstrate what was then known as "the germ theory", and his discovery of this principle showed the way to Lister when he, in turn, applied his antiseptic principle in surgery. Robert Koch (1843–1910) showed how disease-producing organisms could be stained and cultivated, and thus the science of bacteriology was founded.

Another noteworthy example of the discovery of a principle is the work of Paul Ehrlich (1854–1914). His demonstration of the efficacy of Salvarsan (substance No. 606 in his series) was only one of many therapeutic achievements based upon his principle of chemotherapy, the affinity of the drug or dye for the organism. Ehrlich's object was to find a "magic bullet" which would find its way unerringly to the cause of the disease without harming the patient.

METHODS AND TOOLS OF MEDICAL RESEARCH

The discovery of a new method of scientific investigation will naturally lead to further discoveries. Vesalius inaugurated a fresh outlook in anatomy when, in 1543, he produced his fine book "On the fabric of the human body", the *Fabrica*, as it is called. Ambroise Paré had novel ideas regarding the treatment of wounds, and his methods foreshadowed those of Lister. Paracelsus, by advising the use of simple chemical remedies, changed the course of materia medica.

Another Renaissance discovery was the application of measurement to science and medicine. It is indeed most strange to reflect that, for centuries, men preferred to argue about a problem which could be solved at once by simple arithmetic.

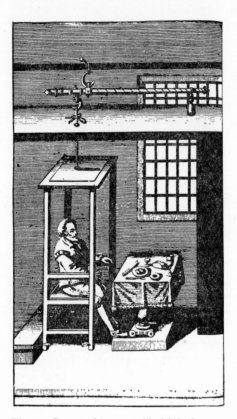

Even this common-sense method first sponsored by Galileo, was adopted very slowly. Almost certainly, Harvey, as a student in Padua, attended the lectures of Galileo and was deeply influenced by his teaching, and by his use of the mathematical method.

Sanctorius, also of Padua, was a memorable exponent of self-experiment. Sanctorius, who published his results in 1614, practically lived in the weighing machine which he had devised in order to determine the daily amount of what he called "imperceptible perspiration". The numerical method was more closely applied to medicine by Louis, of Paris, one of the most popular teachers of medicine a century ago, and this statistical approach is now everywhere followed.

Fig. 4—Sanctorius, seated in his balance: the frontispiece of his work, *Medicina Statica*, 1614

Closely allied to the discoverers of method are the discoverers, or rather the inventors, of tools and instruments of precision. The microscope, at first regarded as a mere toy, the "flea-glass", as it was called, enabled Malpighi in 1661 to complete the work of Harvey by demonstrating the capillary vessels in a frog's lung. A few years later we find Antony Leeuwenhoek, the linen-draper of Delft in Holland, writing numerous letters to the Royal Society, describing the astonishing revelations of his simple home-made microscopes, of which he possessed about two hundred.

Medicine no longer depended upon plain unaided observation, and the field extended as various "scopes" were invented. Two of them came from Paris. The stethoscope, or *cylindre* as it was first named, was visualized by Laënnec as he watched two boys, in the Jardin du Luxembourg, using a felled tree as a gigantic telephone. Laënnec adapted this idea in practice by rolling a quire of paper into a cylinder and applying one end to the patient's chest and the other to his own ear. He then set himself to classify and describe all the curious sounds which were thus rendered more audible. The results were set forth in his book, *Traité de l'Auscultation Médiate*, published in 1819. Not content with mere invention, he had proceeded along the more distant road of discovery.

Another idea, this time one of vision rather than hearing, flashed into the mind of Manuel Garcia, the singing master, in 1854, as he noted reflections on the glazed roof of the Palais Royale. On returning home he found that with the aid of a dental mirror he could clearly see the action of his own vocal cords. This had long been his ambition, but he never imagined that by his discovery he had founded an entirely new special branch of medicine, that of laryngology. The discovery of X-rays by Röntgen, and of other aids to diagnosis, followed each other in rapid succession until, at the present day, instrumental methods are used so widely that every wise teacher of medicine finds its necessary to advise students not to discard the old-fashioned, but still essential, art of simply looking at the patient, before examining him.

HISTORY AND THE INVESTIGATOR

Let me conclude with a brief reference to the value of history as a foundation to all new knowledge.

The specialist, ploughing his lone furrow, may soon find himself out of touch with any knowledge outside his own, even in adjacent fields. A study of the history of medicine will widen his outlook, because one need not journey very far back before reaching the point at which a complete survey of science and medicine was possible for a single human brain. Nowadays, the fragmentation is very considerable, and each special branch has developed its own language, or, shall we say, its own jargon. History is still expressed in the language of the ordinary individual, while science requires an interpreter. A short course in history and philosophy is probably still the best introduction to the study of science or medicine. History, the story of man's past activities, not merely of what happened but of how and why it happened, enables us to act more intelligently in the world of today. History is a guide to thought and action: it is not merely an intellectual pastime, a hobby for senile doctors.

To history there should be added philosophy, because to the facts there should be added deductions and interpretations. History has shown, time and again, that *medicine can never become wholly scientific*. The subject of study is human, and the investigator is in a peculiar position, since he also is human. The teaching and study of disease must needs be clinical; at the bedside of the patient.

The opportunity for justifiable experiments upon living man does not come often to the investigator as it did in 1822 to Beaumont, the army surgeon, or "backwood physiologist" as Osler called him. Beaumont was enabled by circumstances to study the process of digestion in his patient Alexis St Martin, who had recovered from a gunshot wound with a large fistula in his stomach. His experiments show science at its best and simplest, a fine piece of research.

Nevertheless science has its limitations. In quite recent times it was firmly believed that science would eventually solve every problem. Yet many problems are beyond the reach of science. Moreover, as one difficulty is solved, another appears to take its place. The quest for knowledge is never-ending. But, though research is a lottery in which few win a prize, it should not be judged from the point of view of profits. The true investigator, though he may find his way hard and steep, will always have the reward which comes from seeking, although his search may not have resulted in discovery.

At the beginning of this paper reference was made to the

stained-glass window at the Mayo Clinic. The panel showing Lister at work bears a motto which might well be every doctor's ideal: "to cure sometimes, to relieve often, to comfort always." Cure and relief are within the powers of science, but comfort belongs to the art of medicine. Comfort, the necessary complement of cure and relief, may be, at times, all that the doctor can give. It will then be well for him and for his patient if, in the course of his absorbing studies, he has given some little thought to the Art of Medicine, and to the profound truths which extend far beyond physical science.

THE PURSUIT OF THE
INFINITELY SMALL*

WHEN I WAS A LITTLE BOY, of ten years or so, I was taken by
an aunt to visit her friend, whose son was assistant to the Professor of Botany in Glasgow. That young man, confronted with
the awkward necessity of amusing a restless child, produced his
microscope and showed to me, in a drop of water from under
a flower-pot, a number of active and curious creatures, darting
to and fro—Infusoria, as I was to learn later. I shall never
forget the first thrill of gazing down that microscope tube; it
was as though a new world had been opened for my benefit.

CURIOSITY AS AN ASSET

Since then I have tried the same experiment upon some members of a later generation of small boys, not yet past the age of
wonderment. The results were encouraging in the main, although the present-day world has been stripped of some of the
old glamour, and phenomena which provided vivid surprises
for our Victorian ancestors have become commonplace during
an epoch in which children are familiar, almost from birth,
with the ways of atoms and electrons. Nevertheless, this sense of
curiosity, so apparent in early life, is a most valuable asset,
especially to a child, or youth, who is to become a student of
science or medicine.

"When I was a boy", said John Hunter, "I wanted to know
all about the clouds and the grasses, and why the leaves changed
colour in autumn; I watched the ants, bees, and birds, tadpoles and caddis worms: I pestered people with questions about
what nobody knew or cared anything about."

This inquisitive habit John Hunter retained throughout his
life. It is a trait which well deserves cultivation and encouragement. It may even be said that it is an essential attribute of

* An address to The London Hospital Medical Society on 5 October 1948.

every scientist. All great discoverers have possessed it in marked degree. They alternatively wondered and observed. Imagination is a species of active wonder. But, as Claude Bernard pointed out, imagination and observation must be kept in separate compartments, though both are essential. When one enters the laboratory one must shed imagination, like one's overcoat, but one must put it on again on leaving to go home, there to ponder over the results of one's observations (see page 198).

To other factors which promote discoveries we shall return later. In the meantime let us concentrate upon the wonder, and the importance, of the infinitely small. To-day we take the microscope for granted, as one of our common tools, but in the seventeenth century scientists, or "philosophers" as they were then called, hailed it with boyish enthusiasm and with all the curiosity of youth.

"CURIOUS MATHEMATICS" OF "LITTLE CITIZENS"

Sir Thomas Browne of Norwich had doubtless heard of the microscope, although it is doubtful if he ever possessed one. Yet he fell under the spell of the smaller forms of life, as opposed to the larger. We find him remarking (in 1643): "What reason may not go to school to the wisdom of bees, ants and spider? Ruder heads stand amazed at those prodigious pieces of Nature: Whales, Elephants and Camels, ... but in these narrow engines (of the insect world) there is more curious mathematics, and the civility of these little citizens more neatly sets forth the wisdom of their maker."

Twenty years later, that erudite pupil of Robert Boyle, Henry Power, wrote his *Experimental Philosophy* (1644), in which he begins by describing the flea. "The flea", he tells us, "hath two fair eyes, most admirable to behold, ... a black spot, the pupil, is beset around with a green glittering circle which is the iris. His head, body and limbs be all of blackish armour, nature having armed him thus, that he might not be hurt by the great leaps he takes. How incomprehensibly subtle must the animal spirits be, that run to and fro in nerves included in such prodigiously little spindle-shank'd legs?" [Note that word "prodigiously", used in its correct sense.] "How thin must be the liquors that circulate through the pipes and vessels disseminated through those parts". Power also described mites and hairs, seeds and pollen, and the fibres of "silk ribbans", but the flea was the commonest microscopic object in the early days; indeed, the microscope was at first a mere toy, and was known as the "flea glass".

A year later, the year of the Great Plague of London, witnessed the publication of Hooke's *Micrographia*, of which I shall have more to say presently. Samuel Pepys bought both those early works on microscopy, as he mentions in his diary. "I took home Hooke's book of microscopy, a most excellent piece." (20 January 1665). During the previous year Pepys had purchased a microscope for £5 10s.—"a great price, but a most curious bauble it is." (13 August 1664). We also read: "Thence home . . . to read in Dr Power's book . . . . to enable me a little how to use and what to expect from my glasse. So to supper and to bed."

THE INVENTION OF THE MICROSCOPE

It is interesting to recall those early days of microscopy. The origin of the compound microscope is rather obscure. Various means of magnifying were known to the ancients. Seneca, in A.D. 63, noted that: "letters are seen larger through a glass bulb full of water." Although the science of optics is of ancient date, men were very slow to apply the knowledge in practice. That herald of the Renaissance, Roger Bacon, writing in 1276, discusses the value of magnifying lenses which, he said, "might be useful to old men and to those with weak eyes to see the letters sufficiently enlarged." Roger Bacon is sometimes regarded as the inventor of spectacles, which appear to have been used from the fifteenth century onward, although there are other claimants. Nevertheless, for years no use was made of convex lenses except for the magnification of written or, later, of printed works. It was not until the seventeenth century that Malpighi and Leeuwenhoek made their great discoveries with the aid of single lenses.

Zacharias Janssen (or simply Zacharias, according to some writers), a spectacle-maker of Middelburg, in Holland, is usually regarded as the inventor of the compound microscope. In 1590, while still a lad, he chanced to observe the advantage of combining convex lenses in a tube. Janssen's microscope was described in 1655 by Pierre Borel, Physician to Louis XIV, but long before that, in 1619, Cornelius Drebbel, the astronomer, showed a microscope to King James I. It is also alleged that

Galileo, who had already invented the telescope, heard of Janssen's invention and proceeded to construct a microscope for himself about 1610. Galileo was attracted by the infinitely small as well as by the infinitely large. He writes that he constructed instruments (*tele*scope and *micro*scope) which made things appear "a thousand times greater and more than thirty-fold nearer than if observed by the naked eye". The first microscopes were really short-focus telescopes.

John Wedderborn, a Scotsman, wrote from Padua in 1610 that he had heard Galileo relate how, with the microscope, he had seen that the eye of a certain insect was "covered by a thick membrane, that is, nevertheless, perforated with seven holes like the visor of a warrior". From what has been said it is obvious that the evidence is confusing, and that the compound microscope is not clearly the invention of any one individual.

Of more importance are the early observations made with the aid of the microscope. As already mentioned, the microscope was at first a toy or a means of amusement. Nevertheless it made its appearance at an opportune moment. The Renaissance, or revival of learning, was no sudden movement, but a gradual change of attitude, spread over many years. Beginning in Italy at about the end of the fourteenth century, and affecting, at first, the fields of art and literature, it spread from art to anatomy, from literature to science. The spirit of enquiry and observation took a long time to reach England, where medieval ideas persisted even until the eighteenth century, and where the revolutionary discoveries of Vesalius and Harvey gained acceptance very slowly. Various inventions, and notably that of printing, favoured the spread of the new culture, and the discovery of America provided a vast new field for its propagation.

THE LYNX-EYED SCIENTISTS

In the atmosphere of the Renaissance the microscope could not fail to attract attention, and in Italy the first important steps were taken. In 1603 an enlightened nobleman, Duke Federigo Cesi, then only eighteen years of age, gathered around him a company of scientists to form the Accademia dei Lincei (the Academy of the Lynxes, so called from the keen vision attributed to this animal). The Society met at the house of the founder in Rome, and included, besides the Duke himself and Galileo, a number of men prepared to collaborate in a joint scheme of research in the field of microscopy. Much of their work has been lost. Duke Cesi discovered the spores of ferns, "minutely fine dust adherent to the back of Polypodian leaves, and appearing as big as peppercorns" when studied by the microscope.

Another subject of study was the anatomy of the bee, and it is set forth in *Persio tradotto*, published in 1630 by Francesco Stelluti, who did much of the writing. Others who contributed to the work were Johannes Faber, the first to use the word "microscope"; Francisco Fontana, the astronomer of Naples, who drew the illustrations; and Fabio Colonna, a botanist well known for his work on lichens, who carried out much of the investigation.

THE MICROSCOPE IN MEDICINE

This excellent team-work of the Accademia was continued until the early death of Duke Cesi, in 1630. It was the first-fruit of the compound microscope, although simple lenses had been previously used. That well-known pioneer of entomology, and London physician, Thomas Mouffet, had employed a magnifying glass while preparing his *Insectorum Theatrum*. This work, derived in part from Conrad Gessner of Zurich, was completed in 1589, but remained unpublished until 1634, when it was sponsored by the eminent physician to James I, Sir Theodore Turquet of Mayerne.

The lynx-eyed scientists were followed by others. In 1664 Gianbattista Hodierna of Palermo published his observations on the compound eye of the fly, and in 1655 Pierre Borel wrote his *Centuria Observatorum Microscopiarum*, which, according to Professor Singer, is "the first medical work involving the use of the microscope". Borel spoke of minute insects in the air which caused plague, and of worms in the blood of fever patients, visible only on microscopic examination, and although he gives no details, he may well have been the first to produce evidence of the germ theory of disease. This idea had been already suggested, with remarkable clairvoyance, by Fracastorius, the pioneer epidemiologist of Verona, who in 1546 wrote of "seminaria", invisible particles which are "seeds of disease". Nevertheless, the fame of Pierre Borel is overshadowed by that of Athanasius Kircher, who in his famous *Scrutinium Physico-Medicum Pestis*, 1658, described worms in the blood of plague-stricken persons. Kircher, who resided first at Wurzburg, and later at Rome, was a Jesuit priest. He wrote voluminously on many subjects—on dragons in the centre of the earth, on animal sounds as transcribed into music on the Tower of Babel, and on other weird and mysterious topics. His works are a strange medley of nonsense and reason. In his *Ars magna lucis et umbrae*, 1646, he spoke of animalculae in putrid material, and worms in the blood of fever patients. "It is well known", he wrote, "that all decaying bodies abound in worms, but not until after the wonderful invention of the microscope was it found that all putrid substances swarm with an innumerable breed of worms which are imperceptible to the naked eye." This latter observation he repeated during the plague of Rome in 1656, but in his book, printed two years later, he gives no illustration of what he saw. Whether he actually saw bacteria is very doubtful. More probably he saw merely the blood corpuscles, but his idea that disease was due to invisible germs has ensured him a prominent place in the history of medicine.

The value of the microscope as a scientific tool rather than as a mere toy, or "flea-glass", was now fully established. A magnified view of an already visible flea or mite was strange enough, but how much more remarkable was the revelation of structures, and even of entire living creatures, which were invisible to the naked eye. Invention may be a prelude to discovery, and the stage was now well set for discovery. Just as, during the nineteenth century, the invention of the stethoscope, the laryngoscope, and other aids to sight and hearing, opened up large fields of enquiry, even so did the appearance of the microscope pave the way to many discoveries in science and medicine.

THE PIONEER MICROSCOPISTS

Among those who showed the way during the seventeenth century, five names stand out above all others—Malpighi, the Italian; Leeuwenhoek and Swammerdam, the Dutchmen; and Hooke and Grew, the Englishmen. It is worth while to recall the leading facts regarding the lives and work of those great pioneers.

The discovery of the circulation of the blood was made in 1616 or earlier, but William Harvey delayed the publication of his work until 1628. Edward Jenner delayed the publication of *his* great discovery for eighteen years, until 1796, and Darwin collected material and pondered over the idea of evolution for twenty years before publishing *The Origin of Species* in 1869.

Harvey's account of the circulation was complete in almost every detail. "Almost", because one observation was lacking. Harvey, whose classic work appeared in 1628, used no microscope, and he was obliged to presume the existence of capillaries. It was Malpighi who gave the finishing touch to Harvey's discovery, by his demonstration, in 1661, of the capillary network in the frog's lung. The life of poor Marcello Malpighi is a story of ill-health and misfortune. Born at Bologna in 1628, he was faced, in early manhood, owing to the death of his parents, with the necessity of providing for a family of seven younger brothers and sisters. A dispute regarding the property continued for many years, and then his own poor health and the loss of his papers from a fire in his house combined to interfere very materially with his career. Nevertheless he bore those reverses with calmness and patience and produced so vast an amount of original work that he may well be regarded as the Father of Microscopic Anatomy.

For a time Malpighi was a colleague of Borelli of Pisa, well known as one of the founders of the mechanical or mathematical view of physiology, but it was after he became Professor of Medicine at Bologna that his famous discovery was made. Prior to that time the lung was regarded as a mass of fleshy tissue. Malpighi not only showed that it was composed of numerous little air cells, but he noted in the walls of those tiny chambers the capillaries, which serve as a link between the arteries and veins. This was by no means his sole achievement. He proceeded to investigate other tissues—the liver, the kidneys, the brain—and he added many new facts to microscopic anatomy. He also made a valuable contribution to botany. In his treatise on the anatomy of plants he described the spiral vessels of the stem, which he regarded as a respiratory system. Perhaps his chief publication, in 1669, was a monograph on the structure of *Bombyx mori* (the silkworm). In that insect he showed the air tubes or tracheae, the silk glands, and the chain of nerve ganglia. This was the first great contribution to insect anatomy. He also made a valuable contribution to embryology in his study of the development of the chick (1673), which remained the authoritative work on the subject until the nineteenth century. Most of his works were published by the Royal

Society, of which he became a Fellow in 1668. He died in 1694.

Malpighi had enriched many branches of science through his use of a primitive form of compound microscope. Leeuwenhoek, to whose career we shall now turn, used simple lenses of his own construction. This worthy man was perhaps the greatest of all the pioneer microscopists. His life was the longest, and probably the most romantic. Antony van Leeuwenhoek held no academic position, he knew no language but his native Dutch, and his scientific work was entirely a labour of love.

LEEUWENHOEK AND HIS "LITTLE ANIMALS"

Born at Delft, in Holland, in 1632, Leeuwenhoek received no university education and was a self-taught man. For nearly seventy years he conducted business as a linen-draper in his native town. He was twice married, but only one of his five children survived infancy, his daughter Maria, the solace of his later years, who outlived her father and died at the age of 89. Throughout his long life (he died at the age of 91), Leeuwenhoek devoted all his spare time to microscopy. He was probably the greatest amateur microscopist of all time.

Leeuwenhoek made his own microscopes, each of which consisted of a tiny biconvex lens, which he ground himself and mounted between two thin plates of metal, usually silver or brass. The object to be examined was held upon a silver needle, or upon a thin glass plate glued to the needle, adjusted to the required distance by a fine screw. Thus the object was brought into the focus of the lens, which was fixed. "Each microscope", he wrote, "has a particular curiosity stuck before it". No less than 247 of these microscopes were sold after Leeuwenhoek's death, but very few have survived to this day. Only eight specimens are said to exist, five of them in Holland, but none in England, nor in America. Leeuwenhoek used to show his microscopes to visitors, and those visitors were many when he became famous, including even Kings and Emperors. But he always refused to sell the instruments, and he had a few "through which no man hath looked, save myself" which he never exhibited, but kept for his own private use. He appears to have had a secret method of using those microscopes and, according to Dobell (who has produced a magnificent work on Leeuwenhoek), this may have been dark-ground illumination. Whether those special microscopes had lenses of greater magnification we shall never know. The majority of the microscopes magnified from 40 to 120 diameters, and the maximum appeared to be plus 160 (Plate 9). Leeuwenhoek made a practice of measuring his specimens, and his method of measurement was to compare the object with a fine grain of sand which, he stated, was one-hundredth of an inch in diameter. Besides inorganic objects, Leeuwenhoek's researches ranged throughout the vegetable and animal kingdoms and his discoveries were reported in the form of letters to the Royal Society. The Dutch physiologist Regnier de Graaf, discoverer of the "Graafian follicles", wrote in 1673 to inform the Secretary of the Society of "a certain most ingenious person here named Leeuwenhoek, who has devised microscopes which far surpass those we have hitherto seen". Thus began a correspondence which continued until 1717, a few years before Leeuwenhoek's death, and covered a period of forty-four years. Leeuwenhoek became a Fellow of the Royal Society in 1680. Many of the letters were printed in 300 *Philosophical Transactions of the Royal Society*. Those letters are straightforward, modest and sometimes humorous. They were originally written in Dutch, but many of them have been translated into English, and they reveal Leeuwenhoek as a careful and infinitely painstaking observer. The illustrations were not drawn by Leeuwenhoek himself, but by artists employed by him, and they are of no great artistic merit. One of the first letters (1675) related to the "little animals" found in rain-water, in well-water, and in an infusion of peppercorns; it is the first description of protozoa and bacteria. A subsequent observation (1683) concerned the "animalcules" in "the white matter from betwixt the teeth", which appeared to be more numerous than "all the people in our United Netherlands". They were, he stated, more commonly found in those whose teeth were not clean, but although his own teeth were sound, at the age of fifty he found "animalculae" in the molar region of his mouth. Many of the protozoa and bacteria figured in the letters have been identified. He was the first to see *Volvox* (the name applied later by Linnaeus) and *Hydra*, as well as the Rotifera with "their strange little wheels going round in so wonderful a motion". Leeuwenhoek was the first to describe red blood corpuscles, and was the first to note that the blood corpuscles of birds and amphibians were oval, while those of man and mammals were round. He gave a detailed account of the microscopic structure of muscles, and noted the striped character of muscle fibre.

All this, and much more, Leeuwenhoek did with a simple lens of his own construction. Thus, although Leeuwenhoek did not continuously study any one aspect of science, he initiated many advances. Although he was an amateur of no academic rank or distinction, this indefatigable worker founded the sciences of histology, protozoology and bacteriology. Even today the value of his contribution to biological science has not been fully assessed, and much of his work still remains unpublished.

DISSECTIONS IN MINIATURE

The name of Jan Swammerdam is often linked with that of Leeuwenhoek. The son of an apothecary, he was born at Amsterdam in 1637. It was in the museum of his father, a keen naturalist and collector, that the boy developed his taste for investigation and his skill in minute dissection. He studied medicine at Leyden, where he formed friendships with Regnier de Graaf and with the Dane, Nicolas Stensen or Steno, who discovered the parotid duct. All three were students under the distinguished anatomist Sylvius; all achieved greatness, though all died young, de Graaf at 32, Stensen at 48 and Swammerdam at 43.

From early youth Swammerdam had a passion for microscopic dissection. To this he devoted his life, and he may be said to have founded the study of comparative anatomy of invertebrates. This he did in spite of ill-health due to attacks of malaria, and in opposition to his father's desire that he should abandon such unremunerative employment and engage in medical practice. Swammerdam laboured incessantly, from dawn to dusk each day, at his micro-dissections, and developed amazing skill in this fine work. The later part of his career was clouded by religious uncertainty and by an unbalanced mind. He appears to have decided that the pursuit of natural knowledge was an act of impiety, and he devoted the closing years of his life to the worship of the Creator rather than to the study of His works. Most of his notes remained unpublished at his death in 1680, and it was not until 1738 that the famous physician of Leyden, Hermann Boerhaave, bought Swammerdam's manuscripts and caused them to be printed, with the magnificent illustrations, under the title *Biblia Naturae*. The *Bible of Nature* holds a high place among the classics of zoology, and the fame of Swammerdam, a man of little account during his lifetime, has steadily increased since his death almost 300 years ago (1680). His career was a struggle with adversity and a short struggle, very different from the long and placid life of Leeuwenhoek. The studies of Swammerdam were more purposive and limited than those of Leeuwenhoek. Swammerdam did not investigate the smallest forms of life. He was concerned mainly with micro-dissection, and under his dissecting microscope he revealed, in unrivalled fashion, the anatomy of the mayfly, the honey bee, the tadpole and the squid. His greatest achievement was his revelation of the anatomy of insects. His dissections of the nervous system of the bee—also the mouthparts, the compound eye, the generative organs—are all truly marvellous. It is interesting to note that his favourite instrument was a pair of very sharp fine-pointed scissors. He did not believe that new parts were formed during the life cycle, but stated that the perfect insect was there from the first, preformed, and ready to be revealed in due course.

Swammerdam was an experimenter as well as an observer. He discovered the important medico-legal fact, that the lung of the new-born child will float if respiration has taken place. He is said to have been the originator of the injection of blood vessels with a solidifying medium—a technique carried to great perfection by his friend Frederik Ruysch, one of the finest of the technical anatomists. Furthermore, Swammerdam proved the relation of nerve to muscle, and he refuted the idea that muscle contraction was due ·to the addition of fluid which arrived by way of the hollow nerves. For Swammerdam it may be claimed that he was a leading pioneer in minute anatomy, a miniaturist in dissection. The wonders of his *Bible of Nature* are still deserving of careful study. Unfortunately there is no known portrait of Swammerdam; but his artistry in revealing the anatomy of insect forms is a memorial more permanent than any portrait.

ENGLISH MICROSCOPISTS

While the two Dutchmen of whose work we have spoken were making their discoveries in the field of the infinitely small, similar researches were being conducted in England. The

216

"Invisible College" had become the Royal Society, about 1663, and had won general approval. Closely associated with the new Society, first as curator and later as secretary, was Robert Hooke, who had begun his career by assisting Thomas Willis and then Robert Boyle in their chemical and physical experiments at Oxford. On returning from one of the meetings of the Royal Society, Mr Pepys wrote in his diary, in February 1665: "Mr Boyle was at the meeting, and above him, Mr Hooke, who is the most, and promises the least, of any man in the world I ever saw." Robert Hooke was not prepossessing in appearance. Born in 1635, the son of a clergyman in the Isle of Wight, we are told that he was a weakly child, and although in adult life he retained that alertness of movement so often seen in keen students, he was small of stature, very thin and sallow, hunchbacked, and with long and dishevelled hair. Unfortunately, he was of a melancholy and distrustful nature, and suspicious of his fellow scientists. It is not surprising that Newton called him "the irritable philosopher". Nevertheless, Robert Hooke was a man of genius who initiated many new movements and prompted many discoveries in biological science. Perhaps his fame would have been greater if his researches had been less diffuse. Like John Hunter, he appeared to be constantly on the brink of new territory, but he failed to consolidate the victory. His discovery of the balance spring for watches was made during his early years at Oxford, at the time when he was assisting Boyle to produce that important and revolutionary work the *Sceptical Chymist* (1661), and it is only one of his many mechanical inventions. Hooke was "the greatest mechanic of his age". He made an important advance in the physiology of respiration when he showed that an animal could be kept alive by blowing air into the windpipe, even after the chest was laid open. This, in fact, was a demonstration of artificial respiration, but it was not applied in practice until the nineteenth century.

Hooke prophesied the invention of the stethoscope, and came very near to it, when he wrote: "It may be possible, one day, to discover the motions of the internal parts of the body as in a watch we hear the beating of the balance, the running of the wheels, and other noises. I have been able to hear plainly the beating of a man's heart, and the stopping of the lungs is easily discovered by the wheezing sound." A century later Laënnec proved the truth of Hooke's statement.

Furthermore Hooke predicted the discovery of artificial silk, stating, "I have often thought that probably there might be a way found out to make an artificial glutenous composition. . . . as good, nay better, than that out of which the silkworm draws his clew. A frothy kind of artificial stuff. . . . may be made. . . . very like the substance of silk." He hoped that "some ingenious inquisitive person might take the hint".

This versatility was not limited to the natural sciences. After the Great Fire of London which followed the Plague, Hooke was appointed City Surveyor, and took a leading part, along with Sir Christopher Wren, in the production of designs for rebuilding the city; thus he appears to have been no mean architect.

As Curator of Experiments to the Royal Society Hooke was called upon to report upon the letters from Leeuwenhoek describing the animalculae he found when grains of black pepper were steeped in water for some time. Hooke discovered in the water "vast multitudes of those exceeding small creatures", and this observation quickened his interest in microscopy and led to the publication of his classic work, *Micrographia*, in 1665. He began by showing that under the microscope the edge of a sharp razor was really full of ridges and furrows, and that the point of a fine needle showed a multitude of holes and scratches (Plate 9). He used a compound microscope, mounted on a ball-and-socket joint. The objective was a tiny double convex lens, and a wide field was secured by a planoconvex lens at a fixed distance from the cup-shaped upper end of the microscope tube.

It is sometimes stated that Hooke was the first to demonstrate the cellular nature of plant and animal tissue. Certainly he did reveal, in a thin section of cork, a great number of little "pores or cells", but the word *cell* was applied to the empty space. It was not until early in the nineteenth century that Schleiden and Schwann developed the cell theory and proved that the cell, which was a solid particle with a nucleus, was the structural unit of all living tissue. Hooke's observations in his *Micrographia* dealt with common objects—hair, feathers, seeds, mites, spiders, gnats and, of course, the flea, so beloved of early microscopists. Hooke did not follow up the researches of Leeuwenhoek into the tiniest forms of life, but he gave a powerful impetus to microscopy, and the general design of the microscope has changed little since his day. Hooke died at Gresham College in 1703, at the age of sixty-seven.

Alongside the work of Robert Hooke may be placed that of Nehemiah Grew, 1641–1712, another of the bright luminaries of the Royal Society. He studied at Cambridge and graduated M.D. at Leyden, but London was the seat of most of his work. He made a useful contribution to biology in his work, quaintly entitled, *The Comparative Anatomy of Stomachs and Guts* (begun 1676), in which he depicted the alimentary canal of many animals. But his main achievement was in the field of botany, and his chief book was on *The Anatomy of Plants*, 1682. His beautiful drawings of plant structure are explained by a text describing the minute structure of plants, which, before his day, was hardly known. He was the first to show that sex was an attribute of certain plants, as of animals. Grew lived at a time when botany was an integral part of medicine, and his name appears as one of the compilers of the *Pharmacopoeia of the Royal College of Physicians of London*.

MICROSCOPY AND BACTERIOLOGY

The steady advances of microscopic technique since the seventeenth century forms a fascinating story which, however, can be told only by an expert physicist who is more than a mere medical historian. A powerful impetus was given to improvements in microscopy by the new science of bacteriology. The Italian poet and parasitologist, Francisco Redi, showed in 1684 that if meat was protected from flies, maggots did not appear in it. Before his time it was thought that mites developed spontaneously out of cheese, and maggots out of meat. His book, *Observations on living animals which are found within other living animals*, is the pioneer classic of parasitology. There was, in his view, no "spontaneous generation". "Life alone produces life", he said. A century later, in 1765, the argument was transferred from maggots and mites to microbes by another Italian, Lazaro Spallanzani, who proved that micro-organisms do not develop in fluids contained in flasks which had been exposed to heat, and sealed. Yet another century was to elapse before Pasteur (born 1822) demonstrated that fermentation was not a chemical change, but was caused by micro-organisms. Upon Pasteur's foundation Lister built his antiseptic system, which was to revolutionize surgery, in 1865. And it is sometimes forgotten that Lister's father introduced the achromatic system of lenses, which led to much clearer focusing than had been possible.

It is apt to be forgotten, too, that Lister was a great pioneer of bacteriology. His study of "bacterium lactis" occupied his attention for years.

Robert Koch (born 1843) showed how bacteria might be grown on solid media, and how they might be stained and then studied more easily. This discovery, as was to be expected, proved to be the prelude to the revelation of a bacterial cause of many infective diseases—plague, cholera, typhoid and others. This demonstration of bacteria was followed, at a slightly later date, by the discovery of a protozoan cause of malarial fever and by the wonderful discovery that insect vectors played a prominent part in the life history of various other parasitic infections—trypanosomiasis, filariasis and many others. The history of tropical diseases is, as you well know, one of the most romantic chapters in medical history. To discuss it more fully would lead far beyond the present theme.

THE LATEST MICROSCOPES

Let us return, however, to the tool, to the microscope itself. Many advances in its construction have been made since the time of Robert Hooke. During the nineteenth century there was a vogue for small instruments, especially when the physician desired to carry the microscope about with him, just as he carried his stethoscope. John Hughes Bennett, Professor of Physiology in Edinburgh and a leading physician, was one of the first to use the microscope in daily practice (Plate 9). His elegant little microscope, which was made in Paris, recently came into my possession. Since that time the stand has been improved, coarse and fine adjustments have been perfected, the mechanical stage and the oil-immersion system have been introduced; the objective and the condenser have undergone modification in design; and dark-ground illumination has extended the range of visibility. As a result, a most efficient means of magnification has been produced. Naturally, the degree of magnification is determined by the wave-length of light; consequently it is not possible to see a clear image of a greater magnification than about 1,500 diameters.

A little over ten years ago new possibilities were opened up by the discovery and development of the electron microscope. It was found that an electron beam passing through a vacuum carried with it waves of very short length which could be focused by electromagnetic fields, acting after the manner of optical lenses. As the electron wave-length is one hundred thousand times smaller than that of visible light, the increase in magnification, as compared with the ordinary microscope, is very considerable. A magnification of 10,000 to 50,000 diameters, or even as much as 180,000, may be obtained by the electron microscope. There are, of course, many technical disadvantages. One does not *see* the actual specimen, and must be content with what is virtually an X-ray picture or shadowgraph. Since the microscope works only in a vacuum, the specimen must be dry, and this is another serious disadvantage. The cost of the instrument, in the region of £2,000, and the fact that it demands the services of a technical expert, are other factors which, meanwhile, limit its value. Nevertheless it has already proved useful in revealing the nature of the so-called filterable viruses—causes of disease so small that they passed through the finest filter, and whose actual existence had been merely presumed before this pattern—be it cellular or crystalline—was revealed by the electron microscope. Obviously we may expect further discoveries in many fields as the research progresses.

THE WIDER OUTLOOK

You may now feel tempted to ask, "What is the present-day significance of all this obsolete lore regarding the evolution of microscopy?" and I would reply that there are at least two very good reasons why the scientific search for little things should engage our attention. In the first place the early classics of microscopy—such as Swammerdam's *Bible of Nature*, and Hooke's *Micrographia*—are well worth studying today, if only for the beauty of their illustrations.

A second, and more cogent, reason for a study of the work of the pioneers is that it enables us to recapture the wide perspective, the sweeping range of view, which was possible in the days of our forefathers, but which has become almost lost under the narrowing effect of specialism. The pioneers were not content to focus their microscopes on one object. Their range of vision was wide. The biologist was in close touch with the physicist and the chemist, and it is interesting to note that today biophysics and biochemistry are once again subjects of importance, but are now founded upon deeper and more accurate knowledge. Modern science is attempting this synthesis, being well aware of the disadvantages of specialized knowledge, and medicine would do well to follow such a lead. This can be done only by founding our current studies upon the firm basis of history. History is not merely an interesting side-line of science and medicine: it is an integral part of both, and, for the student, an essential means of securing the most enlightened outlook upon his life-work.

ANCIENT AND PRIMITIVE DRUGS

ONE IS OFTEN ASKED whether modern medicine has already fully exploited the innumerable remedies that were in vogue in ancient times and also the drugs that are still used by primitive peoples in many parts of the world. Can we derive therapeutic hints and assistance from these two sources, or has medical science already adopted all that was worth while, leaving the remainder to be cast aside as useless or, at best, to be regarded as mere historic landmarks? Yes, we must admit that those mines are worked out for the most part and that we can hope for no noteworthy addition to our materia medica, derived from ancient herbals or from the primitive medicine in use today.

Nevertheless it is worth while to take count of the obsolete drugs of the past and the primitive remedies of the present which, after all, have formed the basis of modern treatment. In this short paper we shall confine our attention to medicinal remedies, commonly called drugs, although that word is now often used in the restricted sense to designate a narcotic or a poison rather than a remedy.

PRIMITIVE MEDICINE AND FOLK-MEDICINE

How did it all come about, and why were plants ever used as medicines? In prehistoric times our early ancestors discovered, by the tedious and often dangerous process of experimenting on themselves, which plants were foods, which were poisons and which were remedies for diseases. Just as cats and dogs physic themselves with grasses, so did primitive man treat himself and his children. Such "folk-medicine" persists to this day. But that is not the whole story by any means. When men began to use their powers of reasoning, they did not reason in the way we might expect. Primitive man did not, and does not today,

223

regard disease as a natural phenomenon. In accordance with his animistic belief, he drew no distinction between body and soul. Although he dressed wounds with a leaf and soon learned the use of splints for fractures, disease was not so obviously a natural happening as was an injury. Diseases, especially those of an epidemic variety, or those which involved unconsciousness or mental disturbance, were regarded as "supernatural", the work of an enemy or an offended god who must be appeased. A demon had entered the sick person, and treatment consisted in driving it out. This was done by purging, by steam baths, by massage, by unpleasant drugs, or more often, by charms and incantations and other magical means. Perhaps our early ancestors were wiser than we are today, in applying treatment to the soul as well as to the body. Religion still has close affinity with Medicine. In the primitive scheme the magico-religious part of the cure was more significant than the administration of any drug. Nevertheless, the drug had its place and "folk-medicine" or domestic medicine was handed down in families through countless generations. It remains with us to the present time, and many ancient herbal remedies are still in use.

The domestic medicine of rural districts flourishes to this day. In Orkney, I was told that the root of the Buck-bean or Bog-bean (*Menyanthes trifoliata*), known also as the Craw-shoe, was often chewed by the older generation of crofters and was also given to cattle. It is used for much the same reason as Coca leaves are chewed by the natives of Peru, and Betel-nut by Indians. Also in Orkney, the leaves of Coltsfoot (*Tussilago farfara*) are smoked in a pipe and are said to cure bronchitis, while the roots of the common plant known as Thrift, when boiled in milk, will cure all chest complaints.

Each one of those medicinal plants is used in purely empiric fashion. This plant will cure that disease: the reason why, we cannot tell or even guess.

In the medical practice of primitive man, drugs play but a small part. Magic and supernatural methods are, in his view, much more potent. Such drugs as he uses are mainly those of vegetable origin. The lower plants are seldom used, i.e., the fungi, mosses, and ferns. It is from the highly differentiated plants that most remedies are derived. The roots and leaves are the parts most often used, at least in Africa, the country with which the writer is familiar. The juices, wood, stems, and seeds are less frequently employed. Sometimes the leaf or root is eaten raw, but more often it is prepared as a liquid decoction or infusion. The dosage is varied and uncertain. Pharmacologists who have made a special study of those drugs affirm that the great majority are inert.

The native names of the plants are often an inaccurate guide, and one name may be applied to several plants of different species. The therapeutic value of a plant remedy may vary according to the season in which it is gathered, a fact not always remembered. Thus, an accurate investigation of the so-called native remedies is beset by many difficulties. Many of the preparations are purgatives of rather drastic action.

Numerous are the tales of marvellous cures wrought by native practitioners, and the veracity of those who tell them must often be credited. Nevertheless it seems doubtful whether any further spectacular discovery may be expected from this line of research, although it does seem a pity that so few expert pharmacologists have been inclined to pursue it. Of course it is not surprising that a system of medical treatment based not only on empiricism but also, and to a greater extent, upon magic and witchcraft will defy investigation by the coldly material method of modern science. The differing reaction of each individual to the same drug, the idiosyncrasy, as it used to be called, is a factor that may defy analysis. Furthermore, native medicine is more psychic than physical.

MAN'S DISCOVERY OF REMEDIES

It was not until the beginning of the twentieth century, when Ehrlich introduced what he called "Chemotherapy", that the sky became clearer. By this time it had been proved that bacteria were the causes of many diseases and Ehrlich directed his "magic bullets" to hit the mark by combining with, and neutralizing the noxious agent, while avoiding injury to the tissues. This principle was carried a step farther by the introduction of penicillin, and the numerous "antibiotics" which have become so important in modern medicine. Ehrlich altered our entire therapeutic outlook. No longer are we forced to depend upon the trial-and-error method of testing the effect of fruits or berries or other vegetable products, in order to determine whether they are foods or poisons or whether they have some specific effect upon the human body in health or in disease. That was the only method known to our primitive ancestors and also to primitive man as he exists today. The method of pure observation and sheer empiricism soon became mixed with various forms of magic and ritual, and the reasons for the choice of remedies were often very strange. In medieval times, and perhaps even earlier, there arose the curious doctrine of "signatures". For every disease, it was argued, there must be a definite remedy, if only it could be found.

The idea of signatures was that of curing a bite by taking a hair of the dog that bit you. For example, the leaves of *Cyclamen* were shaped like the human ear and were therefore to be used for ear diseases, while the spotted leaves of the plant called *"Pulmonaria"*, which in appearance resembled the lungs, were a specific for chest affections. Saffron, on account of its yellow colour, was advised for jaundice. It was a strange system of treatment, but at least it was better than the blind gropings of earlier seekers after cures. As time went on, the search became more purposeful, although treatment remained empiric because of the lack of knowledge of the causes of disease. We still use many drugs without knowing exactly how they act.

I have said that in early times religion and medicine were one, and the doctor exercised a priestly function. Magic and religion played the major part in the treatment of disease.

About 460 B.C., Hippocrates, the father of medicine, arrived on the scene, and taught that there was no such thing as a sacred or supernatural cause of disease. All disease was perfectly natural, and could be cured by natural means. Our bodies, he said, were the physicians of our diseases. Nature was the great healer. Never was truer word spoken, and fortunately the Hippocratic attitude to disease remains with us still. Hippocrates used few drugs: he trusted largely to diet and regimen, and to the healing power of Nature.

Galen, who lived 600 years later, and died about A.D. 200, developed a system of medicine which lasted for more than a thousand years, and was based upon the doctrine of the humours—heat and cold, moisture and dryness. He used many drugs, and his name is perpetuated in the world "galenicals", drugs prepared from plants, as opposed to synthetic chemical remedies.

After the fall of Greece and Rome, medicine passed into the

hands of the physicians of the great Moslem Empire, which extended from Persia to Spain. It may be claimed that those Arab physicians were the orginators of pharmacy and *materia medica*. They introduced the processes of distillation, sublimation, and crystallization, and discovered many new drugs. The word "drug" is of Arabic origin, as also are syrup, sugar, alcohol, and many others. During this period, sometimes erroneously called "The Dark Ages", medicine was kept alive also by the Christian Church, and in many a monastery, manuscripts were copied, and medicinal plants were cultivated. The chemists of that time were more concerned with the search for the philosopher's stone, which would turn base metals into gold, than with the preparation of new remedies.

Furthermore, poisons of many kinds were used, and antidotes were numerous. The main ingredient of the famous antidote Theriac, was the flesh of vipers. Theriac remained in use for centuries. Indeed, it is listed in the London Pharmacopoeia of 1724, and the prescription contains sixty-two ingredients.

Into this strange atmosphere of medicine there came Paracelsus, a man whose work is not even yet fully appreciated. He focused the attention of alchemists upon the preparation of drugs, and he greatly simplified prescribing, by seeking out the "quintessence" or "active principle" of each remedy.

The Revival of Learning, about the fifteenth century, brought new knowledge in abundance, and of course the invention of printing and the discovery of the New World each made an enormous contribution.

The discovery of America was followed by the introduction of all manner of new drugs into Europe, and the "herbals", or books in which they were described, grew larger and more complicated than ever. Samuel Hahnemann's system of homeopathy helped to check the vogue for lengthy prescriptions containing large and even dangerous doses. That was early in the nineteenth century, a century during which there also appeared a wave of "therapeutic nihilism", when physicians were more interested in postmortem findings than in the recovery of patients. Once again the pendulum has swung toward carefully planned therapy, and in the antibiotics and other tools of precision we have weapons against disease that would amaze our forefathers.

UNICORN AND MUMMY AS SOURCES OF DRUGS

As a complete contrast to the present situation, it is interesting to recall some of the remedies that had a high reputation in the days of old.

Consider, for example, the story of the unicorn, a very strange tale indeed. The mythical unicorn, it was said, could be captured by a virgin in whose lap the animal innocently laid its head, while the hunters rushed up and slew it. As every child knows, the unicorn was the traditional enemy of the lion, and it has been identified variously with the rhinoceros, the oryx, and the narwhal. The oryx antelope, to be sure, has two horns, but they are not clearly separate when viewed at a distance, and sometimes one is missing: hence the myth of the unicorn. It is easier to note how the rhinoceros was called the unicorn. Rhinoceros horn, made into a cup, was regarded as an infallible protection against poison, and the powdered horn is still highly esteemed in native medicine. The relationship of the unicorn to a marine creature, the narwhal, is not so easy to understand. Nevertheless the horn of the unicorn, as it was displayed in churches and in museums, was certainly the single tusk or horn of the narwhal.

Jerome Cardan, on his way from Milan to attend the Archbishop of Scotland in 1552, spoke of seeing in the Church of St Denis at Paris "the rare and perfect horn of a unicorn". One of the chief contributions to the literature on the subject was *De Unicornu*, by Thomas Bartholin, Professor of Anatomy in Copenhagen (1616–80), a strange work dealing with every variety of horned creature, real or imaginary. Unicorn was a medieval remedy for numerous ills. One of the first to demonstrate its uselessness was Ambroise Paré, when he wrote, in 1582, his *Discours de la Mumie et de la Lincorne*.

Mummy was a remedy even more ancient than unicorn. Originally it was a product of Egyptian mummies, but, if that source was not available, any dried corpse might be used. The mummy of commerce, for use as a drug, was a resinous substance that sold at an enormous price. Paré stated that its source was always doubtful, and, like unicorn, it was quite inert. Nevertheless each of those curious drugs had a great vogue, and even such distinguished men as Lord Bacon and Robert Boyle extolled the virtues of mummy as a wound dress-

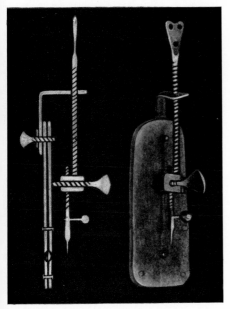

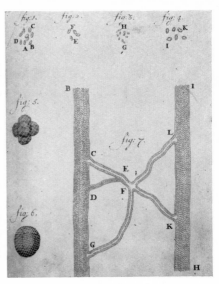

Capillaries and blood corpuscles as seen by Leeuwenhoek

Leeuwenhoek's microscope, showing the tiny lens and the screw controls for focussing the object

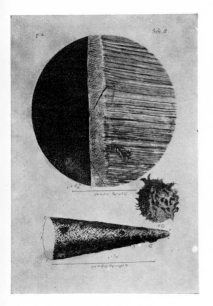

Edge of a razor blade, speck of London dust, and point of a needle, illustrated by Robert Hooke in his *Micrographia*

Pocket miscroscope used by Professor Hughes Bennett in 1848 (Author's collection)

PLATE 9

Dr William Heberden

(From the portrait by Sir William Beechey in the Royal College of Physicians)

PLATE 10

ing, which may have been quite justifiable, as the embalming resins doubtless had some antiseptic value.

Sir Thomas Browne, in his work, *Urn Burial*, published in 1658, tells us that "Mummy is become merchandise, Mezriam cures wounds and Pharaoh is sold for balsams", which suggests that even in his day it was not entirely discarded.

BEZOAR STONE AND VIPER'S FLESH

Antidotes against poisoning were in great demand during the Middle Ages. One of the best known of those antidotes was bezoar stone, the concretion or enterolith sometimes found in the intestines of goats and other animals. Bezoar stone was highly prized, not only as an antidote to all manner of poisons but also, according to Pomet's *History of Drugs* (1712), as a remedy for vertigo, jaundice, dysentery, and colic. The dose was 6 grains of the powdered stone, but even the carrying of the stone as a charm or amulet was believed to render the bearer immune to poison.

Still more strange was the use of the flesh of vipers as an antidote to poison. This was the principal ingredient in the substance known as theriaca or Venice treacle, the name treacle being at one time applied to any thick fluid. Theriaca contained, besides vipers' flesh, coral, pearls, and many other ingredients. Indeed its composition was so multiple that one recipe mentions no less than 250 ingredients. It was a modification of the earlier compound called "mithridatium", which derived its name from Mithridates VI, King of Pontus (132–63 B.C.), who discovered that he could immunize himself against poisons by the use of gradually increasing doses of them. The physician to the court of Mithridates was Crateuas, who made such accurate drawings of plants that he has been called the father of plant illustration. Theriaca, on the other hand, was first compounded by Andromachus, physician to the Emperor Nero, about the year A.D. 50. Such was its popularity that it was described in every herbal and, later, in every pharmacopoeia, and it was listed even in the French Codex of 1884. In England theriaca remained an official drug of the London Pharmacopoeia until 1746, although by that time it no longer contained vipers' flesh and was merely a mixture of opium, caraway, honey, and wine. Its expulsion from the pharmacopoeia followed the publication by Dr Heberden, in 1745, of his *Essay on Mithridatium and*

Theriac, in which he showed that the so-called remedy was quite useless. Someone has remarked of theriaca that, "Never has a medicine containing so much cured so little".

MANDRAGORA: AN EARLY ANAESTHETIC

One of the most famous drugs of history was the mystic mandrake, Mandragora. This solanaceous herb, with a very long

Fig. 5—Male and female mandrakes illustrated in *Ortus Sanitatis,* 1491

forked taproot, is still common in Greece and elsewhere. The root gives the plant a fancied resemblance to the human body, and there were even male and female mandrakes described in early herbals, the precursors of pharmacopoeias. Mandragora was used as an anaesthetic, and Dioscorides stated that after drinking "the wine of the bark or of the root", the patient may be "cut or cauterised", as he is so "overborne with dead sleep" that he does not feel the pain. It is not easy to understand how such a nonvolatile preparation could be used as an anaesthetic by inhalation: nevertheless it was a common practice to mix opium, mandragora, and henbane with water and to hold this mixture to the patient's nostrils on a sponge—the so-called *spongia somnifera* mentioned by Nicolas of Salerno in his *Antidotarium*, compiled in the eleventh century. Shakespeare has many references to mandragora, "the insane root that takes the reason prisoner". This refers to the gathering of the plant, which was not without danger, as it was believed that the mandrake, when uprooted, uttered a shriek that caused either death or insanity to all who heard it. Accordingly the root was first loosened and then tied to a dog, which completed the process of uprooting and then fell dead. Medieval illustrations often show how the mandrake root has been used as a tether for the dog.

CINCHONA AND QUININE

The discovery of America added largely to the number of drugs in the sixteenth century, and for many years new vegetable remedies continued to arrive from the Western Hemisphere. Among them was quinine in the crude form of cinchona bark, and its discovery forms a romantic story. About 1630, the Countess of Chinchon, wife of the Viceroy of Peru, was cured of a fever by the use of a native remedy prepared from the bark of a tree. It became known as the "Countess's Powder", and large quantities were distributed to the people of Lima by the Countess, who also introduced the drug into Spain. In this way, cinchona, as it was called after Linnaeus had omitted, in error, the first "h" of the word, became widely known in Europe. In England it was used as a secret remedy by Sir Robert Talbor who acquired a large fortune in this way, and, later, it was popularized by the leading physician Thomas Sydenham. The legend of the Countess of Chinchon has been disproved, as, it seems, she never went to Peru at all but lived and died in Spain, and it has also been shown that cinchona bark, or quinaquina, was often confused with Peruvian bark, from an entirely different tree, which yields balsam of Peru. Errors of this nature are not uncommon in the history of drugs. So many cinchona trees were cut down that there was a danger, early in the nineteenth century, that the supply might entirely fail. Charles Ledger, a Londoner who was buying alpacas in Bolivia, collected a quantity of cinchona seeds and offered them to the British Government. The offer was rejected, but the Dutch Government, with greater foresight, bought them for about a hundred dollars. From those seeds, in Java, were raised the plants that formed the nucleus of a vast industry, which yielded tons of quinine and immense revenues. Today, quinine has been largely superseded by other remedies, but the story of its appearance is a landmark of history.

TOBACCO, DIGITALIS AND ERGOT

Among other plants introduced from the New World was tobacco, and one of the first illustrations of the tobacco plant appears in the book by Nicolas Monardes of Seville who, although he never visited America, set himself to study the effect of many of the new plants. His work was translated into English in 1577 by John Frampton, who gave it the quaint title, *Joyfull Newes out of the Newe Founde Worlde*. Another remedy that owes its popularity to folklore is digitalis. For many years an infusion of foxglove leaves was used by the country folk of Shropshire as a cure for dropsy. This fact, noted by Dr William Withering while practising among them, led to the introduction of the plant into regular pharmacy. In his book, which has become a medical classic, *An Account of the Foxglove*, published in 1785, Withering described 163 cases of dropsy treated by digitalis. At that time dropsy was regarded as a disease and not merely as a manifestation of cardiac or renal disease. Withering did, however, recognize that digitalis had, "a power over the motion of the heart to a degree yet unobserved in any other medicine".

As an example of a plant disease which can cure human disease, there is Ergot. *Claviceps purpurea* is a fungus parasitic on rye, sometimes on other cereals. Its poisonous effects were early recognized. In the ninth and tenth centuries thousands of people died during epidemics of "ergotism" which caused gangrene of the limbs and was fatal. Since then there have been many epidemics: even as recently as 1926 in the Balkans and Russia. In modern times, it came to be used for haemorrhage after childbirth, and instead of causing deaths it saved many lives. Truly, a drug with a strange history.

HERBALS AND PHARMACOPOEIAS

A study of the ancient literature brings to light numerous interesting facts regarding vegetable remedies. Some drugs still in use, such as castor oil, are mentioned in the Ebers Papyrus, the oldest known medical book (or record) written about 1500 B.C.

Dioscorides, who lived in the first century A.D. wrote the first known account of medicinal plants. Many similar works followed: they were known as "herbals", and some are now very valuable. One of the first to be printed was the "Ortus sanitatis", dated 1491. Illustrations in the early herbals were very crude, but Otto Brunfels had made more accurate pictures of plants in his "Herbarium vivae incones", in 1530. William Turner, Dean of Wells, sometimes called "The Father of English Botany", published his Herbal in 1548, while that of Leonhard Fuchs, who gave his name to the fuchsia, appeared in 1542. The Herbal of John Gerard (1636) has an illustration of the potato, then a rarity, which Gerard grew in his garden at Holborn. Gerard perpetuates the myth of the Goose or Barnacle tree which bore shells on its branches from which Barnacle geese hatched out. A legend even more surprising is that of the Vegetable Lamb, which decorates the title-page of the herbal of John Parkinson (1629). This hybrid between animal and vegetable was often illustrated, becoming more plant-like as time went on.

John Parkinson was the last of the great herbalists. His book is entitled *Paridisi in Sole, Paradisus Terrestris*, the "Park in Sun" being a play upon his own name, and it appeared in 1629. The vegetable lamb was a creature that grew upon a stalk and that died after it had eaten up all the foliage within its reach. It was described and illustrated by Elizabeth Blackwell in her beautiful herbal dated 1737 and entitled *A Curious Herbal*. The hairs of the "animal" were used as a hemostatic, and this remedy

Fig. 6—"Vegetable lamb" from the title-page of Parkinson's *Paridisi in Sole, Paradisus Terrestris*, 1629

was discussed by Sir Hans Sloane in a paper to the Royal Society in 1698, although by that time it had become obvious that the plant-plus-animal was merely a species of fern that bore a remote resemblance to a lamb.

233

A well-known writer in herbalism was the notorious Nicolas Culpeper who published the Pharmacopoeia of the Royal College under his own name in 1649. That Pharmacopoeia was the first official list of approved remedies in English. Printed in 1618, it listed almost 2,000 remedies, some of them simple, others having many ingredients. In the tenth and last edition (1851), less than 300 drugs are mentioned. There had been earlier Pharmacopoeias in Italy, Germany and France, and the Royal College of Physicians of Edinburgh sponsored one in 1699 which continued through fourteen editions. All were superseded when the General Medical Council first issued the British Pharmacopoeia (1864), now in its 9th Edition (1958).

More might be written regarding the strange drugs and remedies of early times, but enough has been said to show the interest of this aspect of medical history, so peculiar to our enlightened minds, yet representing the first stages of the age-long war against disease.

A HUNDRED YEARS OF
CHLOROFORM*

I HAVE BEEN ASKED to address you at this centenary meeting
on "The Discovery of Chloroform Anæsthesia", and no doubt
the University has acted wisely in apportioning the duty to one
who is neither an anæsthetist nor an obstetrician, but simply a
worker in the neutral field of history.

It is good to praise famous men and to recall great achievements, and surely the discovery of chloroform anæsthesia by
Professor James Young Simpson was one of the most important
advances, as well as one of the most dramatic episodes, in the
long history of medicine, which we do well to celebrate upon
this, its hundredth anniversary. As we do so, we may find it
hard to realize that the discovery was so long delayed, and that
only so recently as the middle of last century was surgery completely revolutionized by the introduction of anæsthesia and
antisepsis.

The quest for some means of relieving pain had been pursued
down the ages since prehistoric times. Nepenthe, used by Helen
of Troy, was followed by mandragora, a drug which retained
its popularity for many centuries. Other pain-relieving agents
—opium, and henbane, and various "drowsy syrups", as well
as physical means, such as freezing or pressure, were employed
with very varying degrees of success.

Animal magnetism, or mesmerism, was the anæsthetic
method which held the popular imagination and the attention
of surgeons in this country about the middle of last century,
when there arrived from America news of the spectacular use of
ether by inhalation. The first public demonstration of the value
of ether anæsthesia in surgery was given by William T. G.

* An Address delivered in the Upper Library Hall, University of Edinburgh, on
4 November 1947, at a reception to celebrate the centenary of the discovery of
chloroform anæsthesia by Sir James Young Simpson.

Morton at Boston, on 16 October 1846. There were other claimants to the priority of the discovery—Crawford Long, Horace Wells, and Charles Jackson. There is no need to revive this complex controversy, so widely publicized a year ago. Suffice it to say that our present festival in no way detracts from the merit due to the American pioneers of ether anæsthesia.

Robert Liston, at University College Hospital, London, is usually regarded as the first to employ ether anæsthesia in major surgery in Britain in December 1846; while James Young Simpson was the first to introduce it into obstetric practice, in January 1847. On hearing of the American discovery, Professor Simpson had written to his brother, "It is a glorious thought; I can think of naught else." Here was the solution to a problem which had intrigued him since his student days, and now he readily grasped the opportunity of testing its efficiency. As he continued to use ether, it became apparent to Simpson, and to many others, that this was not yet the ideal anæsthetic. It was uncertain in action, irritating to the air passages, and required special apparatus for its administration. Simpson resolved that he would find some anæsthetic which would be free from such disadvantages.

He inhaled all manner of gases and vapours, and it is said that on one occasion at least, before his discovery, he rendered himself unconscious, greatly to the alarm of his family. In his search for a new anæsthetic he enlisted the services of his assistants, Keith and Matthews Duncan. On many an evening, when each day's work was over, the trio sat around his dining-room table at 52 Queen Street, engaged in a strange but heroic experiment upon themselves. Early each morning, Simpson's next door neighbour, Professor Miller, would call to ascertain the results, or, as he himself remarked, "to find out whether everyone was still alive".

The little team of investigators had been at work for several months, and a variety of substances had already been tested. Shortly before the night in question, David Waldie of Liverpool had mentioned to Professor Simpson that it might be worth while to try the effect of perchloride of formyle, or chloroform. Waldie, a medical man who had become a chemist, deserves credit for his suggestion, although he made no experiments on his own account.

A small quantity of chloroform had been prepared for Simpson by the professor of chemistry, William Gregory, but it had been laid aside as it appeared heavy and unpromising. On the night of the discovery, after several substances had been tested without result, this little phial was searched for, and found under a heap of waste paper. Simpson himself was the first to inhale it, and his companions followed his example on observing that it seemed effective. Naturally he was also the first to regain his senses, and the thought prominent in his returning consciousness was that something "far stronger and better than ether" had been discovered. Then he noticed that Matthews Duncan was snoring in his chair with open mouth and staring eyes, while Keith, having reached only the stage of excitement, had slipped under the table and was kicking it vigorously. Each of them on recovery echoed Simpson's satisfaction with the effect of the new agent.

The witnesses of this strange scene, who must surely have been much alarmed, included Mrs Simpson, her sister Miss Grindlay, and her niece Miss Petrie. When further trials were made, Miss Petrie insisted upon inhaling the drug, and thus became the first woman subjected to its influence.

Some few days later in the Royal Infirmary of Edinburgh, Professor Simpson administered chloroform to three patients, two of whom underwent operation by Professor James Miller, the third by Mr John Duncan. The first of them was a Highland boy, whose name is unrecorded and who could speak only Gaelic. A large fragment of diseased bone was removed from his arm. He continued to sleep soundly after the operation and felt no pain.

Simpson lost no time in making known his discovery. Within a week, on 10 November 1847, he presented to the Medico-Chirurgical Society of Edinburgh his "Account of a New Anæsthetic Agent". Chloroform rapidly became the anæsthetic of choice, and soon superseded ether in this country and on the continent.

Nevertheless Simpson continued his researches, hoping to improve the method. Every member of his household was now eager to share in the work. At one time Professor Simpson resolved to try the effect of drinking a mixture of chloroform and champagne. Hearing of this, his butler, named Clarke, administered a dose of the potent cocktail to the cook, who promptly fell insensible on the kitchen floor. Clarke rushed upstairs to his master, calling "Come down, sir, come down for God's sake, I've poisoned the cook". Fortunately the victim rapidly recovered.

It seems advisable that one should include in this brief survey some account of the life-story of the discoverer, of whose accomplishment this University may well be proud. Born at Bathgate in 1811, the youngest of a family of eight children, James Simpson climbed the ladder of fame from a lowly rung. From his earliest years he had an insatiable appetite for learning, and even at the village school he was known as the "wise wean". Poor though they were, his father and mother resolved that Jamie would proceed to the University, and this he did at the age of fourteen.

"Thus, I entered Edinburgh University", he told the audience on receiving the Freedom of the City many years later, "very young, very solitary, very poor, and almost friendless." His estimate of the relative values of nourishment and knowledge is shown by an entry in his diary of expenses as a student: Finnan haddies, 2d.; Book on Osteology, 21s. During his student days he was so repelled and shocked by the dreadful scenes of suffering in the operating theatre that on one occasion he actually resolved to abandon medicine and to devote himself to the study of law. Leaving the Infirmary he proceeded to Parliament House with this object in view. Fortunately, his better judgement prevailed. He accepted the existing conditions as a challenge rather than as a deterrent, and it seems probable that from that very day he gave much thought to the clamant need for the prevention and relief of pain in surgery.

After graduating M.D. in 1832, he became assistant to John Thomson, the professor of pathology, and it was Thomson who advised him to specialize in midwifery. In 1840 the Town Council of Edinburgh, by a majority of one vote, appointed him professor of midwifery in succession to Professor Hamilton. He brought great repute to the chair and he contributed very materially to the progress of midwifery and gynæcology.

Nevertheless he did not allow his speciality to monopolize all his energies. A versatility such as his could not accept the limitations of specialist practice. His advocacy of the control of hæmorrhage by needles in places of ligatures, acupressure, as he called it, brought him into conflict with some of his

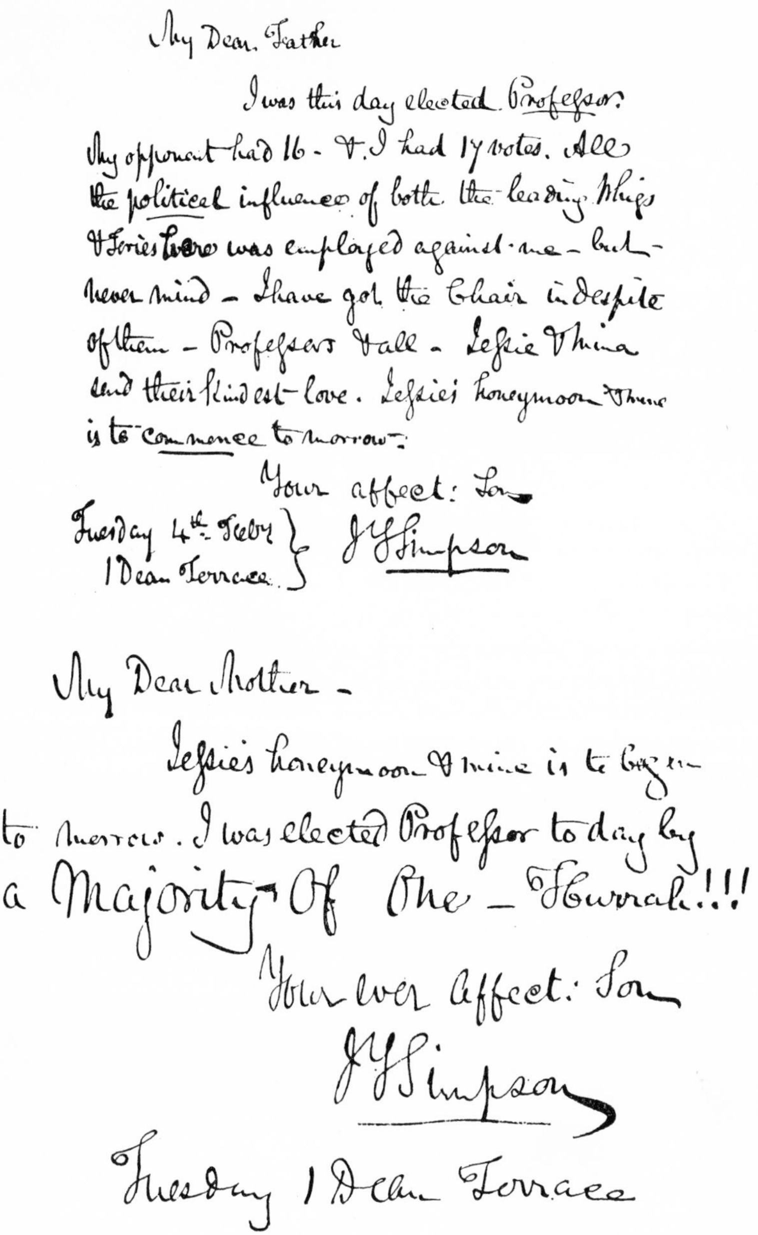

My Dear. Father

*I was this day elected. Professor.
My opponent had 16 - & I had 17 votes. All
the political influence of both the leading Whigs
& Tories &c was employed against me - but -
never mind - I have got the Chair in despite
of them - Professors Vall - Leslie & Mina
send their kindest love. Leslie's honeymoon & mine
is to commence to morrow.*

*Your affect: Son
Tuesday 4th Feby } J Y Simpson
1 Dean Terrace. }*

My Dear Mother -

*Leslie's honeymoon & mine is to begin
to morrow. I was elected Professor to day by
a Majority Of One — Hurrah!!!*

*Your ever affect: Son
J Y Simpson*

Tuesday 1 Dean Terrace

Fig. 7—James Young Simpson's letters to his father- and mother-in-law; from the originals in Edinburgh University Library

surgical colleagues. Simpson regarded this discovery as equal to the discovery of chloroform anæsthesia, although acupressure has now become a mere historical curiosity. Another campaign of Simpson's was directed against the evil of large hospitals, the so-called hospitalism. In place of the great solid structures, so conducive to septic infection, he advised the building of small temporary hospitals. His conclusions were not always correct: indeed, he was one of the strongest opponents of Lister's methods. Nevertheless his arguments were always supported by evidence carefully collected.

Nor did he confine his researches to medicine. On archæology he was an acknowledged authority, and he published papers on leprosy in Scotland, on the buildings on Inchcolm, on medical officers in the Roman army, to mention only a few. Well, indeed, might Dr John Brown remark to a friend, as Simpson passed along the street, "There is not one man, but many men, under that coat" (Plate 11).

His residence at 52 Queen Street, now known as Simpson House, was constantly filled by numerous patients, distinguished visitors, and post-graduate students, to all of whom he extended a cordial welcome. At every meal, even at breakfast, there were guests, invited and even uninvited.

His well-stored mind and multiple interests made him an ideal host, and he delighted in argument and debate, being gifted with an unsual fluency both of pen and tongue.

In the conduct of his practice he was obliged to undertake many a long and weary journey, but fortunately he had the aptitude for sleeping anywhere and at any time. The short journeys and the daily round he accomplished by carriage, for which Messrs Croall supplied a pair of spirited horses and a coachman who was not always sober. Summoned one evening to Hopetoun House, Professor Simpson wondered why he was taking so long to reach Queensferry, until he discovered that for over an hour he had been driven round and round the garden railing side of Ainslie Place, from which the driver alleged that he could find no way out!

Simpson's address as Promoter at the Graduation Ceremony of 1868 was a masterly performance, and in it he prophesied the discovery of X-rays, remarking that "one day, by means of electric lights, we may render the human body transparent to the eye of the surgeon". Two years before that date he had been the first medical man in Scotland to receive a baronetcy, and it is significant that he chose as his motto: *Victo dolore*. His race was now nearly run. Although he died at the age of fifty-nine, he had crowded into that lifetime a full and varied career.

Of course Simpson did not discover the substance chloroform. That discovery had been made in 1831–32, independently and almost simultaneously by three chemists, Souberian, Liebig, and Guthrie, in France, Germany and America. Chloroform had been used internally in medicine and indeed it is still so used. It is also used very largely to flavour confectionery, and as a solvent in many industrial processes. Simpson, however, was the first to describe and demonstrate its employment as a general anæsthetic.

Others played minor parts in the discovery. David Waldie, for example, the Linlithgow doctor who became a chemist in Liverpool, suggested to Simpson that chloroform was worthy of a trial, but he published no observations of his own, if indeed he made any experiments. Simpson's assistants, Keith and Matthews Duncan, deserve a share of the credit, and it has been alleged that the latter made a personal trial of chloroform before the classic day, just as it is also said that Simpson tested the drug in advance. Such tales may or may not be true, and are of little significance.

One other name, however, deserves mention alongside that of Simpson. Dr John Snow of London, the first professional anæsthetist, introduced many technical improvements, and it was he who administered chloroform to Queen Victoria at the birth of Prince Leopold in 1853.

It is a strange commentary on the times in which he lived that Simpson was obliged to defend anæsthesia against those who objected to its use in obstetrics on religious grounds. He answered the critics in their own tongue, showing an amazing acquaintance with the Hebrew text. The controversy continued for several years, and it was the Royal patronage of the new drug which finally silenced the narrow-minded opposition.

By the medical profession, the advantages of chloroform over ether were at once recognized. For a time, chloroform entirely displaced ether and became almost the only general anæsthetic in use all over the world. It was even stated by some authorities, including Lister, that chloroform was perfectly safe, provided due attention was paid to the respiration. Professor Syme could point to 5,000 cases of chloroform administration without a death. Nevertheless reports of deaths in this and other countries shook the original optimism, leading to a revival in the use of ether, to the use of nitrous oxide, and various mixtures of ether and chloroform, and to the introduction of dosimetric methods, as opposed to the uncertain drop method, the so-called "rag and bottle" anæsthesia, so highly favoured in Edinburgh. Perhaps the most beneficial effect of the argument regarding the virtues of this or that anæsthetic or method was the development of anæsthesia as a speciality, and of the anæsthetist, who devoted all his time to this work.

Since its introduction by Simpson a century ago, chloroform has retained its place as a general anæsthetic, although it is no longer employed in random fashion. Regarding its present use, I am not qualified to speak, and in any case the question was admirably discussed by three eminent anæsthetists this morning. This, however, one may say with confidence, that the very name "chloroform" reflects credit upon the University of Edinburgh. It is right and proper that we should celebrate the birthday of our centenarian. During those hundred years many a sufferer has had reason to be thankful for "the thick, sweet mystery of chloroform", which has transformed an unspeakable anguish into what Henley called, "an immense, complacent dreamery". Looking back, we now salute the memory of James Young Simpson, who, by his discovery of chloroform anæsthesia, achieved immortal fame. *Victo dolore.*

BY-WAYS
IN BIOGRAPHY

Dr Joseph Bell operating at the Royal Hospital
for Sick Children, Edinburgh, about 1890 (see page 290)

Professor Sir James Young
Simpson wearing the fur
coat presented to him by
a grateful patient (see
page 240)

PLATE 11

Alexander Monro primus
(1697–1767)

Alexander Monro secundus
(1733–1817)

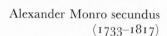

Alexander Monro tertius
(1773–1859)

Plate 12

(see page 304)

"RELIGIO MEDICI":
A TERCENTENARY TRIBUTE

SIR THOMAS BROWNE'S *Religio Medici* (The Religion of a Physician) can be classed neither as a medical nor as a scientific work, yet it occupies a unique place in literature because of the perennial freshness of its message and the delightful manner and style in which that message is presented. It has had many imitators. All manner of "religios" have appeared, pertaining to numerous callings. Thus we have *Religio Clerici, Religio Jurisprudentis* and such-like publications; but none of them can match the original model.

Many men of letters have paid homage to Sir Thomas Browne. Coleridge, Lamb, Lowell, Johnson and many another has acknowledged his influence, and in our own day Sir William Osler has done much to revive the peculiar attraction which the *Religio* must ever hold for the medical man. Needless to say, Browne has also had his critics since the fashion was set by the dreary Aberdonian philosopher, Alexander Ross, whose *Medicus Medicatus or the Physician's Religion cured by a lenitive or gentle Potion* only added to Browne's popularity. Sir Kenelm Digby's *Observations upon Religio Medici* did still more, and thereby hangs the tale of the publication which may be here retold.

THE STORY OF THE FIRST EDITION

Dr Thomas Browne, the son of a mercer of Cheapside, London, had studied in Oxford, spent three years in the medical schools of Padua, Montpellier and Leyden, had started practice in Norwich, and had married Dorothy Mileham, before the authentic edition of *Religio Medici* appeared in 1643. Originally written at Shipden Hall, Halifax, just after the author's return from the Continent, it was not intended for the press, but was composed as "a sort of private diary of the soul". The writer was still young. "My life, it is a miracle of thirty years", he observes in one place, and in another, "nor hath my pulse beat thirty years". The manuscript was circulated among friends, and frequently copied, as a number of manuscripts still exist although none in Browne's handwriting. The publication of such a document was a temptation too great to be resisted; one of the manuscripts reached a printer in 1642 and was "most imperfectly and surreptitiously published". Worse was to follow, when a copy of the pirated edition was bought by the forceful and versatile Sir Kenelm Digby, then in prison for a political offence. Within twenty-four hours, if we are to believe him, the prisoner had written and published a review and criticism which caught the public imagination. Browne was now obliged to take action. With characteristic liberality he supplied to the same publisher the corrected edition and thus, early in 1643, *Religio Medici* became available for all readers. The alterations do not appear to have been very extensive. Even the frontispiece of the "surreptitious" edition was used, and has been reproduced many times. It represented a man, falling from a high cliff, caught and rescued in mid-air by a hand emerging from a cloud in the heavens, and it bears the legend "*a cælo salus*".

THE "RELIGIO" AND ITS MESSAGE

It is not easy to explain in a few sentences the nature of *Religio Medici*; indeed it is by no means easy to read, for it is a work which must be studied and pondered for many a day before its magic and fascination captures the average reader.

The very title of the book was a paradox when it appeared; the medicus of that day was held to be a sceptic in matters of religion, and the new learning, already in full flood on the Continent and gradually extending to Britain, tended to widen the gulf between religion and science. Yet Browne sets out to state his argument in favour of a wide and liberal interpretation of Christianity, for "those who do confine the Church of God either to particular Nations, Churches or Families, have made it far narrower than our Saviour ever meant it". At the outset the work claims that he "dare without usurpation assume the honourable title of Christian"; but, he continues, "I borrow not the rules of my Religion from Rome or Geneva, but the dictates of my own reason". His views are "not wrung from speculations and subtilties, but from common sense and observation; not pickt from the leaves of any Author, but bred

246

amongst the weeds and tares of mine own brain". He has no antipathy to "Turks, Infidels and Jews", but, for himself, he finds that "there is no Church whose every part so squares unto my Conscience", so "consonant unto reason" and so "framed to my particular Devotion, as the Church of England".

Having said this, he is not prepared to argue further, for he has "no Genius to disputes in Religion", however argumentative he may be in other matters. "In Philosophy, where Truth seems double-fac'd, there is no man more Paradoxical than my self; but in Divinity I love to keep the Road; and, though not in an implicite, yet an humble faith, follow the great wheel of the Church." "As for those wingy Mysteries in Divinity, and airy subtleties in Religion, which have unhinged the brains of better heads, they never stretched the Pia Mater of mine." Like many another man of Science he keeps his Religion in a separate compartment, for "many things are true in Divinity which are neither inducible by reason nor confirmable by sense". Of course he was faced by problems, but he was content merely to state them and to believe that "there is some other hand that twines the thread of life other than that of Nature. I am sure we do not err if we say it is the hand of God". For instance: "For the first chapters of Genesis, I must confess a great deal of obscurity", and "I would gladly know how Moses with an actual fire calcined or burnt the Golden Calf unto powder, for that mystical metal of Gold, exposed to the violence of fire, grows onely hot, and liquefies, but consumeth not".

We are not surprised to find Browne sceptical of Hell, a grim reality in his time. "I thank God", he writes, "that I was never afraid of Hell, nor ever grew pale at the description of that place." "I can hardly think there was ever any scared into Heaven; they go the fairest way to Heaven that would serve God without a Hell." Nor can he "dream that there should be at the last day any Judicial proceeding or calling to the bar as indeed the Scripture seems to imply, and literal Commentators do conceive".

So futile is religious argument, that he considers it would be for the benefit of learning, were it possible to limit the literature of religion to "a few and solid Authors; and to condemn to the fire those swarms and millions of Rhapsodies, begotten only to distract and abuse the weaker judgments of

247

Scholars, and to maintain the trade and mystery of Typo-graphers". One shudders to think how Browne would have regarded the books of today.

As a medical man he must needs refer to the mystery of the soul, stating that "amongst all those rare discoveries and curious pieces I find in the Fabrick of Man, there is no Organ or Instrument for the rational Soul; for in the brain there is not anything of moment more than I can dis-cover in the crany of a beast, and this is an argument of the inorganity of the Soul. Thus we are men, and we know not how; there is something in us that can be without us, and will be after us; though it is strange that it hath no history what it was before us, nor cannot tell how it entered in us."

The Medicus makes further reference to his anatomical studies when he refers to those patients, so well known to every medical practitioner, who "think health an appurten-ance unto life, and quarrel with their constitutions for being sick"; "but I", writes Dr Browne, "that have examined the parts of man, and know upon what tender filaments that Fabrick hangs, do wonder that we are not always so; and do thank my God that we can die but once". Not content to contemplate such mysteries of Nature as the Tides, the Nile floods and the Magnetic Pole, he "studied to match and parallel those in the more obvious pieces of Nature, which without further travel I can do in the Cosmography of myself". "We carry with us the wonders we seek without us: there is all Africa and her pro-digies in us. . . ." Extending his observations to the animal world, he remarks that "there are no Grotesques in Nature", and "no deformity in any kind or species of creature whatso-ever". It is not surprising that he was more intrigued by the habits of insects than by such "prodigious pieces of Nature, Whales, Elephants and Dromidaries". There was "more curious Mathematicks" in bees, ants, and spiders, and "the civility of these little Citizens more neatly sets forth the Wisdom of their Maker".

In the second part of *Religio Medici* the author turns from the theme of Faith to that of Charity.

Browne had a truly international outlook which must have been as rare in the seventeenth century as it is today. His was "a constitution so general, that it consorts and sympa-thiseth with all things. I have no antipathy, or rather Idio-

248

syncrasie, in dyet, humour, air, any thing. I wonder not at the French for their dishes of Frogs, Snails and Toadstools, . . . but being amongst them, make them my common Viands". "At the sight of a Toad or Viper, I find in me no desire to take up a stone and destroy them." "National repugnances do not touch me, nor do I behold with prejudice the French, Italian, Spanish or Dutch." This he writes at a time when "whole Nations miscall each other by opprobious Epithets" and when scholars wielded pens which "carried farther and gave a louder report than Thunder". "All places, all airs, make unto me one Countrey; I am in England every where, and under any Meridian."

How could men judge aright, with such imperfect knowledge? "No man", answers Browne, "can justly censure or condemn another, because indeed no man truly knows another." How many of us could echo such noble sentiments? Thus he continues, condemning intellectual snobbery, philosophizing on sleep and dreams, and discussing the voice of Conscience; "another man within me that's angry with me, rebukes, commands and dastards me."

Browne's experience as a physician leads him to pray, "Let me be sick my self, if sometimes the malady of my patient be not a disease unto me", and to feel "not only ashamed but heartily sorry, that there are diseases incurable; yet not for my own sake, or that they are beyond my Art, but for the general cause and sake of humanity".

LATER LIFE IN NORWICH

No series of extracts from *Religio Medici* can convey the charm and interest of the complete work. It is like a piece of music, which must be played in its entirety to be fully appreciated. Of course Browne had his faults. We find it hard to understand how so saintly a man could write "I have ever believed, and do now know, that there are witches", and could even supply the evidence upon which two unfortunate women accused of witchcraft were condemned to death at Lancashire Assizes in 1635. Perhaps one should rather marvel that in other respects the author of *Religio Medici* held views far ahead of his time. As so often happens, the *Religio*, his first work, was also his greatest. His second, *Pseudodoxia Epidemica*, was published in 1646. It was an inquiry into certain "vulgar errors" and is full of quaint and picturesque argument. Did moles possess eyes? Did swans sing whilst dying? Were the legs of the badger shorter on one side so that it could run on the side of a hill? Could the ostrich digest iron? Such are a few of the "errors" discussed in this curious book.

Two other books followed in 1658, *Urn-burial* and *The Garden of Cyrus*. Dr Browne was a physician of high repute, his large medical practice including such well-known families as the L'Estranges and the Pastons and extending far beyond the city of Norwich. He was also a keen naturalist and archæologist and it was natural that he should be informed of a number of cinerary urns near Walsingham. Yet no-one can regard his book, *Hydriotaphia, Urn-Burial* as a contribution to archæology. The urns are simply the text of a magnificent discourse upon man's mortality. It is strangely ironical that the skull of Sir Thomas Browne, he who had that horror of being "knav'd out of our graves", was on view in the museum of the Norfolk and Norwich Hospital from 1840 until 1922, when it was decently reinterred in the church of St Peter Mancroft. Browne himself had written, "Who knows the fate of his bones, or how often he is to be buried?" To day he would have been a strong supporter of cremation.

The Garden of Cyrus contains as little of horticulture as *Urn-Burial* does of archæology. Obsessed by the geometrical form known as the "quincunx," the writer wanders on in tantalizing fashion, often becoming almost unintelligible, until at the end he rises to the very summit of English prose in a grand peroration.

Of the closing years of Browne's life we have little information. For forty-six years he practised in Norwich, but his fame extended throughout the world of letters. He lived in troublous times and was a good Royalist, but he was too wise to dabble in politics. Throughout all the current turmoil, he and his wife Dorothy enjoyed long and happy lives. Edward, the eldest of their ten children, attained a distinction almost equal to that of his father. He travelled far and widely in Europe and wrote an account of his journeyings, then became a leading physician in London, a fellow of the Royal Society and physician to the king. It was that king who knighted the father during a visit to Norwich in 1671. Charles II was about to confer this honour upon the Mayor, but that honest man informed the king that a more worthy recipient of the royal favour was present in the person of the famous doctor, who thereupon became Sir Thomas Browne.

He died fourteen years later, on his 77th birthday. Some twenty editions of the *Religio* had appeared during his lifetime and the book had been translated into Latin, Dutch, German, French and Italian. It has been reprinted many times since then. Although it proclaimed no new discovery, nor even any new idea or method, the influence which it exercised in its day has steadily grown and it continues to attract an ever-increasing circle of devoted readers.

JOHN HUNTER:
SURGEON AND NATURALIST*

PROFESSOR JOHN CHIENE,† whose apt maxims of surgical practice still ring in the ears of those of us who were fortunate to be his pupils, was wont to advise us to avoid becoming mere "hewers of wood and drawers of water". Such counsel would have delighted John Hunter who, with a vision far ahead of his time, laboured to prevent surgery from becoming an affair of carpentry and plumbing.

In the present era of specialism and super-specialism it is indeed salutary to recall this great figure of medical history, and although the work of John Hunter has been the theme of a dozen biographers and nearly a hundred Hunterian Orators, the remarkable story remains of perennial interest.

PARENTAGE AND YOUTH

John Hunter, the youngest of a family of ten children, was born on 14 February 1728, at the farm of Long Calderwood, some seven miles south-east of Glasgow. His father, already an old man, died when John was ten years old, and he remained in the care of an indulgent mother and appears to have been a "spoiled child". It is indeed remarkable that such a genius, at the age of seventeen, could neither read nor write. But, as is well known, the brilliant schoolboy does not always fulfil the pro-mise of early years, and, conversely, the boy who has no inclination for scholarship may grow to be a clever man. John Hunter was one who blossomed late; nevertheless his education did progress, although along unusual lines, for in his own words he "wanted to know all about the clouds and the grasses, and why the leaves changed colour in autumn: I watched the ants, bees, birds, tadpoles and caddisworms; I pestered people with

---

* Address to the Royal Medical Society on 28 November 1941.
† Professor of Surgery, University of Edinburgh, 1882-1909.

questions about what nobody knew or cared anything about".
His sister Janet, eldest of the surviving children, had married a
Mr Buchanan, a Glasgow cabinet-maker. To him John was
apprenticed, as it appeared obvious that his livelihood must be
gained by handicraft rather than by scholarship. But as John
Hunter grew to manhood his ambition became at length
aroused, and indeed it is uncertain whether he was engaged in
woodwork for more than a short time.

EARLY DAYS IN LONDON

At the age of twenty he joined his brother William in London,
and entered upon a career which became steadily more
strenuous and more fruitful of results until his death, forty-five
years later. William, ten years his senior, was already making
a name for himself as an anatomist and obstetrician, a strange
combination to our way of thinking but not unusual at that
time.

William Hunter was originally destined for the Church, and
he had received a good education before he came under the
spell of Dr William Cullen, who practised medicine in the town
of Hamilton, and who afterwards became Professor of Medicine
in the University of Edinburgh. After assisting Cullen for several
years, William Hunter went to London, and there he lived with
Dr Smellie, of Lanark, who had come to London two years
previously and was already a successful accoucheur and
apothecary, with a shop in Pall Mall.

William Hunter also assisted Dr John Douglas, the anatomist, whose name survives in the "pouch of Douglas", and he
succeeded him as lecturer in Anatomy a few years later. It is
interesting to note that William Hunter became a member of
the Royal Medical Society in 1775.

An older brother, James, who had been a Writer to the Signet
in Edinburgh, forsook Law for Medicine and joined his brother
William, embarking upon a career of great promise. Unfortunately, however, he was stricken with pulmonary tuberculosis
and returned home to die at the age of twenty-nine years. A
sister, Dorothea Hunter, married Rev. Dr James Baillie, who
became Professor of Divinity at Glasgow. Of this marriage were
born three children—Matthew, a distinguished physician of
London and one of John Hunter's trustees; Joanna, who made
a name for herself in literature and was a friend of Sir Walter

Scott; and Agnes, who, "if not distinguished in life, was at least tenacious of it", as she died in her 101st year.

Certainly the Hunter family possessed brains, and there can be no doubt that William, himself a great man, blazed the trail for his greater and more brilliant young brother, John. John set out from Glasgow and arrived in London in September 1748, after a journey on horseback which occupied about a fortnight. William gave him an arm to dissect, just as many a student starts with "the upper limb" today, and the excellence of his work was immediately apparent. It was William who sent John to study surgery under Cheselden at Chelsea Hospital, and under Percival Pott, of fracture fame, at St Bartholomew's; subsequently he was a house surgeon at St George's Hospital. For a short time he was in Oxford, as it was deemed necessary that he should have some acquaintance with the classics, but this was an unsuccessful experiment. John Hunter preferred to study the book of Nature. The two brothers worked together in London for a time, discovering the lachrymal ducts and the tubuli seminiferi and making researches on congenital hernia and on the circulation in the placenta, until a misunderstanding and estrangement arose which lasted until William's death. William is often quoted as having said on his deathbed, "If I had the strength to hold a pen I would write how pleasant and easy a thing it is to die". Commenting later upon those "last words", John Hunter remarked, "Ay, but it is a poor thing when it comes to that".

Ottley, whose *Life of John Hunter* has influenced all subsequent biographers, tells us that "Jack" Hunter, as he was then called, was "not very nice in the choice of his associates", and that he was a favourite with the "resurrection men", mingling with them in the theatre galleries in order "to damn the productions of unhappy authors".

ON MILITARY SERVICE

But let us return to the early struggles of brother John. In 1759, eleven years after his arrival in London, he developed symptoms of tuberculosis and he was advised to seek some rest in a warmer climate. Doubtless remembering the fate of his elder brother James, he took the advice, but gave it a somewhat original interpretation by enlisting in the Army, truly a graceful compliment to the Medical Corps of that time. England had become involved in the Seven Years War and was about to lay siege to Belleisle, near the mouth of the Loire. Staff-Surgeon John Hunter accompanied this expeditionary force, and in the following year he went to Portugal, to whose aid, threatened with invasion by France and Spain, the British force had proceeded. Belleisle and Portugal afforded valuable experience to John Hunter, for not only did he acquire first-hand experience of gunshot wounds, but in the intervals of fighting he studied the flora and fauna of the countries and added continually to his knowledge. He made experiments on lizards, forcing food into their stomachs and noting that it remained undigested during the period of hibernation. He also investigated the hearing organ of fishes, as he mentioned in his paper of that title to the Royal Society some years later. Indeed, his four years of foreign service must have given John Hunter ample opportunity to indulge his favourite study of comparative anatomy.

LIFE AT GOLDEN SQUARE AND AT EARL'S COURT

We have only a scanty record of the eight years which intervened between his military service and his marriage, but we know that they were very busy years. On his return to civilian life in 1763, John Hunter had resumed, or rather begun, practice in Golden Square. He opened a room for dissecting and taught classes in Anatomy. At first the classes were small, the number of students at no time exceeding thirty, for he was never a good lecturer, and it is said that on one occasion he asked the porter to bring in the skeleton so that he might preface his remarks with the word "Gentlemen". The lectures were given from 7 to 8 P.M. on alternate evenings during the winter months.

Ottley tells us that "he appeared to little advantage as a lecturer; his language was inelegant and often coarse, his delivery heavy and unengaging, as he rarely raised his eyes from his book". It was said that he used to calm himself with a dose of laudanum before his lecture. Nevertheless, he schooled himself to lecturing, as he felt that the practice was of benefit to himself as well as to his hearers. His insistence upon accurate observation is shown by a remark to a student who was taking notes, "You had better not write down that observation, for very likely I shall think differently next year". He had been in practice for ten years, had been made a Fellow of the Royal

Society, had been appointed Surgeon to St George's Hospital, and had married and succeeded to his brother William's house in Jermyn Street, before he began the first course of lectures on Surgery, which contained the fruit of much study and hard thinking and comprised "the whole circle of the sciences round Surgery". In the notice he stated that the course would include "so much of the Animal Œconomy as may be necessary to illustrate the Principles of those Diseases which are the object of Surgery". His pupils included Abernethy, Physick, Astley Cooper and Cline, and further details will presently be given of his long friendship with his most famous student, Edward Jenner.

Practice came slowly to Hunter, but he made good use of the time and was never unemployed. Indeed, he appeared to regard private practice as an unfortunate necessity, and in that respect resembled a more modern physician who remarked that "medicine would be intensely interesting if it were not for those damned patients". John Hunter's remark to a friend was, "Well, Lynn, I must go and earn the damned guinea, or I shall be sure to want it tomorrow". It was during these early days of practice that Hunter began those vast researches in comparative anatomy and physiology to which the rest of his life was to be devoted. He argued that in order to understand the nature of disease it was necessary first of all to study the structure and functions of healthy tissue, not in man alone, but in the whole animal series and even also in plants. "Instead of referring to the discoveries detailed in books, he appealed directly to Nature herself, and rested nothing upon the facts related by others until, by the evidence of his own senses, he had ascertained their truth."

As such a programme of research could scarcely be carried out in the centre of a city, John Hunter acquired a small piece of ground and a house at Earl's Court, which was then in the country, two miles from London. Here he kept all sorts of animals and birds and fishes. There was a pond for the fish and a den, or "dug-out", for the more dangerous animals, among which were two leopards, which created a lively diversion by attempting to escape on one occasion. Another inmate was a bull which the Queen had given him, and with which one day he had been wrestling, when he was thrown down and might have been seriously injured had not one of his servants come to his aid. Mention of bulls reminds one that it was said that Hunter used to drive down Piccadilly in a cart drawn by two buffaloes, showing that he was not without his eccentricities! He kept rabbits, pigs, goats, dormice, hedgehogs, opossums, a jackal, a zebra and other animals. Of birds, there were fowls, ducks and geese, and there were silkworms and hives of bees.

Around the house was a covered area about six feet below the level of the ground, which was excellent for keeping small animals in cages and for the rough work of anatomy. It must have been an unsavoury spot, for here were dissected, among many other creatures, the whales on which Hunter contributed a paper to *Philosophical Transactions of the Royal Society*. Like many other anatomists, Hunter was greatly interested in whales. He would have appreciated *Moby Dick*. He even engaged a surgeon, at considerable expense, to accompany a Greenland whaler in order to collect material, but his only return was "a bit of whale's skin, with some barnacles sticking to it".

The size of the anatomical "subject" intrigued him. "The heart of the spermaceti whale appears prodigious", he tells us, "the aorta measuring a foot in diameter. When we consider these facts applied to the circulation and figure to ourselves that 10 to 15 gallons of blood are thrown out at one stroke, the whole idea fills the mind with wonder." In his *Curiosities of Natural History*, Frank Buckland relates the following tale regarding Hunter's most famous technical assistant, William Clift:

Some years before I was born, a large whale was caught at the Nore, and towed up to London Bridge, the Lord Mayor having claimed it. When it had been at London Bridge some little time, the Government sent a notice to say the whale belonged to them. Upon which the Lord Mayor sent answer, 'Well, if the whale belongs to you, I order you to remove it immediately from London Bridge'. The whale was therefore towed downstream again to the Isle of Dogs, below Greenwich. The late Mr Clift, the energetic and talented assistant of his great master, John Hunter, went down to see it. He found it on the shore, with its huge mouth propped open with poles. In his eagerness to examine the internal parts of the

257

mouth, Mr Clift stepped inside the mouth, between the lower jaws, where the tongue is situated. This tongue is a huge spongy mass, and being at that time exceedingly soft, from exposure to air, gave way like a bog; at the same time he slipped forwards towards the whale's gullet, nearly as far as he could go. Poor Mr Clift was in a really dangerous predicament; he sank lower and lower into the substance of the tongue and gullet, till he nearly disappeared altogether. He was short in stature, and in a few seconds would, doubtless, have lost his life in the horrible oily mass, had not assistance been quickly afforded him. It was with great difficulty that a boat-hook was put in requisition, and the good little man hauled out of the whale's tongue.

That Hunter was also attracted by the infinitely small is proved by his experiment with bees, in which he discovered that wax was secreted by the insect and not collected, like the honey, as had been imagined. "The wax is formed by the bees themselves; I have found that it is formed between each scale on the under side of the belly". It is told of Hunter that on one occasion a pupil who wished to see him was told to call at the early hour of 4 A.M. and then found him dissecting beetles! "I want everything respecting the bee tribe", he wrote to a correspondent in Africa, "such as wasps and their nests, also hornets and theirs." His "Observations of Bees", read at the Royal Society a year before his death, was a masterly contribution revealing long and patient study. He used to say that his head was like a beehive, an expressive metaphor when one realizes the multiplicity of the problems he investigated.

In his house at Earl's Court there was a large copper tank, used for preparing skeletons, the most famous of which was that of Bryne, or O'Brien, the Irish giant. He was 8 feet 4 inches in height, and was wont to light his pipe from a street lamp. Bryne had learned that John Hunter coveted his bones, and he therefore left strict orders that on his death his body should be guarded day and night until, enclosed in a leaden coffin, it was buried at sea. On hearing of the death of Bryne, Hunter set forth to interview the men engaged to watch the body. He began by offering them £50 if they would allow the corpse to be kidnapped, but they said they must have a hundred. Hunter agreed, but when the men found him so eager they increased their demands and continued to do so until they raised the price to £500!

The feet of the skeleton thus acquired appear in the famous portrait of John Hunter by Sir Joshua Reynolds which now adorns the Royal College of Surgeons. Of this portrait is told the following tale: As might be expected, Hunter was a restless sitter, and Reynolds was almost in despair until one day Hunter, as he sat, became immersed in thought. The artist at once turned the canvas upside down and painted a new head between the legs of the figure he had already drawn. The engravings of the portrait, by William Sharp, were greatly in demand and have become relatively rare.

Another portrait of John Hunter, by his brother-in-law, Robert Home, is now in the possession of the Royal Society, and it shows him seated, his hand resting on the head of a large dog.

Ottley paints his portrait in words thus: "In person he was about the middle stature, of a vigorous and robust frame, and free from corpulency. His shoulders were high, and his neck short. His features were rather large and strongly marked; his eyebrows projecting, his eyes of light colour, his cheeks high and his mouth somwhat underhung. In dress he was plain and gentleman-like; and his hair which in youth was of a reddish-yellow, and in his later years white, he wore curled behind."

MARRIAGE AND FAMILY

In July 1771 John Hunter married Anne Home, the daughter of a former fellow-officer, Mr Robert Boyne Home, surgeon to Burgoyne's Regiment of Horse and afterwards of Greenlaw Castle, Berwickshire. John Hunter was forty-three, and Anne Home twenty-nine, and there is no doubt it was a happy union, although Anne loved gaiety while John must have been "gey ill to live wi'" at times. In order to defray the expenses of his marriage, John Hunter published his first work, *On Diseases of the Teeth*. Anne was a clever and handsome lady, fond of lively society, a taste which sometimes conflicted with her husband's studious life, as on the occasion when he returned home to find his house full of guests. "I knew nothing of the kick-up", he announced, ". . . but as I am now returned home to study I hope the present company will retire!"

Mrs Hunter was more than a mere consort of her distinguished husband. She published a volume of poems and wrote the

259

lyric, "My Mother bids me bind my hair", which, set to Haydn's music, has become immortal, and she also wrote the words for Haydn's "Creation".

The Hunters had four children. Two died in childhood. The elder survivor, John, entered the army, but did not marry; the younger, Agnes, was twice married but had no issue. Thus the family of John Hunter became extinct.

Mrs Hunter survived her husband for twenty-seven years and died at the age of seventy-nine.

FRIENDSHIP WITH JENNER

"I don't know anyone I would as soon write to as you. I do not know anybody I am so much obliged to." Those words were written by John Hunter to his friend and former pupil, Edward Jenner, who practised at Berkeley in Gloucestershire. Jenner had spent two years in the household of John Hunter as one of his resident pupils, and was one of the small coterie who revered John Hunter as the "dear man". It is fortunate that many of Hunter's letters to Jenner have been preserved. Jenner carried out all manner of experiments and investigations at Hunter's suggestion and also kept him supplied with material. Of this there is ample evidence in the letters. "I thank you for your experiment on the hedgehog", wrote Hunter on 2 August 1775, "but why do you ask me a question by the way of solving it? I think your solution is just; but why think? Why not try the experiment? Repeat all the experiments on a hedgehog as soon as you receive this . . . and let me know the result." The experiments upon the hedgehog to which he refers were a part of an investigation on the vital heat of animals and plants. It must be remembered that the clinical thermometer was not then in use and Hunter contructed his own thermometers. Hunter sought to prove the thesis "that living bodies possess a power of maintaining their heat against the influence of external cold, and this in degree proportioned to their rank in the scale of organization".

Not only did Jenner record the temperature of the hibernating hedgehog, but he sent hedgehogs to London, where they did not always survive.

Condoning Jenner in regard to a love affair, Hunter wrote: "Let her go, never mind her. I shall employ you with hedgehogs." Another letter gives one a glimpse of animal tragedies at Earl's Court: "If you could send me a colony of hedgehogs, I should be glad, as I have expended all I had except two; one an eagle ate, and a ferret caught the other. I am hedge-hogless." Apparently the hedgehog was Hunter's laboratory animal, his guinea-pig in fact, and it is interesting to note that quite recently the hedgehog has again been pressed into the service of the laboratory ("New Laboratory Animals from Wild Species." R. N. Ranson, *Journal of Hygiene,* vol. 41, No. 2, Sept. 1941).

Hedgehogs were by no means the only creatures referred to in this correspondence. Together, Hunter and Jenner studied the mating habits of the cuckoo (that peculiar bird, still a subject of controversy), the spawning of salmon, the life story of eels, the plumage of blackbird nestlings and their feather patterns, the temperature of growing trees, and many another problem.

Hunter at one time proposed that Jenner should return to London and collaborate with him in founding a school of comparative anatomy, but Jenner declined the invitation. There is something idyllic about this friendship of pupil and teacher, of city surgeon and country practitioner, and there can be no doubt that Jenner was inspired by Hunter, although his discovery of vaccination was not announced until after Hunter's death.

THE MUSEUM IN LEICESTER SQUARE

Throughout his life in London John Hunter was a keen collector. Nevertheless, he built up his great collection on a definite plan, designed to illustrate the whole range of comparative anatomy, physiology and pathology.

For many years he worked almost incessantly to accumulate and study the 13,600 specimens which the museum eventually contained at the time of his death. This represents, as Hey Groves has told us in his Oration of 1930, one specimen for each day of his life "How many", asks Hey Groves, "would continue this self-imposed slavery right up to the end, even when fame and fortune smiled upon them?" "Ah, John, you are always busy", said Dr Gartshore who had called and found him, as ever, at work. "Yes", was the reply, "and when I am dead you will not soon meet another John Hunter."

John Hunter did not set out to make a fortune. He gave his

services freely to the poor, and to those in reduced circumstances he was always kindly and considerate in the matter of fees. He spent lavishly, and it is said that his museum must have cost him altogether some £70,000. Although he became the leading surgeon of London, his income never exceeded £5,000 a year, and reached that figure only a few years before his death. The fact that he spent lavishly is shown by the price he paid (£500) for the skeleton of the Irish giant. All the money he could spare was devoted to the museum He was a persistent beggar for any curio which pleased him, as is shown by the story of a specimen of an extrauterine gestation which was the pride of a certain Dr Clarke. "Come, doctor", said John Hunter, "I positively must have that preparation." "No, you positively shall not", was the reply. "Well, then," said John, "take care I don't meet you with it in some dark lane at night, for if I do, I'll murder you to get it."

Bland Sutton said in his Hunterian Oration for 1923 that the museum contained "everything, big and little, that Hunter could obtain; shrimps and sharks, tits and ostriches, shrews and whales, and of human kind, dwarfs and giants. It was . . . an anatomical Valhalla".

It is not surprising that his house in Jermyn Street soon proved too small to accommodate all his specimens and, as his practice was also increasing, he removed, in 1785, to larger premises in Leicester Square, or Leicester Fields, as it was then called. This was not only his home but also his consulting and lecture-rooms and his museum. A stuffed specimen of a giraffe, or camelopard, to use the current name, stood in his hall, but, even so, the entire creative world could not be accommodated, and John Hunter amputated its legs so that it might be more easily inspected. Although he had a good income, the upkeep of this establishment was very heavy, and it is not surprising that Hunter died a comparatively poor man notwithstanding the fact, related in the biography by Adams, that such was the afflux of morning patients that they overflowed into the drawing-room. His door plate bore the plain legend "John Hunter".

Leicester Square and Earl's Court, between them, demanded a large staff, and it is recorded that the Hunter household, consisting of family, pupils, servants, gardeners and workmen, formed such a goodly assemblage that there were never fewer than fifty persons daily provided for at Mr Hunter's expense. A detailed list of them is given in Stephen Paget's biography of Hunter.

ILLNESS AND DEATH

The sadder aspect of Hunter's life now falls to be recorded. In 1773, when he was forty-six, there occurred the first attack of angina pectoris, which ultimately caused his death. Few ordinary men could have survived the hard work and long hours which he imposed upon himself, and he seldom took more than four hours' sleep in the twenty-four. He was wont to remark that his life was in the hands of any rascal who chose to annoy him, knowing, as he did, that any worry or excitement might precipitate a seizure. In addition, we must accept Sir D'Arcy Power's view that John Hunter suffered from cerebral syphilis as the direct result of a somewhat foolhardy experiment upon himself. This took place in 1767 when, seeking to ascertain whether gonorrhœa and syphilis were one and the same disease, he inoculated himself with pus from a patient, and this was followed by typical manifestations of syphilis which under mercurial treatment took three years to "cure". There is no reason to believe that he transmitted the disease to his wife or family, his marriage taking place five years after the infection, but the angina pectoris and the cerebral symptoms were almost certainly of syphilitic origin. His illness has been described in detail by his brother-in-law, Sir Everard Home, who acted as his assistant in the later years. The first of the cerebral attacks appeared in 1777, four years after the first anginal attack, when "he had no sooner lain down that he felt as if suspended in the air, and soon after the room appeared to go round. . . . and the quickness of motion became very rapid. . . . The idea he had of his own size was that of being only two feet long, and when he drew up his foot, or pushed it down, it appeared to be moving a vast way. . . . He could not bear the least light . . . his hearing was also painfully acute". At the end of ten days the symptoms gradually abated, the vertigo persisting for some weeks.

The attacks of angina continued, however, until in 1786 they occurred almost daily. Two years later cerebral trouble was again manifest, and he suddenly was stricken with complete loss of memory, which lasted for half an hour. A fortnight later, while making a round of professional visits, he was seized with sickness and vertigo. Again there were the peculiar symptoms now known as "Lilliputian hallucinations", for, according to Home, "objects were smaller than the natural recollection of them, his idea of his own size was that of being only four feet high; objects also appeared to be at an unusual distance as if seen through a concave glass". For a week he could not raise his head from the pillow; recovery was slow and some impairment of memory persisted until his death.

As was to be expected, the end came suddenly. On 16 October 1793 he was attending a meeting of Governors of St George's Hospital, and a question arose regarding the eligibility of two young Scottish students who wished to attend the hospital. Having had no previous medical training, they were debarred from attendance, according to the existing rule. John Hunter spoke in support of the candidates. During his speech he made a statement which one of his colleagues at once contradicted. Hunter, seeking to suppress his anger, ceased speaking, staggered into an adjoining room and fell dead. Thus died the great John Hunter, on the very day, curiously enough, that Marie Antoinette was beheaded in Paris.

He was buried in St Martin's-in-the-Fields and there his body remained until 1859, when it was reinterred in Westminster Abbey. This reburial took place at the instance of Frank Buckland, whose four little volumes of *Curiosities of Natural History* are still well worth perusal. Buckland, reading in *The Times* that the vaults of St Martin's Church were to be built up and closed, immediately obtained permission to search for Hunter's remains. For sixteen days he searched among the 3,260 coffins, hardly a task to be envied, for he tells us that "the sickly effluvia which emanated from these vaults were truly overpowering and poisonous". In No. 3 vault, where Hunter was believed to be buried, there were over 200 coffins. Amid the piles of coffins revealed by the light of his bull's-eye lantern were those of another John Hunter and of a Mrs John Hunter, both burials of more recent date. At last there were only five coffins to examine and one of them was that of John Hunter. This was re-interred on 25 March 1859 in Westminster Abbey by the Royal College of Surgeons, who erected a suitable memorial and conveyed to Mr Buckland their thanks for his valuable services in honouring so illustrious a man.

WILLIAM CLIFT AND SIR EVERARD HOME

John Hunter was careless in matters of money. At his death his estate yielded only £1,500. His widow was granted a civil list pension until the museum, in accordance with his wishes, was offered for sale to the Government. But times were hard, and Pitt, the Prime Minister, retorted "Buy preparations? We have hardly money to buy gunpowder". It was not until 1799 that the collection was purchased for £15,000 and placed in the custody of the Royal College of Surgeons. In the interval it remained at Leicester Square, guarded by the faithful William Clift who, out of respect for his master, remained as custodian for the beggarly salary of 7s. per week and occupied himself in transcribing the large mass of Hunter's unpublished manuscripts. It was fortunate that he did so, because when the museum was transferred to the Royal College of Surgeons, Sir Everard Home removed to his own house what was literally a cartload of manuscripts, in order, he said, that they might be better examined and cared for. There they remained until 1823, when Sir Everard Home burned them all, and nearly set fire to his house in the process. He alleged that John Hunter had instructed him to destroy the manuscript notes, but unfortunately there is strong reason to suppose that in the twenty-three years' interval he had made use of the material for his own advancement. Fortunately, Clift had laboriously copied out nine volumes of notes and some twenty other monographs, and these were subsequently published under the editorship of Sir Richard Owen.

William Clift (1775–1849), whose name has already been mentioned in Buckland's story of the decomposing whale, was a Cornish boy who, at the age of seventeen, had entered the service of the Hunter household only the year prior to John Hunter's death. He was the first Curator of the Hunterian Collection, and he was succeeded by his son-in-law, Sir Richard Owen (1804–1892), the eminent comparative anatomist and palæontologist.

JOHN HUNTER'S LEGACY TO MANKIND

It is not easy to explain the secret of Hunter's greatness nor to assess the results he achieved during his strenuous life in London. The fact that he published nothing until his forty-third year indicates the accuracy of his researches and his meticulous adherence to his rule of proving all things. His papers to the Royal Society were prepared with scrupulous care, although his style of writing is sometimes trying to the reader. He made no definite discovery, and yet, in a sense, he was the originator of many discoveries. The pioneer may not find the largest nugget, but at least he shows where gold may be found. Although he was a skilful surgeon, operating was distasteful to him. In his lectures he states that "to perform an operation is to mutilate a patient whom we cannot cure by other means, and it should therefore be considered as an acknowledgement of the imperfection of our art".

Nevertheless, his operation of ligature at a distance, of ligation of the femoral artery in "Hunter's canal" in the treatment of poplitael aneurysm was the means of saving many limbs. His experiments of grafting a spur or a human tooth into the comb of a cock were the precursors of the modern procedure of bone-grafting. By his investigations on the developing embryo in the eggs of geese he advanced the science of embryology. On many other subjects did he write—on bees, on whales, on the blood and inflammation, on post-mortem digestion of the stomach, on the gizzard or Gillaroo trout, on electric organs in fishes, on animal heat and on the olfactory nerves. He also wrote descriptions of the Kangaroo, the Potoroo (Kangaroo rat) and the Wha Tapoua Roo (Phalanger), specimens of each having been sent to him from New South Wales. Some of the papers were collected and reprinted under the title *Animal Economy* in 1786, while his *Lectures on Surgery* were published under the editorship of Mr James F. Palmer, Surgeon to St George's Hospital, in 1835.

The construction of the Museum* was an achievement which would have brought fame to any man. But neither the writings nor the museum represent the end-result of John Hunter's labours. This fact has been stressed by many Hunterian Orators. Sir James Paget, in 1877, said that although he was unequalled as a comparative anatomist, he did more by the questions he set than by the answers he worked out. Indeed, the true value of Hunter's discoveries is to be found in the number of the discoveries to which they have given birth. The Orator of 1899, Sir William MacCormac, remarked that "the surgery of the

* Almost completely destroyed by enemy action in May 1941.

Middle Ages was a trade. Ambroise Paré and Jean Louis Petit converted it into an art; John Hunter elevated it to the rank of a science. Lister crowned the edifice whose corner-stone John Hunter laid".

In our own time (1932) perhaps the most brilliant of all Hunterian Orators, Mr Wilfred Trotter, pointed out that Hunter achieved greatness not as surgeon or as discoverer but by his example in the use of the scientific method, and wrote of him: "He saw, as from a peak in Darien, the illimitable ocean of biology before him and he addressed himself unhesitatingly to explore it all."

Never content to remain a "hewer of wood" or "drawer of water", John Hunter, by his originality of thought, raised Surgery from the level of a technical accomplishment to that of a defined science, securely based upon physiology and pathology. Indeed, he may be regarded as the founder of surgical pathology. He improved the status of the surgeon, and he reunited Medicine and Surgery, which had been progressing along diverging lines.

It is a good thing to remember such men. It would be a matter of great regret if the student could pass through his five or six years of training without knowing at least a few leading facts regarding the lives and times of some of the great leaders of medicine in the past. To make no provision for a study of the History of Medicine is surely a short-sighted policy. It is true that the student is already overburdened with masses of detail, but an occasional lecture on the rise and progress of medical science would not only add interest to the routine subjects, but might serve also as a stimulus and as a refreshment. That is why I have ventured to submit to this great and honoured Society some account of the life and work of John Hunter.

BIOGRAPHIES OF JOHN HUNTER

Life of John Hunter, Sir Everard Home, 1794.
The Life of John Hunter, Jesse Foot, 1794.
Life and Doctrines of the late John Hunter, Joseph Adams, 1817.
Life of John Hunter, Drewry Ottley, 1835.

Memoir of John Hunter, Sir William Jardine, 1843. (Vol. X of Naturalists' Library.)

Two Great Scotsmen, William and John Hunter, George Mather, 1893.

John Hunter, Stephen Paget, 1897. (Masters of Medicine Series.)

Memoirs of William and John Hunter, George A. Peachey, 1924.

DR WILLIAM HEBERDEN*

THE TALL AND SPARE, YET STATELY FIGURE of Dr William
Heberden must have been a familiar sight to many Londoners
of the eighteenth century. That period was rich in great
physicians, and in London the leading practitioners were
at first Radcliffe and Mead, to be followed by Fothergill,
Lettsom, Baillie, and Heberden. Heberden was second to none,
and although he held no hospital appointment and made no
discovery, his contribution to medical progress was considerable.
Samuel Johnson, who was his patient, called him the last of the
great physicians, *ultimus Romanorum*, although he might be
regarded more correctly as the first of the modern physicians,
so fresh and unbaised was his outlook.

At that time London was the centre of practice, just as Edinburgh was the centre of teaching. Heberden was still a student
at Cambridge when in 1726 Alexander Monro returned from
Leyden to found the Edinburgh Medical School. Born in 1710,
William Heberden died in 1801, and thus his long life-span
almost coincided with the eighteenth century. Our knowledge
of his domestic life is scanty. He was born at Southwark, the
son of Richard Heberden, and was educated at the grammar
school of St Saviour, and from 1724 at Cambridge, where he
became a fellow of St John's College in 1731. For ten years
after graduating M.D. in 1739 he practised in Cambridge, and
taught *materia medica*;† then he removed to London, where for
many years he conducted a large and fashionable practice,
living first at Cecil Street, Strand, and later at 79 Pall Mall,
with a country residence at Datchet, near Windsor. He was
twice married, and had seven sons and three daughters from
whom a succession of physicians and clergymen is descended,
but the only member of his family to survive him was a son of

---

* Read before the Heberden Society in Edinburgh on 10 May 1951.
† The cabinet of *materia medica* used by Heberden in teaching that subject is
still preserved in the Library of St John's College, Cambridge.

269

the second marriage, usually known as William Heberden the Younger.

Our patron retired at the comparatively early age of seventy-two, and such, in brief, is his biography, so far as it is known. That he was a classical scholar of distinction is evident from the fact that he edited some of the plays of Euripides. He had many friends in the field of literature, some of whom were his patients. Dr Johnson we have already mentioned; George Crabbe described him as "tender, ardent, and kind", and the poet Cowper wrote of him:

> *Virtuous and faithful Heberden, whose skill*
> *Attempts no task it cannot well fulfil.*

Among his friends was a certain Dr Conyers Middleton, who had composed an unorthodox work entitled "The Inefficiency of Prayer" which was left unpublished at his death. When the widow consulted Heberden regarding its publication he found a publisher who offered £150 for the manuscript; thereupon Heberden sent a cheque for £200 to the widow and consigned the work to the fire, since he considered that, if published, it would be injurious to the memory of the writer. The action was characteristic of the man, and he deserves to be remembered not only for his learning, but for those qualities of modesty, sympathy, and kindness which he possessed in full measure.

Heberden's earliest published work was a tract written in 1745, while he was still teaching at Cambridge, entitled "Antitheriaca; An Essay on Mithradatium and Theriaca", pointing out the uselessness of those remedies. The poison antidote used by Mithradates, king of Pontus (who died in 63 B.C.), consisted of twenty leaves of rue, one grain of salt, and two dried figs. Celsus (A.D. 30) mentions thirty-eight ingredients. Nero's physician, Andromachus, added viper's flesh to the remedy and called it Theriac. The Theriac of the Pharmacopoeia of the Royal College of Physicians of London, dated 1724, contains sixty-two ingredients, but in spite of Dr. Heberden's exposure it remained an official remedy until 1788. In 1725, shortly after his removal to London, Heberden was admitted a Fellow of the Royal Society, and contributed four papers to the *Philosophical Transactions*: "On the Effects of Lightning", "On Rain-gauges", "On Salt found in Teneriffe", and "An Account of a very large Calculus".

For the *Medical Transactions* of the Royal College of Physicians he wrote other papers, of which "Observations Upon the Ascarides", "Of Night-Blindness or Nyctalopia", "Of the Diseases of the Liver", "Remarks on the Pulse", and "Account of the Noxious Effects of Some Fungi" are only a few.

Throughout his many years of practice, William Heberden was in the habit of making notes "relating to the nature and cure of disease", and of transcribing and arranging them at the end of every month. In this manner he collected a vast mass of material, written in Latin and English, and from it compiled, in 1782, his "Commentaries on the History and Cure of Diseases", which he entrusted to the care of his son, to be published after his death. The book appeared in 1802, and remains to this day one of the most useful and readable of medical classics. In it are described the *Digitorum Nodi* which we call "Heberden's Nodes", little hard knobs, frequently seen upon the finger, and continuing for life. Even more worthy of mention is Heberden's classic description of "Pectoris Dolor": "A disorder of the breast marked with strong and peculiar symptoms, considerable for the kind of danger belonging to it, and not extremely rare. The seat of it, the sense of strangling, and the anxiety with which it is attended, may make it not unproperly be called *angina pectoris*."

The disease had already been described in 1632 by the Earl of Clarendon, who spoke then of the death of his father: "the pain in his arm seizing upon him, he fell down dead, without the least motion of any limb."

Naturally, we wish to know what Heberden had to say of Rheumatism, which he defines as "a common name for many aches and pains, which have yet no peculiar appellation, though owing to very different causes". He describes two varieties, "acute and chronical", telling us that "both kinds attack indiscriminately males and females, rich and poor".

Heberden's description of "chicken pox" was opportune, at a time when it was often confused with smallpox. Edward Jenner's discovery of vaccination in 1796 had not yet met with general adoption. At that time, too, malaria was still prevalent in England. Heberden shows that the quartan fever is more serious than the tertian, and more resistant to treatment by Peruvian bark. Another topical description deals with "malignant sore throat" which occurred in epidemic form and was described in 1748 by Fothergill. Heberden regarded it as a form of scarlet fever, remarking that "both are names for the same disorder, and both are epidemical at the same time". One of the longest and most interesting chapters deals with jaundice, and the shortest dismisses hernia in a single sentence: Ruptures require no other remedy than a truss.

But no extracts from the Commentaries can be adequate; the clinical pictures, clear and concise, must be studied and pondered. It is not surprising that the book had an enormous popularity although good copies are now rare.

The portrait of Heberden here reproduced is an engraving from the original in oils which hangs in the Royal College of Physicians. Sir William Beechey, R.A., a famous artist of the day, went down to Windsor in 1796 to paint it, but he forgot his canvas, and it is said that he painted it on one of his subject's shirts! (Plate 10).

Heberden's son, William Heberden the Younger (1767–1845), was also a distinguished physician, although his fame, as so often happens, was overshadowed by his father's achievement. He lived to the age of 78, but retired early from practice and devoted his attention to theology and to the education of his nine children. Nevertheless, he attained eminence sufficient to warrant his appointment as Physician to St George's Hospital in 1793, and to King George III in 1809. The King's illness dragged on for years, with Matthew Baillie and Heberden in attendance, and Francis Willis as mental consultant, a collaboration recorded by a contemporary in this doggerel:

> *The King employs three doctors daily—*
> *Willis, Heberden and Baillie;*
> *All extremely clever men—*
> *Baillie, Willis, Heberden,*
> *But doubtful which most sure to kill is—*
> *Baillie, Heberden or Willis.*

He published "Observations on the Increase and Decrease of different Diseases" (1801), and "Morborum puerilium epitome" (1804), Eng. trans., (1805), both interesting and useful works.

REFERENCES

BULLER, A. C., (1879). *Life and Works of Heberden*, Bradbury, Agnew and Co., London.

PETTIGREW, T. J. (1839). *Biographical Memoirs*, vol. 3, no. 7. Whittaker, London.

LAËNNEC AND HIS
STETHOSCOPE*

SOME TIME AGO, when I rashly undertook to contribute to this Society a paper dealing with the history of tuberculosis, I greatly under-estimated the magnitude and the difficulty of such a task.

Given the necessary time and perseverance, a fair knowledge of general medicine and an interest in past events, the writing of a History of Medicine presents no insuperable difficulty. The history of a special branch of medicine, however, demands a historian who is also a specialist. Of tuberculosis, quite a series of histories might be written, each varying in its aspect of the subject. The history of the disease, the views of pathologists and of clinicians, the rise and development of sanatorium treatment, the evolution of laws and regulations concerning tuberculosis could each fill a volume, so that it is not easy to select. Speaking personally, however, my ignorance has considerably narrowed the field from which selection is possible, and I can indicate only a few of the principal signposts which may perhaps guide those of you who feel drawn more deeply into the study of the past.

The main object of this paper is to direct attention to some classic works on tuberculosis which are still well worth reading, although generally regarded as "out of date". The latest view on any subject may be, or ought to be, the most enlightened view, but it is not necessarily the most correct view. Osler spoke truly when he said, "it is a dry age when the great men of the past are held in light esteem". Old work need not be obsolete work.

So far as I am aware, only two detailed histories of tuberculosis have appeared in recent years, both of American origin.

* Read at a meeting of the Tuberculosis Society of Scotland held in Edinburgh on 10 May 1946.

They are *The Development of our Knowledge of Tuberculosis*, by Laurence Flick, 1925, and *The Story of Clinical Pulmonary Tuberculosis*, by Lawrason Brown, 1941. To those books I am largely indebted for the information which, not without some diffidence, I am about to place before you.

In the writing of history there is one inflexible rule; one must preserve a definite time-sense or chronology, so that each fact may be recorded in its particular sequence.

One of the best methods of presenting the subject is to pick out one striking or sensational event—in general history, a conquest, an empire, a dynasty; in medical history, a discovery, a great teacher, a school—and around this event to group all other minor or accessory events. In surgery, the dominant figure is Lister, and every history of surgery is an account of events before and after Lister.

What was the most definite landmark in the history of tuberculosis? Was it the discovery of the bacillus by Koch in 1882? Or was it the early attempt of Bodington, in 1840, to establish sanatorium treatment?

LAËNNEC AND HIS ACHIEVEMENT

I wonder if you will agree with me when I suggest that a more significant event than any was the publication by Laënnec, in 1819, of his classic work on Auscultation—*Traité de l'Auscultation Médiate*. Laënnec accomplished much during his short life. Today, he is remembered as the inventor of the stethoscope, but that was only the first step in his great achievement, the tool which enabled him to explore a new field. His book is no mere description of the stethoscope; it describes what the stethoscope can do. It is one of the great medical classics.

René Théophile Hyacinthe Laënnec was born in 1781, at Quimper in Brittany, the son of a local lawyer. He had the misfortune to lose his mother when he was six years old, and as his father was a fickle and purposeless man, young Théophile, as he was called, was consigned, with his brother Michael, to the care of his uncle William, a physician at Nantes. Seven years later, when his father married again, Michael returned to Quimper, but Théophile remained, as he was determined to become a doctor like his uncle. Indeed, Laënnec owed little to his father, and everything to his uncle. He studied in the Medical School of Nantes, and then in Paris. His health was feeble, he was often very poor, but he was fortunate in his teachers and fellow students. His chief friend was Gaspard Bayle, his senior by seven years, who exercised upon him that beneficial influence which so often passes from a senior student to a junior. Bayle himself is an important landmark in the history of tuberculosis. Before he died of tuberculosis at the age of forty-two, he had performed nine hundred post-mortem examinations in cases of that disease, many of which he had also investigated clinically. Almost certainly Bayle was a martyr to science. He corrected many errors; he showed that early and advanced pulmonary tuberculosis was one disease and not a whole series of diseases, and he was the first to use the term "miliary" in describing small tuberculous lesions.

Let us return, however, to the student life of Laënnec. Another senior associate was Guillaume Dupuytren, who later won great fame as a surgeon; a cynical and intolerant man, it is not surprising that Laënnec and he did not always agree. Laënnec studied medicine at the Charité under Corvisart, of whom more will be said. Bichât was the brilliant teacher of morbid anatomy and when Bichât died of tuberculosis in 1802, at the age of thirty-one, Laënnec began to lecture on the subject and it was then that he discovered the sub-deltoid bursa, and proved that hydatid cysts were caused by a parasite. At this early stage of his career he busied himself in the study of Greek, the better to understand Hippocrates, and his thesis for which he received his diploma in 1804 dealt with "The Hippocratic Doctrine in relation to the Practice of Medicine". During the next few years Laënnec worked strenuously, writing papers on many subjects, conducting a rapidly increasing practice, and studying and teaching at the Necker Hospital to which he was appointed Physician. All his work was based upon observation and experiment. Like Sydenham, he held that the practice of medicine should consist in observation rather than speculation.

It was in September 1816 that he made his great discovery. While examining a stout young woman it suddenly occurred to him that just as the scratch of a pin at one end of a log of wood is audible to the ear placed against the other end, even so might the sounds within the thorax be conducted to the ear of the observer. Rolling a note book into a tight roll he applied one end to the patient's chest and put his ear to the other, when he was "surprised and gratified" at being able to hear the heart sounds with great clearness and distinction. For a time he continued to use rolls of paper. Then he constructed a wooden cylinder which answered very well and was known as the "cylinder", the "baton", the "pectoriloquer" and, eventually, the "stethoscope". Yet Laënnec was no mere inventor of an instrument, though that was a clever piece of work. His real service was to show what might be accomplished by the aid of this tool, and to this task he devoted the remaining years of his short life. All those strange, unfamiliar sounds within the chest —whistlings, murmurs, wheezings, bleatings and crackling— were all to be analysed and arranged, and this was Laënnec's great accomplishment. It is little short of miraculous that this wasted, hollow-cheeked little man, already in the grip of the disease he was so closely studying, should have been able, within a few years, to produce a book in which are described and classified all the sounds heard by the stethoscope. The first edition is dated 1819. It is a pleasure to read, and is universally regarded as a medical classic. But it almost killed the author. He was obliged to leave Paris, and naturally he returned to his beloved Brittany, where he had a house, Kerlouarnec (the place of foxes), facing the Bay of Douarnenez. There, his health improved and two years later, in 1821, he returned to Paris and literally threw himself into his work. He knew that it might kill him, but what was the loss of one life, he argued, if others could be helped. So he lectured and practised and laboured hard at the second edition of his book. He was now Physician at the Charité, Professor at the College of France and with a wide reputation as physician and teacher. He often lectured in Latin, for the benefit of foreign students who knew that language better than French, and he preferred the term "rhonchus" to "râle", which meant death-rattle and might be so interpreted by patients. He married Madame Argon in 1824, but he was to enjoy only two years of happy married life. In May 1826 he was again obliged to retire to Brittany, and on the afternoon of 13 August of that year he removed the rings from his fingers, explaining to his wife that he preferred that no one should have the trouble of doing this for him. Two hours later he died. The second edition of his book had been published just as he left Paris for the last time. It was translated into English by Sir John Forbes, a man of culture and a good linguist, who graduated at Edinburgh in 1807 and, after serving in the Navy for some years, conducted a large practice at Chichester and eventually became physician to Queen Victoria. There were four editions of his translation of Laënnec's book, the last in 1834. A still better translation, though abridged, was published, with a *Life of Laënnec*, by Sir William Hale-White in 1923.

Mention has been made of Laënnec's teacher Corvisart, who was then at the height of his fame, soon to become a Baron, and physician to Napoleon. Jean Nicholas Corvisart was a great teacher, though rather dictatorial in his methods. It was characteristic of him that his M.D. thesis was entitled "The pleasures of the study of medicine and the disagreeableness of its practice". He was a keen student of physiognomy and a master in the art of diagnosis at a distance, now, perhaps fortunately, a lost art. Nevertheless he was most thorough in his examination of patients. "These", he told his students, "these are your books and you will find them more difficult to read than printed books." Corvisart was an authority on diseases of the heart, but his chief claim to fame lies in the fact that he drew attention to the neglected discovery of Auenbrugger, which must ever be linked closely with that of Laënnec. Leopold Auenbrugger (Laënnec calls him Avenbrugger), was born in 1722, the son of an innkeeper of Graz, and it is said that his idea of percussion was derived from the practice of ascertaining, by tapping, the level of the fluid in his father's wine casks. He studied under Van Sweiten in Vienna, became a popular court physician, and wrote an opera entitled "The Chimney Sweep". His only contribution to medical literature was a little book of ninety-five pages, now extremely rare, which bore the long title, *A new invention for the Diagnosis of obscure internal diseases of the chest by percussion of the Thorax.* Written in Latin, it is usually named from the first two words of the title, "Inventum Novum". In this classic of medicine, Auenbrugger compares the normal percussion note to that of a drum covered with woollen cloth. He suggests that percussion should be carried out "with a linen glove on the hand to avoid the disturbing sound of striking the bare skin". He confirmed his facts by injecting water into the chests of cadavers, and he made use of his method for seven years before publishing his book in 1761. Nevertheless it attracted little notice until Corvisart translated it into French twenty years later. The English version appeared in 1824, when it was included by Forbes in his translation of Laënnec's work. Laënnec had a high regard for Auenbrugger and he believed that percussion and auscultation had each an important part to play in diagnosis. Corvisart used the open hand in percussion, a sort of slapping rather than tapping. The plessimeter, or pleximeter, a little plate of metal or ivory placed on the chest, was a later refinement introduced by Piorry of Paris in 1826. William Stokes of Dublin, who did so much to popularize the new methods in his book on *The Diagnosis and Treatment of Diseases of the Chest*, 1837, and who was one of the first to recognize the importance of early diagnosis, percussed against his finger placed with its dorsal surface on the chest.

Another physician who popularized the methods and views of Laënnec in this country was his pupil who afterwards became Sir James Clark (not to be confused with Sir Andrew Clark), and to whom the second edition of Forbes's translation of Laënnec's book was dedicated. In his own treatise, published in 1835, Clark drew attention to the importance of early diagnosis, and he sounded a warning against the practice of sending tuberculous patients away on long sea voyages.

Josef Skoda, who was the first to lecture in German (instead of Latin) in the Vienna School, added much to physical diagnosis by assigning to each of the sounds its musical pitch. Thus were the great contributions of Laënnec and Auenbrugger gradually accepted and employed.

It is not my intention to attempt to give a complete account of the history of tuberculosis, but the central position of Laënnec will become more obvious if we glance at the state of affairs before and after his time.

BEFORE LAËNNEC

It appears probable that tuberculosis existed in prehistoric times and although of course there is no written evidence, we may read it in the pathological appearance of Egyptian mummies, 1000 B.C., and in the votive offerings of Greek temples of Aesculapius of about the same date. One of the earliest written records, as we should expect, appears in the work of the Hippocratic School. There are a number of references in the Aphorisms to phthisis, although other wasting diseases may have been included under this category. "Phthisis was most common between the ages of 18 and 35; it was worse during autumn; diarrhœa was a mortal symptom." "In persons who cough up frothy blood, the discharge of it comes from the lungs." "Such persons as become humpbacked from asthma or cough before puberty soon die."

For the first clear description of pulmonary tuberculosis one must pass to the works of Aretaeus, who lived at Alexandria in the second century A.D. He distinguished between phthisis and empyema, thus :"If an ulcer form in the lungs from abscess, from cough, or from haemoptysis, the disease is phthisis. If matter form in the chest or side it is called empyema." Aretaeus goes on to describe phthisis: "All parts are slender and without flesh, no vestige of mammæ, joints prominent, eyes hollow and brilliant." "The persons most prone to the disease are the slender, those with prominent throats and whose scapulæ protrude like wings, who are pale and have narrow chests." Aretaeus classified disease as acute cases (including hæmoptysis) and chronic (including phthisis). The relationship between them was as yet unknown, and even Laënnec focused his study upon the later stages of the disease. Aretaeus, however, was one of the first to recognize the benefit of living on or close to the sea, and he laid stress on the value of milk as a food. "If the patient live on the sea," he wrote, "it will be beneficial, as sea water is dessicant to the ulcers." It was not until 1796 that John Coakley Lettsom, the well-known Quaker physician, founded the Royal Sea Bathing Hospital at Margate for tuberculous children. After Aretaeus little advance was made in tuberculosis until the seventeenth century. Brief mention may be made of the use of the Royal touch for "King's Evil" swellings, tuberculosis of bones and joints and lymph nodes. The Royal touch had a long history, reaching its zenith in England in the reign of Charles II, who "touched" 4,000 persons a year and attained a grand total of over 90,000. Richard Wiseman, the Father of English Surgery, condoned the practice, though he added that a surgeon might cure when the King was not available.

It was about this time that the study of morbid anatomy began and that an effort was made to correlate the clinical with the postmortem findings. The great work of Morgagni of Padua on the subject did not appear until 1761. Entitled

On the Seats and Causes of Diseases, it described 700 cases. Morgagni located disease in the organs; Bichât in the tissues; Virchow, in the cells. Nevertheless, long before Morgagni's day, the method of investigation had been adopted.

Franciscus Sylvius (1614–72), one of the first to teach clinically in the Medical School of Leyden, suggested that there were lymph nodes in the lung which might be attacked by scrofula, in the same manner as other lymph nodes. Not every disease with emaciation was to be called phthisis. Sylvius suggested that "tabes" should signify emaciation; phthisis, an ulcer of the lung. But the next important contribution to the pathology of tuberculosis at this time was made by Richard Morton, whose *Phthisiologia* appeared in 1689. Morton, like Sylvius, thought that the lungs were "full of innumerable little glands." "No wonder", he writes, "that those who have King's Evil also have tubercles in their lungs." Morton described sixteen varieties of pulmonary tuberculosis and recognized the tubercle, which he distinguished from ulceration and regarded as the primary lesion. Among the causes of tuberculosis, besides "imprudent diet, over-study, thick smokey air, and troublesome passions", he mentioned "excessive salivation and spitting, which withdraws the nutritious juices from the body". One of his astute observations was that it was "surprising that anyone past his youth could die without a touch of consumption". That he recognized natural cure is evident from his remark that "sometimes the tubercles go off of their own accord". This is remarkable when we remember that tuberculosis was regarded as incurable in his day. He hastens to add that "every consumption, though cured, is apt to return". Another observation was that "Chalky stones, bred in the lungs, are wont to tear the tender parts and cause bleeding". He also alleged that "he who coughs lives long" and he explained this by stating that such persons usually take good care of themselves. Poor Morton, like his father before him and his son after him, died of tuberculosis. Morton's detailed account of tuberculosis was a remarkable achievement, but it was too detailed. In all fields of knowledge, advance is not just a steady progress. A subject becomes more and more detailed and complicated and specialized, until it reaches a bewildering complexity. Then some genius arrives on the scene and simplifies it all at a single stroke.

So it happened that in the following century there lived yet another medical victim of the disease, William Stark of Birmingham who, during his short life of twenty-nine years, showed that the numerous varieties described by Morton were simply various stages of the same disease. His demonstration of the unity of tuberculosis was a great advance. Meanwhile, the infectious nature of the malady was an accepted fact. Francastorius, one of the great medical figures of the Renaissance, not only gave its name to syphilis, but wrote the first book on epidemiology, *De Contagione*, 1546, in which he stated that many diseases, including phthisis, were caused by "minute seeds, or seminaria, which multiply rapidly", and which spread infection by contact or even at a distance, through the air. Of course no one had seen them, but the idea took root, and we find Sydenham, one of the greatest of all physicians, writing that "certain diseases are caused by particles in the atmosphere".

There was no lack of material for those early investigators. John Locke, the philosopher and physician, the friend of Sydenham, wrote an essay on Tussis (Cough) in 1685 in which he said that 20 per cent of all deaths in London were due to phthisis. Locke referred to the benefit accruing from horseback exercise, but he failed to recognize that the improvement was due to the open air rather than the exercise. Many more names might be mentioned, but perhaps enough has been said to illustrate the state of knowledge before the times of Laënnec. Laënnec did not arrive on the scene unheralded. That genius of the seventeenth century, Robert Hooke, a pioneer of microscopy and a founder of the Royal Society, wrote "who knows but that it may be possible to discover the works going on in man's body by the sounds they make, as in a watch."

AFTER LAËNNEC

Although Laënnec added greatly to the methods of diagnosis, the death rate remained high. No cure had been discovered. The first to recognize the importance of early diagnosis was another physician of Paris, Pierre C. A. Louis, whose results were based upon the careful statistical analysis of 2,000 cases. Indeed, his second great service was to show that exact figures are more valuable than vague impressions, and it is interesting to note that this statistical method is again becoming important in medicine. Louis's work, published in 1839, drew attention to the early signs of pulmonary tuberculosis, and to the fact that the apex of the lung was usually involved. Louis was a popular teacher and a good clinician. He always began by asking two questions. First, "How long have you been ill?" and then, "Before that, were you perfectly well?" and, having thus fixed the time of onset, his examination proceeded. Many American students attended his clinic, including Oliver Wendell Holmes, who learned three things from him: "not to accept authority when he could have facts, not to guess when he could know, and not to think that a man must take physic because he is sick".

Meanwhile another Morton, George Morton, in America, who had been a pupil of Laënnec, had written his *Illustrations of Pulmonary Consumption* (1834) and had noted the signs of incipient tuberculosis. Another excellent description of early tuberculosis was written in 1846 by Henry Bowditch of Boston, a pupil of Louis. He called it *The Young Stethoscopist or the Student's Guide of Auscultation*. Lawrason Brown considered it the best account of early pulmonary tuberculosis that has ever been written. A later American authority, who has been called "The American Laënnec", was Austin Flint of New York, well known for his work on cardiac disease and on tuberculosis. He analysed 670 cases of tuberculosis in a book (1875) which is still in use.

I shall not attempt in this paper to deal with the work of Jean Antoine Villemin, the French army surgeon who, in 1865 (the year of Lister's discovery), proved that tuberculosis could be produced in rabbits by inoculation. Nor shall I do more than mention the immense services of Robert Koch, and the medical revolution which followed his discovery of the tubercle bacillus in 1882.

In the short time now at my disposal I should like to refer to the early days of open-air treatment, as the facts are perhaps less familiar, though doubtless well known to the present audience. Recognition of the disease in its early stages naturally led investigators to search for a cure. No longer was tuberculosis to be regarded as a hopeless and incurable disease. And as so often happens in the history of medicine, the first step was taken by an obscure general practitioner. Born in the last year of the eighteenth century, George Bodington was in practice at Erdington, near Birmingham, when he wrote his famous *Essay on the Treatment and Cure of Pulmonary Consumption*, 1840.

He condemned the prevailing practice of "shutting patients up in a close room and forcing them to breathe over and over again the same foul air". "To live in and breathe freely the open air was the one essential remedy." The cooler the air was the better. Therefore he advised early rising so that the "cool pure morning air might have its sedative effect upon the interior surface of the lungs". He also advised abundant food (nourishing diet and wines) but he did not recognize the value of rest, and he perpetuated the tradition of exercise on horseback and of long walks. Nor did he realize the need for sleeping in the open air. His attention was more closely drawn to the problem when he observed that few of the awl grinders of Sheffield lived beyond the age of thirty. The town hospital, in his opinion, was the "most unfit place imaginable" for cases of tuberculosis. There should be special hospitals in country surroundings, with "provision for horse and carriage exercise" and "gardening and farming for convalescents". After treatment the patient should not return to town but should continue out-door work. "There ought to be a class of practitioners who would pursue this practise as a special branch and receive patients into their own houses in the country."

Bodington gives details of six cases, treated with good results. In 1843, he transferred to Sutton Coldfield, near Lichfield, and continued his plan of treatment. Nevertheless he met with scant encouragement and was obliged to turn his establishment into a mental hospital.

Another pioneer, who apparently was unaware of Bodington's work, was Henry MacCormac of Belfast, who graduated M.D. at Edinburgh in 1824. Bodington became discouraged and gave up his fight for fresh air, but MacCormac preached his gospel for years, in season and out of season and refused to accept defeat. He lived at a time when night air was considered a deadly poison and the atmosphere of every sickroom was foul and stuffy. On more than one occasion he poked his umbrella through the window pane of his patient's bedroom, and once he was obliged to defend such a practice in the police court. "If I had a Stentor's voice and an angel's pen", he wrote, "I should employ them to enlarge my views". "There can be no immunity from phthisis until medical practice and popular conviction concur as to the indispensableness of pure fresh untainted air, at all hours, at all times and in all places." When his paper on "The Preventibility of Consumption" at the Royal Medical and Chirurgical Society of London in 1861 was read in his absence by the Secretary, it was received so adversely that the meeting declined to pass a vote of thanks. Nevertheless his treatise on *Consumption* was published in 1855, and his enlightened views were welcomed on the Continent where Hermann Brehmer held similar views amid the jeers of his colleagues and eventually opened the first sanitorium at Goerbersdorf in Silesia in 1859. One of Brehmer's patients, Peter Dettweiler, built his own sanatorium at Falkenstein in 1876 and he was probably the first to recognize the value of rest and the possible danger of exercise. It is not known whether either of those German physicians was aware of the similar views of Bodington and MacCormac.

In America, the pioneer of open air treatment was Edward Livingstone Trudeau, whose sanatorium for persons of moderate means began its work at Saranac Lake in 1884.

Trudeau, himself a tuberculous patient, laid stress upon the pre-tuberculous stage of the disease. He drew attention to the method of bringing out latent râles by a cough at the end of expiration.

Here the story must end. I have left much unsaid: the progress of organization and control and prevention; the introduction of artificial pneumothorax; the development of X-ray diagnosis; and various other aspects of the great problem. It is fitting that at this point I should remind you of the greatest of Scottish phthisiologists, perhaps the greatest of all, Sir Robert Philip, whose teaching was an inspiration to some of us and whose gracious personality was so helpful to many a student and patient. His dispensary for tuberculosis was opened in Bank Street, Edinburgh, in 1887.

One could not hope, in a short paper, to tell the whole story of pulmonary tuberculosis. But in this mechanical age, with its attempts to produce a rule-of-thumb medicine based upon technical principles, it is salutary to remember the past and to honour the pioneers. Although I am no longer a clinician and although perhaps I have no right to express an opinion, I make bold to say that it will be a sad day when the stethoscope becomes an obsolete instrument, and when the classics of Morton and of Laënnec are no longer read. Especially Laënnec, for he is the central figure of the story, the Lister of tuberculosis, the most doughty knight who ever bore a lance against "the captain of the men of death".

REFERENCES

ADAMS, FRANCIS (1856), Trans. by, *The Extant Works of Aretaeus the Cappadocian.*

AUENBRUGGER, L. (1761), *Inventum Novum ex percussione thoracis humani* (Vindobonae). (French translation of above by Corvisart, 1808; English translation by Sir John Forbes, 1824.)

BAYLE, GASPARD L. (1810), *Recherches sur la phthisie pulmonaire.* (Paris.)

BODINGTON, G. (1840), *Essay on the Treatment and Cure of Pulmonary Consumption.*

BOWDITCH, H. (1846), *The Young Stethoscopist, or the Student's Guide of Auscultation.*

BROWN, LAWRASON (1941), *The Story of Clinical Pulmonary Tuberculosis.*

FLICK, LAWRENCE F. (1925), *The Development of our Knowledge of Tuberculosis* (Philadelphia).

FRACASTORO, G. (1546), *De Contagione et Contagiosis Morbis et Curatione* (Venetiis).

LAËNNEC, R. T. H. (1819), *Traité de l'Auscultation Médiate*, 2 vols. (Paris). (Translation of above by Sir John Forbes, 4th Edition, 1834. Translation of above, with *Life of Laënnec* by Sir William Hale-White, 1923.)

LOUIS, P. C. A. (1925), *Recherches Anatomico-Pathologiques sur la phthisie* (Paris).

MACCORMAC, H. (1855), *On the Nature, Treatment and Prevention of Pulmonary Consumption.*

MORGAGNI, G. B. (1761), *De Sedibus et Causis Morborum*, 2 vols. (Venetiis).

MORTON, RICHARD (1689), *Phthisiologia* (English translation, 1694).

MORTON, SAMUEL GEORGE (1834), *Illustrations of Pulmonary Consumption* (Philadelphia).

STOKES, WM. (1837), *Treatise on the Diagnosis and Treatment of Diseases of the Chest* (Dublin).

VILLEMIN, JEAN ANTOINE (1868), *Études sur la tuberculose* (Paris.)

SHERLOCK HOLMES AND MEDICINE*

EVERYONE KNOWS, or at least has heard of, Sherlock Holmes, the most real character in fiction. So real has he become that many people believe that he actually existed, and was not merely fictitious.

Societies have been founded in many countries to pay tribute to his memory. His sayings and doings have been studied from every angle, and the original stories regarding his life and work have formed a pattern for subsequent "thrillers". Every visitor to London who has read the tales is eager to see Baker Street, and letters addressed to "Mr Sherlock Holmes, Baker Street, London" still baffle the authorities at the General Post Office.

Sherlock Holmes has a special appeal to members of the medical profession. The doctor, reviewing the signs and symptoms which guide him to a diagnosis of his patient's malady, has much in common with the detective who studies the clues which guide him to a solution of the crime he investigates. Besides this, the author, Conan Doyle, was a medical man, as also was Joseph Bell, the model from which Doyle drew the character of Sherlock Holmes, and more than twenty medical men make their appearance in the pages of the famous stories, though most of them allow us only a brief acquaintance with their doings.

THE AUTHOR AND HIS MODELS

Dr (later Sir) Arthur Conan Doyle was born at Edinburgh in 1859 and graduated in medicine at that University in 1881.

He was conducting a small general practice at Southsea when he wrote his first book *A Study in Scarlet*, in which he

---

* An Address to the Vancouver Medical Association, sponsored jointly with the Department of the History of Medicine and Science, The University of British Columbia, 17 June 1961.

introduced Dr John H. Watson to Sherlock Holmes, and those two famous characters to the reading public. The idea of making a detective the hero of a tale had already been exploited by Edgar Allan Poe (*The Murders in the Rue Morgue*, 1841), and by Wilkie Collins (*The Moonstone*, 1868), but Conan Doyle went a step farther by developing the new technique of portraying, in each of a long series of stories, the same two characters, one, Mr Sherlock Holmes, the Prince of Detectives, the other Dr Watson, who acts as the Boswell and records the various adventures,

This famous partnership was continued throughout the sixty stories, four of them long, and fifty-six short, which appeared as books, or as items in the *Strand Magazine*, during a period of forty years.

The demand for the first of the "Adventures", in the *Strand Magazine* of May 1891, was enormous and widespread. Holmes and Watson were already popular figures, having made their reputation in *A Study in Scarlet* (1887) and *The Sign of Four* (1890).

The Adventures of Sherlock Holmes consisted of twelve episodes, and was reprinted in book form in 1892; *The Memoirs*, with eleven episodes, in 1894. Each episode or tale was complete in itself.

The last Memoir was the tragic story of how Holmes met his death as he grappled with the criminal Professor Moriarty, and both were precipitated over the cliff at the Reichenbach Falls in Switzerland. The author, Conan Doyle, had killed his hero, and great was the consternation, and even anger, on the part of many readers. "You brute, how could you?" wrote a lady enthusiast.

Perhaps the reason was that Doyle was becoming a little tired of being regarded as only a writer of detective stories. He wished to become acclaimed because of his historical novels. He had written several, and was eager to continue. But the public insisted that he should remain a writer of detective fiction.

It has ever been so. Dr Doyle gave up practice when he turned his attention to literature, and many another medical man has had this experience. If a doctor wishes to write some work not exclusively medical, he had best do it under an assumed name. Thus Doyle found it worth while to change his profession, but even then, the public would not admit that he could shine in two different fields, in historical novels as well as detective tales.

Accordingly he was obliged to restore Holmes to life, or rather, to explain how he had had a miraculous escape from death, in order to satisfy the insistent demand of his readers for further exploits. So *The Hound of the Baskervilles* was published in 1902, and the series of shorter tales was resumed in the *Strand Magazine*, and eventually reprinted in three more books entitled *The Return of Sherlock Holmes* (1905), *His Last Bow* (1917), and *The Case-Book of Sherlock Holmes* (1927)—in all, thirty-three further tales.

It is generally acknowledged that the later tales are not so good as the earlier series. Holmes had recovered after his disastrous encounter with Moriarty, but he was never quite the same man.

In the meantime, Conan Doyle had continued his other literary work, had contested a seat in Parliament, and had espoused the cause of spiritualism and lectured extensively in its defence. His knighthood had been awarded in 1902 for his services in the South African War. He died in 1930 at the age of seventy-one. Such, in brief, is the story of the author and his work.

It is necessary to add a few words regarding the models or originals of Holmes and Watson. Watson is supposed to be the recorder, and some have concluded that Doyle based this character upon himself.

He acknowledged, however, that his description of Sherlock Holmes and his work was inspired by one of his teachers when he was a medical student at Edinburgh.

THE INFLUENCE OF JOSEPH BELL

Dr Joseph Bell was the teacher who inspired in the mind of his pupil the idea of the greatest detective in fiction. In May 1892, when the enthusiasm for Sherlock Holmes was at its height, Conan Doyle wrote to his old teacher: "It is most certainly to you that I owe Sherlock Holmes, although, in the stories, I have the advantage of being able to place him in all sorts of dramatic situations."

Then followed a correspondence in which Dr Bell suggested that a "bacteriological criminal" might be a good idea, but Conan Doyle replied that "the only fear is lest you get beyond

289

the average man, who won't be interested unless he thoroughly understands".

Nevertheless Doyle continues, "I should be very grateful for any 'spotting of trade' tips, or anything else of a 'Sherlock Holmesian' nature."

Dr Joseph Bell came of a long dynasty of surgeons. His great-grandfather, Benjamin Bell (1749–1806), was the first in Edinburgh to restrict his practice to surgery. Benjamin Bell became surgeon to the Royal Infirmary at the age of twenty-four, and wrote *A System of Surgery*, in six volumes, which has a wide circulation and was translated into French and German.

Joseph Bell, "Joe Bell" to his students, was born in 1837, and became assistant to Professor James Syme, Lister's teacher and father-in-law. Joseph Bell, like his great ancestor, became surgeon to the Royal Infirmary, and later, he was the first surgeon to the Royal Hospital for Sick Children, 1887–97, and President of the Royal College of Surgeons of Edinburgh (Plate 11).

He excelled as a teacher, and taught the students much else besides surgery, as he was wont to diagnose not only the disease or injury, but also the occupation and personal characteristics of each patient. Seated in his chair, his finger-tips pressed together, he would study closely the gait, expression and mentality of each patient, and would surprise both patients and students by the accuracy of his deductions. It might have been Holmes addressing Watson, when Bell taught his students the importance of the observation of trifles.

The comparison, however, ends there. Holmes had some habits which were quite foreign to Joe Bell—his incredible untidiness, addiction to tobacco and even cocaine, music at strange hours and indoor revolver practice, all belonged to Baker Street and were unknown at Melville Crescent, Edinburgh. The writer, as a junior medical student about 1905, remembers seeing Bell driving in his carriage and pair, a tall, stately man with aquiline features and alert expression: much beloved by colleagues and patients, and revered by students.

A study of hands and finger nails revealed to Bell the nature of a man's craft; the colour of the mud on his boots indicated a certain district of the city; wood shavings or metal filings in folds of clothing, dialect or manner of speech, each had its tale to tell.

So much for the real live author, and the real persons who may have been his original models. Before discussing some other relationships between detectives and doctors, let us glance at the background against which the dramatic tales are portrayed,

THE VICTORIAN SCENE

One of the attractions of the Sherlock Holmes stories is the author's vivid description of the London of Queen Victoria. In the centre of the stage are the rooms tenanted by Holmes and Watson at Number 221B Baker Street, an address which has hitherto defied all efforts to identify the house.

I have explored the district like many another admirer of Sherlock Holmes. Much of the street was destroyed by enemy action in 1941, and has been rebuilt, but I agree with those who allege that the number was really Number 111, about the centre of Baker Street. This house is directly opposite Number 118, from which Holmes's enemy fired with a rifle at his shadow when visible on the window blind, though it actually was a wax model of his head, as those who have read the story will remember.

Be that as it may, the opening scene of each tale grips the reader's attention. One can almost see V.R. picked out on the mantelpiece by revolver shots, the unanswered letters transfixed by a jack-knife, the tobacco in a Persian slipper. Outside (let Watson now continue), "the wind howled down Baker Street, and the rain beat fiercely against the windows. It was strange here in the very depth of the town, to feel the iron grip of Nature. To the elemental forces, London was no more than the molehills that dot the fields." On another day, "A thick fog rolled down between the lines of dun-coloured houses, and the opposing windows loomed like shapeless blurs through the heavy yellow wreaths. Our gas was lit, and shone on the white cloth, and on the glimmer of china and metal, for our table had not yet been cleared."

Again, this time in summer, "It was a blazing hot day in August, Baker Street was like an oven, and the glare of the sunlight on the yellow brick-work was painful to the eye."

In some of the opening scenes there is a casual allusion to an unrecorded case. But soon the problem appears on the scene, as a letter or a telegram (there were no telephones then), or the arrival of a distracted client, or, it might be, a clue such as the hat in "The Blue Carbuncle", or Dr Mortimer's cane in *The Hound of the Baskervilles*.

Then the two friends set forth in a cab or a hansom, or travel by rail to the seat of the trouble, which was seldom a murder, and not always even a crime, but just a problem.

In the first twelve adventures, there are only three murders.

The scene of the exploits is not always London; indeed the action is confined to London in only nineteen of the sixty stories. Often, the reader is taken to the Home Counties; Surrey is the favourite ground. On two occasions the scene is laid in Norfolk; on two others, in Dartmoor. We may even find ourselves in Aldershot or Birmingham, or may discover Holmes and Watson on holiday in distant Cornwall when confronted by a problem. Yorkshire was the most northerly of Holmes's journeyings. Twice he was called to the Continent, but we are sorry that he never visited Scotland, where Dorothy Sayers found such a good background for adventure, as also did John Buchan.

Holmes did not visit Edinburgh, the early home of Conan Doyle, as well as that of Dr Joseph Bell, the Holmes original.

In ten of the twenty-three tales in the *Adventures* and *Memoirs*, the action begins in the rooms occupied by Holmes and Watson in Baker Street, but after Dr Watson settles in practice in the Paddington district, and marries, five of the tales open with Watson calling on his friend Holmes, while in two of them, "The Blue Carbuncle" and "The Red-headed League", the story begins with the words "I had called . . ."

A more dramatic beginning was the occasion when Watson, in visiting an opium den in London to rescue one of his patients who was an addict, finds Holmes there, disguised as an opium smoker, and in search of a missing man, the "Man with the Twisted Lip", as the tale is entitled.

"The Adventure of the Reigate Squires" begins when Watson is summoned to find Holmes lying ill at Lyons, and brings him home to recuperate in the house of Colonel Hayter at Reigate.

On three occasions, it is Holmes who calls on Watson to invite his co-operation. There are also two tales regarding earlier cases, related to Watson by Holmes as they sat together by the fire one winter's night. Although Watson is the narrator of all the early stories, two of the later ones, "The Blanched Soldier" and "The Lion's Mane", appear as though written by Holmes himself.

Of course Holmes was well qualified to write. He had already published a treatise on The Ashes of Various Tobaccos, enumerating no less than 140 varieties of cigar, cigarette and pipe tobacco, with coloured plates to illustrate the different appearances of the ashes. We also know that after his retirement to Sussex, he wrote a book entitled "A Practical Handbook of Bee Culture", which he called "the fruit of my leisured ease" (*His Last Bow*).

Throughout the entire series of tales, the atmosphere of Victorian times is well preserved, and this seems to add to the interest. In every tale, we are conscious of the trappings of the time—the gas lamps, the clanging door-bells, the sound of horses' hooves, and four-wheeler cabs, the dark lanterns and the golden sovereigns. Holmes knew nothing of microscopy or of modern psychiatry, or even of finger-prints. X-rays were not discovered until 1896. His outfit was simple, a magnifying glass and tape-measure, a hunting crop and a revolver.

Among his addictions was tobacco. He was an inveterate pipe smoker, and he alleged that a concentrated atmosphere aided a concentration of thought—a statement with which few would agree today. We may let that pass, and leave him to his "three-pipe problem", but we really must protest when the author tells us that Holmes was addicted both to morphia and cocaine.

"What is it today?" asks Watson in "The Sign of Four"—"cocaine or morphine?" (Three times a day for many months he had witnessed the performance.) "It is cocaine," he replies; "would you care to try it?"

We might allow him the morphine, remembering that De Quincey, Coleridge, and others, were opium addicts.

At cocaine, however, we draw the line. We have the authority of A. R. Cushny for the statement that: "The cocaine habit leads more rapidly to mental and physical deterioration than the morphine habit." Conan Doyle once said that "You must not make your detective too human", so perhaps we should not grudge Holmes his cocaine.

It is a relief to find Watson writing in the tale of "The Missing Three-Quarter": "For years I had gradually weaned him from that drug mania which threatened once to wreck his remarkable career."

DETECTION AND DIAGNOSIS

There is a close kinship between the work of the detective and that of the medical practitioner. The former looks for clues which will point the way to the criminal; the latter, for signs and symptoms which enable him to make a diagnosis, or, more important still, to give a prognosis, or forecast of future events.

The importance of clear logical reasoning in medical work is not always fully recognized. Another Holmes, one of real life, Oliver Wendell Holmes, observed that "medical logic does not appear to be taught in our schools". The great physician of the eighteenth century, Thomas Sydenham, replied to Sir Richard Blackmore, who asked him to name a good text book of medicine: "Read *Don Quixote*, a very good book." I can remember our Edinburgh Professor of Surgery, Professor Chiene, saying, when a student put to him a similar question: "Try the Sermon on the Mount; there is nothing better."

For my own part, I would counsel students to study Sherlock Holmes and his methods. Good detective tales supply a lesson in logic. The doctor is a kind of detective, and he does well to follow the principles laid down by Sherlock Holmes. Even from the simple-minded Watson he may learn; Watson the humble narrator who must remain in the background in order to emphasize the more erudite Sherlock Holmes.

Watson was often surprised by Holmes, and often deceived. When in "The Dying Detective", Holmes pretends to suffer from a rare tropical disease, disguising himself with beeswax and Vaseline, Watson is completely baffled, and Holmes remarks to him, "You are a practitioner of limited experience. What do you know of Trapanuli Fever, or of the Black Formosa Corruption?" The real fact was, of course, that neither ever existed.

Holmes was a master of disguise. Three years after his presumably fatal encounter with Moriarty, when he appeared before Watson as an old bookseller in a London street, and made himself known, Watson "fainted for the first and only time in his life".

You may remember other disguises used by Sherlock Holmes: a venerable Italian priest, an unshaven French ouvrier, a drunken groom, a nonconformist clergyman.

Clever as were his physical changes of person, his alert

brain and his simple logical reasoning are even more admirable.

His scathing indictments of poor Watson were many. "Elementary, my dear Watson" has now passed into common use. "I can see nothing," said Watson on one occasion. "On the contrary, Watson," retorted Holmes, "you see everything. You fail, however, to reason from what you see."

The subtle difference between seeing and observing was a favourite theme of Sherlock Holmes.

"However did you see that?" said the Police Inspector, as Holmes pointed to a hole in the window sash. "Because I looked for it," was the reply. This leads us to mention the importance of little things, upon which Sherlock Holmes repeatedly insisted: "You know my method; it is founded upon the observance of trifles" ("The Boscombe Valley Mystery"). "The little things are infinitely the most important," Holmes remarked in "A Case of Identity", and in the same tale, he advised Watson: "Never trust to general impressions, but concentrate upon details." Another of his maxims, revealed in "The Reigate Squires", was that he made a point of: "never having any prejudices, and of following docilely wherever fact may lead me."

All these counsels and pithy sayings may be applied with equal significance in the practice of medicine, although spoken by the greatest detective of fiction.

Of course they are not all original. Lister was fond of telling his students that, "success depends upon attention to detail", and Sir William Gull, a leading London physician a little more than 100 years ago, insisted that nothing which concerned the well-being of the patient was too minute for the doctor's attention.

SHERLOCK HOLMES AND THE DOCTORS

It is perhaps unfortunate that the twenty or more medical men associated in some way with Sherlock Holmes flit so rapidly across the stage and are lost to view.

There was old Dr Farquhar, from whom Watson bought a practice, Dr Verner, to whom he sold it, and Jackson and Anstruther, who acted for Watson when Holmes called him away from his medical work.

We have been given only brief glimpses of Sir Leslie Oakshott, the surgeon who attended Holmes when he was assaulted and nearly killed, and Dr Moore Agar, who advised him to take the complete rest he so much needed.

Two fleeting figures are Dr Barnicott, collector of Napoleonic relics, and another collector, Dr Hill Barton, who appears as a complete fiction on a visiting card handed to Watson by Holmes, so as to give him an "alias".

Other medical men in the *Adventures* and *Memoirs* are Dr Percy Trevelyan and Dr James Mortimer who came to Holmes as clients.

On one occasion the murdered man was a doctor, Dr Ray Ernest, and in two of the stories the criminals were doctors, Dr Grimesby Roylott, in "The Speckled Band", one of the best of the short tales, and Dr Leon Sterndale, who in "The Devil's Foot" used a West African root to get rid of his victim.

Two other doctors appear, but not doctors of medicine, Dr Huxtable of "The Priory School", who was a PH.D., and Rev. Dr Shlessinger, a D.D. who, but for Holmes and Watson, would have poisoned Lady Frances Carfax. Sir James Saunders, "the austere figure of a great dermatologist", Dr Ainstree, "a world authority on tropical disease", Dr Wood, the village practitioner at Birlstone, Dr Ferrier of Woking, Dr Richards and Dr Horsom, are other fleeting figures in the stories.

Holmes is always in the centre of the picture, and perhaps that is why Watson did not appear to advantage, and the other doctors made such temporary appearances.

RECONSTRUCTIONS AND RESEARCHES

Seldom in the history of literature has so much liberty been taken with the original text as with the Sherlock Holmes tales. Time and again, the chronology has been investigated, so that each story has been dated and re-dated. It is a fascinating game, or cult. From the facts as stated, the lives of Dr Watson and of Mr Sherlock Holmes, and even those of Mycroft Holmes his brother and of Mrs Hudson his landlady, have been reconstructed and written.

As for Holmes, where did he go during the years of disappearance, from 1891 until 1894?

What was his relation to Mrs Hudson, if any? Or to one of the few women he admired, Irene Adler? Irene Adler, then aged 101, wrote to *The Scotsman* at the time of the Conan Doyle Centenary in 1959, telling us that "dear Sherlock" died in her arms at the age of 100, after his long years of retirement, and pre-occupation with beekeeping on the Sussex Downs.

It has been alleged that Holmes and Moriarty were the same person. As for the number of unpublished stories, which have come to the light of print in recent years, they are legion.

Numerous editions of the stories have been printed, and remain in steady demand. Naturally, they are now obviously "dated". But few of the imitators have ever produced any detective stories quite so good. "Sherlock Holmes" may still be confidently recommended to all readers, and especially to medical readers. There is as yet no sign of any lessening in his popularity.

DYNASTIES OF DOCTORS*

THE STUDY OF GENEALOGY has an attraction for many people. Long ago, the strong-minded Paul exhorted Timothy not to "give heed to fables and endless genealogies, which minister questions rather than godly edifying". (I Tim. 1, 4.) Nevertheless, both fables and genealogies are worthy of study. Who has not, at some time or other, followed the ramifications of his own family tree, perhaps with the assistance of an octogenarian aunt or grandparent? The results of this search have a strange fascination. To have Jacobite ancestry or a forebear who was killed at Waterloo may be just as satisfying, on this side of the Atlantic, as it is to be a direct descendant of a Mayflower pilgrim, on the other side.

Some are led to investigate genealogies, not merely out of curiosity, but for practical reasons. It may be that the possession of wealth or position, of the succession to a title or an estate, or both, will depend entirely upon an examination of ancestral records. Applied genealogy, as we may call it, is not mere amusement or intellectual exercise, although there are many who do actually revel in the tracing of ancestors, and even of ancestors other than their own. Biography, always a popular branch of literature, has more devotees today than ever, and almost every biography, even that of an unimportant person (and there are many), begins with a chapter entitled "Ancestry and Parentage", frequently the best chapter in the book.

The study of biography provides strong proof in favour of the widespread belief that intellectual ability is an asset derived from ancestors, and in no branch of learning is heredity of more significance than in medicine.

But before mentioning the medical families which form the subject of the present study, it is essential to make a few general observations and to define certain terms.

* An Address delivered to the Scottish Genealogy Society.

HEREDITARY GENIUS

Since the appearance in 1869 of Sir Francis Galton's famous work, *Hereditary Genius*, interest in the subject has grown, but little has been added to his interesting investigations. Galton, the founder of what he then termed Eugenics, now known as Genetics, knew his subject well. He was himself a cousin of Charles Darwin and thus, a member of a family which enriched many aspects of science. He tells us in the preface that he ought to have called the book, "Hereditary Ability", because the word genius implies, or ought to imply, an ability quite unusually high, and of a very rare order. Certainly not more than one person in a million is a genius. Nowadays the term is applied loosely. We speak of so and so being "almost a genius" or "having a genius" for this or that. The true genius is the man for whom a whole nation mourns when he dies, and who ranks in the future as a character in history. A genius is born, not made, and he will come to the top, whatever his education, his circumstance or his social position.

Eminence, on the other hand, is a quality much less rare. An "eminent" person, according to Galton, is one who has achieved a position attained by 250 per million or by one person in 4,000. It would be difficult to define more explicitly what is meant by genius and eminence. In the assessment of mental ability, one should as a rule exclude those whose claim to fame rests upon notoriety, upon local reputations, or upon ability to acquire wealth. Statesmen and rulers are so largely subject to their environment that they form a class by themselves. Their eminence is no criterion of their natural gifts. Often they have been pushed into their high position and if to this fortuitous opportunity there is added unusual mental ability they may rise to a fame of the highest order.

It is a profound error to suppose that any child, born with an average or mediocre brain, can be educated to become eminent. "If it is not in you, it will not come out", is the old Scottish proverb, and it has proved true, time and again. All who are concerned in education do well to bear in mind that heredity contributes more than environment to a successful result. Ancestry counts, and the parent may be more important than the teacher.

History abounds with examples of hereditary ability, in

literature the Brontes, in Art the Teniers, in Divinity the Erskines and the Wesleys, in Music the Bachs. The last-mentioned family had eight generations of gifted musicians, and 120 of them attended a family reunion in 1750.

In the field of medicine, one may also note the influence of heredity upon intellectual ability. In early times medical knowledge was passed on from father to son. The Hippocratic Oath suggests to the student of medicine that he should regard his teacher as equal to his parents, and that he should pass on the learning to his own sons and to the sons of his teacher. Frequently the teacher was also the father, and throughout the long history of medicine, the "Art", as Hippocrates called it, has been a hereditary accomplishment. Doctors' sons do not always become doctors, but many of them do, and we need not search very far to find examples of two or more generations of doctors, like the Heberdens, the Bells, and the Pagets and scores of other similar families.

Paracelsus (1470–1541), whose importance as an original thinker had so profound an influence on the progress of medicine, was the son of a physician.

Vesalius (1514–64), who revolutionized anatomy, had a father, grandfather and great-grandfather who were all physicians. Some famous doctors have derived benefit from relatives other than their parents. For example, Ambroise Paré (1510–90), the great French surgeon, had a brother, and a brother-in-law, who were both barber-surgeons, as he tells us in his delightful autobiography. Again, Laënnec (1781–1826), who invented the stethoscope, drew all his early inspiration from his uncle, a physician at Nantes, before he went to Paris to earn fame by his discovery of auscultation. The great William Harvey (1578–1657), the only one of the seven sons of Thomas Harvey to become a doctor, had no head for finance, and might have been a poor man but for his faithful brother Eliab who managed the business affairs of the family. And, nearer our own time, Joseph Lister (1827–1912) derived his interest in the microscope from his father, a prosperous London wine merchant who was awarded the Fellowship of the Royal Society for his improvements in microscopic technique.

One need not explore the past for further instances of the influences of parents and relatives upon the embryo doctor.

Each of us can give examples of the heredity of medical practice within our own circles of friends.

A London physician of my acquaintance comes of a family with an unbroken line of doctors in each generation since early in the eighteenth century, and with seven doctors in the present (his own) generation. And, although a medical practice is no longer a saleable asset and a valuable bequest from father to son, it cannot be denied that there is still a tendency for the sons and daughters of doctors to follow the medical profession.

At this stage it may be profitable to recall the familiar story of the Gregory family, so often quoted as an illustration of hereditary ability.

THE ACADEMIC GREGORYS

This unusually gifted Aberdeen family produced sixteen professors in various universities within five generations. There is reason to believe that the "brains" were brought into the family in the sixteenth century when Janet Anderson married Rev. John Gregory of Drumoak. Janet was the daughter of David Anderson, who was known in Aberdeen as "Davie do a'thing". Among other accomplishments, Davie designed the spire of St Nicholas Church, and he removed a dangerous submerged rock from Aberdeen Harbour by harnessing it to a raft of barrels and allowing the tide to do the rest. Janet's son James might be fitly termed a genius. He became professor of Mathematics at St Andrews, in 1669, and then in Edinburgh, in 1674. He invented the reflecting telescope, and has been regarded as a forerunner of Newton. James Gregory's brother David, whose family numbered twenty-three children, had three sons and two grandsons who became professors of Mathematics, Astronomy and History at St Andrews, Oxford and Edinburgh. James Gregory had a son, also James, who was professor of Medicine from 1725–32 at Aberdeen, where Medicine was taught earlier than at any other university in Britain, a "mediciner" having been included among the original staff when the University was founded in 1494. His son, still another James, succeeded him in this post, which on his death in 1755 passed to his younger brother John. John Gregory had a brilliant career, at first in Aberdeen, and later when he was elected to succeed Robert Whytt as professor of Medicine in Edinburgh in 1766. John Gregory did much to raise the standard of medical conduct and to state those principles of medical ethics which still obtain in practice. He was succeeded in the Chair by the famous William Cullen. After the death of Cullen, John's son, James Gregory, was appointed, the fifth of his family to occupy a professorial chair in Edinburgh. A teacher of great ability, he was, until recently, remembered mainly on account of the nauseous powder which bears his name.

His son William became professor of Chemistry, while his nephew, William Pulteney Alison, held three medical chairs at Edinburgh, in succession.

Thus was the Gregory dynasty carried on until the middle of the nineteenth century. The story of the Gregorys is often cited as an illustration of the hereditary transmission of intellectual ability.

In order to approach the problem more closely and to note the effect of education and environment, and their relative importance, let us now glance at two other medical families, the Hunters and the Monros, and in particular John Hunter and Alexander Monro primus.

THE STRANGE STORY OF JOHN HUNTER

Although John Hunter made no great discovery, he changed the entire outlook in surgery, raising it from the status of a craft to that of a science. After his time, surgeons ceased to be mere artisans. Viewing "the whole circle of the sciences round Surgery" John Hunter set out to explore that field. His marvellous museum of comparative anatomy was a monument to his achievement until it was destroyed by a bomb at the Royal College of Surgeons in 1941. Yet his early life showed no promise of this great work. Born in 1728 at the farm of Long Calderwood near Glasgow, he appears to have been quite a dunce at school. When he was ten years old, his father died and he remained the spoiled child of his mother. At the age of seventeen he could neither read nor write, and so it seemed as though he must gain a living by the work of his hands rather than his brain. His sister Janet had married a cabinetmaker named Buchanan, and to him John was apprenticed for a time.

But in 1748, when he was twenty, he reached a turning point in this unpromising career. His brother William, ten years his senior, after a short partnership in medical practice at Hamilton with Dr William Cullen, had gone to London where he was already making a name for himself by teaching anatomy and practising obstetrics, a strange combination, but not an un-common one in the eighteenth century. William invited John to join him in London, and it soon became obvious that the young and stupid boy was in reality the more brilliant of the two brothers. He excelled in the study of the book of Nature, although he had no taste for scholarship. What he did possess, in full measure, was the gift of curiosity, so strongly developed in many children but so sadly lacking in adult life. There could be no better illustration of the value of observation than the lifework of John Hunter. What a vast gulf lay between him and his brother William, that scholarly, well-educated and polished figure, contrasting so strangely with John, the uncouth and downright man, so full of ideas that he used to say that his head was "like a beehive"!

It is not surprising that the Hunter brothers quarrelled, and never repaired the breach. William was probably greatly surprised when John rose to fame, and if he felt a little jealous, who can blame him? William did not attend John's wedding and John was not present at William's funeral. William was unmarried, John married the talented Anne Home who wrote songs, including "My mother bids me bind my hair". Of their four children, two died in childhood. The elder survivor, John, did not marry; the younger, Agnes, was twice married but had no family. Thus the direct line ended with the sudden death of John Hunter in 1793. His body rests in Westminster Abbey. Nevertheless, ability did appear again in the next generation. Dorothea, the sister of William and John, married Rev. James Baillie, and her son Matthew Baillie became a London physic-ian of great distinction, while her daughter Joanna was a poetess whose work was praised by Sir Walter Scott.

Such is the strange story of the rise to fame of the "ne'er do weel" boy who became one of the greatest surgeons in history, undoubtedly a case of hereditary genius, a child who was bound to become famous and who was one of those rare people who are best left alone to educate themselves. School can do little for such boys beyond teaching them how to tolerate others and how to be useful citizens. Teachers may even dislike pupils who question their statements and who propound all manner of awkward problems. John Hunter was perhaps quite right to refuse to be moulded to pattern, preferring to plough his lone furrow.

Besides family heredity, there is such a thing as the heredity of knowledge, from teacher to pupil. Many a teacher today can proudly point to his former scholars who have risen to occupy positions of eminence.

Herman Boerhaave, perhaps the greatest medical teacher of all time, when he was professor at Leyden in the early years of the eighteenth century, had among his pupils Monro who founded the Faculty of Medicine in Edinburgh, Haller, who inaugurated medical education at Gottingen, and Van Swieten, who reconstructed the Medical School of Vienna. Other famous teachers have been the academic parents of students or assistants who attained distinction. The great Viennese surgeon Billroth had no less than forty-two disciples who became eminent surgeons; and today Sir Robert Muir of Glasgow is the scholastic parent of more than twenty professors of pathology in various universities. This aspect of genealogy would appear to deserve further study.

When we turn from those reflections upon medical education and upon the life of John Hunter to the career of Alexander Monro, the founder of the Edinburgh Medical School, we find an entirely different tale of the climb to fame!

THE DYNASTY OF THE MONROS

The story of the three Alexander Monros, named primus, secundus and tertius, who in succession held the Chair of Anatomy at Edinburgh University for 126 years, shows that inborn talent is not the only ingredient in the recipe for success. In each case the career had been deliberately planned by the father, notably so for Alexander Monro primus, whose father, the Army Surgeon John Monro, had studied at Leyden, and had resolved that Edinburgh should have a Medical School conducted on similar lines. With a foresight quite unusual, he visualized his son Alexander, then at the tender age of three years, as the instrument of his great ambition, and he planned the boy's education with the idea that he should become Professor of Anatomy and Founder of the first Faculty of Medicine in Edinburgh University (Plate 12).

The plan proved to be a complete success. But was it so strange? The Monro family could trace its ancestry back to the twelfth century, the Munros of Foulis, in Ross-shire. They had money and they had brains. There is something to be said for vocational training from earliest childhood such as was planned for the infant Monro primus. Perhaps this is better than the random search for a career which so many boys have to face when schooldays are over. John Hunter would never have submitted to a planned education, but he was reared in a very different nest from that of Alexander Monro. The attempt to control the destiny of any individual is an extremely uncertain experiment, and in general, the Hunter method of self expression may be better than the Monro method of applied discipline. Perhaps heredity is more important than environment. Who can tell? Loyalty to an age-long family tradition spurred the Monros to fame. A child's destiny may be guided by parents and teachers, and also by brothers and sisters and by fellow students or workers. John Hunter owed much to his brother William, Alexander Monro owed almost everything to his father, John Monro. The value, to a medical student, of having a brother, or even a friend, one or two years ahead in his studies is incalculable. The older man has faced the difficulties and can advise his junior colleague better than anyone. The younger student may be stimulated by hero worship and it is well that he should have a pattern of life worthy to be followed. Monro had such an example in his father.

Alexander Monro primus, born in 1697, received all the instruction that Edinburgh could give, and supplemented it by two more years of medical training at London, Paris and Leyden. Leyden was at the height of its fame as a centre of medical education, and young Monro was fortunate in being a favourite pupil of Boerhaave, for whom he would often act as interpreter when patients from Scotland or England came to consult him. One-third of the students at that time were English-speaking and many were from Scotland. On his return to Edinburgh, Alexander Monro was appointed professor of Anatomy and Surgery, and in 1726, along with four other medical professors—Rutherford, St Clair, Plummer and Innes—he established the Faculty of Medicine in Edinburgh University. Those five founded a Faculty which now (1958) numbers thirty-five members. Alexander Monro primus, together with Lord Provost Drummond, and his father John Monro, his constant guide and adviser, founded, in 1741, the Royal Infirmary of Edinburgh in Drummond Street. The interesting experiment of educating his son from early years with a definite object in view,

305

conducted so successfully by John Monro, was repeated by Alexander Monro primus, whose son Alexander Monro secundus succeeded him in the chair.

It is not always an advantage to be the son of a distinguished father but that statement did not apply to the second of the Alexander Monros.

The achievement of Monro secundus was even greater than that of the first Monro, at least from the scientific point of view. Monro primus, a talented teacher and an able adminis- trator, made no definite discovery, but Monro secundus, who, like his father, had studied at Leyden, first described the fora- men of Monro in the brain, the lymphatic channels of the body, and various other structures, besides conducting a large private practice. When Monro secundus retired to his house at Craig- lockhart in 1808 he was, like his predecessor, succeeded by his son Alexander Monro tertius, specially trained for the task. But on this occasion the idea proved less successful, and the third Monro did not uphold the tradition of his father and grandfather, although he held the Chair for nearly forty years. It is said that he simply read his grandfather's lectures a cen- tury old, and even remarked, "When I was a student at Leyden in 1719", but that story is probably apocryphal. He has often been cited as an example of failure of ability in the third genera- tion. But there were reasons for the collapse of a career which showed promise at the start.

The first two Monros had little competition to face, but in the time of the third Monro there were other brilliant ana- tomists engaged in teaching—John Barclay for example, who was succeded in 1824 by the dramatic Robert Knox. Monro tertius may have lost heart; certainly he was a dull lecturer in his later years. Although he had twelve children, not one of his sons was prepared to succeed him. But the hereditary ability was not extinct. One son, Sir David Monro, became a famous politician in New Zealand, and other descendants have held high posi- tions.

HEREDITARY ABILITY, AND THE CHOICE OF A CAREER

We have seen, then, as exemplified in the families of the Hun- ters and of the Monros, two very different routes of approach to the medical profession; the one, John Hunter, left to educate himself, and doing so with wonderful results; the other, Alexander Monro, apparently influenced and guided by his father from his earliest years, and very successfully. Would the results have been the same if the Monro and the Hunter infants had been exchanged? Very probably they would, as there seems to exist among the various "genes" which are transmissible, a gene of the desire to learn, a bump of curiosity and of wonderment. If that is not already there, no amount of education can create it. There are brilliant students who will always rise to the top however steep the path and however formidable the obstacles. And this holds good, whether the Hunter method or the Monro method is applied in education. This reflection should be a great comfort to parents and teachers alike.

It would be interesting to discuss the motives which influence a young man or woman in the choice of medicine as a career, but that is beyond the scope of this address. Suffice it to say, that while the motive may arise from an interest in animals, a curiosity regarding the wonders of living matter; a desire to reduce suffering; a wish to organize public health; an interest in one's fellow-beings or even the presonal experience of an illness or operation; all may attract the boy or girl towards a medical career, the example of one's forebears plays also an important part. All young people are hero worshippers and the hero whose pattern they desire to follow may be a medical parent or relative, a doctor who may have attended them, or a famous pioneer in medicine, such as Pasteur or Lister, of whose life and work they have heard or read. Naturally, all those influences should be fostered and guided by those who have the great responsibility of advising in the choice of a life-work. At times there is no difficulty. To some, it would appear that there is a "call" to medicine, just as there is a call to become a minister of religion. Most of us have known schoolboys who resolved to become doctors, and doctors they did become. Of course, there are doctors who say that medicine would be most interesting if only there were no patients, but even for those who hold this view there is a wide field of usefulness, as a large proportion of medical men and women today never deal directly with any patient. There is ample scope in the medical profession for those who promote health as well as for those who heal. Nevertheless there remain, and will always remain, many problems relating to the choice of medicine as a career, and to the changing needs of medical education. Let me conclude by remarking that to the solution of those problems, and to the guidance of the younger generation, the science of genealogy and the study of heredity will contribute very materially. The family tree is no mere ancestral monument. It may well be a guide to the coming generation, and an incentive and example to all who plan for their future.

INDEX